FORESTRY IN
THE ENGLISH LANDSCAPE

FORESTRY
IN THE ENGLISH LANDSCAPE

*A study of the cultivation of trees
and their relationship to natural amenity
and plantation design*

by ROGER MILES, M.A., B.SC. (OXON.)
Fellow of the Society of Foresters of Great Britain,
Licentiate of the Institute of Landscape Architects

With an introduction by Victor Bonham-Carter, M.A. (CANTAB.)

FABER & FABER, 24 Russell Square London

First published in mcmlxvii by
Faber and Faber Limited
24 Russell Square London WC1
Printed in Great Britain by
R. MacLehose and Company Limited
The University Press Glasgow

To Sybil, my wife

A man of eighty, planting!
To build at such an age might be no harm,
Argued three youngsters from a neighbouring farm,
But to plant trees! th'old boy was plainly wanting.
'For what, in Heaven's name,' said one of them,
'Can possibly reward your pains,
Unless you live to be Methusalem?
Why tax what little of your life remains
To serve a future you will never see?'

'Is it so?' said he

'My children's children, when my trees are grown,
Will bless me for their kindly shade :
What then? has any law forbade
The Wise to toil for pleasure not his own?
To picture theirs is my reward to-day,
Perhaps tomorrow also : who shall say?'

JEAN DE LA FONTAINE, 1621–1695

AUTHOR'S FOREWORD

The writing of this book began eight years ago with a forestry survey in Exmoor; that developed into a thesis at Oxford; finally, the material was rearranged for publication.

During all these processes, my debts of thanks to many people and organizations for many things have mounted steadily. To begin with, I am grateful to the Somerset and Devon County Councils or, more particularly, to the National Park and Joint Advisory Committees for Exmoor, for the use of certain information from their files. At the same time it must be explained that neither the County Councils nor any of their Committees necessarily agree with the views expressed or the conclusions drawn in the text. Generally, I have tried to show, as clearly as possible, where the known policies of public authorities end and my own investigations or reflections begin.

A number of those to whom my thanks are due for information or expert assistance are recorded in the *Notes*; and the authors of works upon which I have often drawn freely are listed in the *Bibliography*. But there are others who do not appear in those sections. For instance, among my past and present colleagues at Taunton, Anthony Giles must receive recognition for the sketches included in the illustrations of Parts II and III; Sydney Banks and Rita Price also took a load from my shoulders by preparing line drawings and plans for reproduction.

Indeed, in the matter of illustrations, many more names spring to mind. Behind the organizations, which I gladly acknowledge as the sources of material, I remember also the courteous and often generous responses which my enquiries received from numerous individual officers or members of staff who remain anonymous.

The Forestry Commissioners, besides supplying Plates 2, 12 and 14, have allowed me to re-print Diagrams C, D, E and F as

7

well as Plan A, from their official publications. The National Parks Commissioners provided me with Plates 15, 20–25, 27, 28, 30 and 38, and Plan B is reproduced with their permission. For Plan C I am indebted to the *Daily Telegraph*; and the Harvard University Press has allowed the use of Diagrams A and B from R. G. Albion's *Forests and Sea Power*.

I also wish to thank the National Portrait Gallery, London, for Plates 1 and 6, the original of the latter being on loan to the Gallery from Mrs. Humphrey Morrice, in memory of her husband. Sir Richard Acland kindly made the oil painting of Holnicote available for Plate 36, and Major R. L. Coke gave me much of his time and enabled Plates 18 and 19 to be made.

I am also grateful to Alfred Qvist for Plate 10; the Dartington Hall Estate Trustees for Plates 4, 5 and 16; *Country Life* for Plate 7; Aerofilms Ltd. for Plates 8 and 39; Leonard and Marjorie Gayton for Plate 9; and V. Blankenburgs for Plate 11.

The quotation on the dedication page is taken from *The Fables of Jean de la Fontaine*, translated by Edward Marsh and published by William Heinemann Ltd. in 1931. It is reprinted by permission of the publishers.

Finally, there are three special people without whose help I would never have completed my work. At the Oxford Department of Forestry, J. J. MacGregor was always ready with kindly guidance; discussions with him never failed to broaden my thinking. In Somerset, it was Victor Bonham-Carter who first set me off on the literary road; he has influenced me with his infectious energy and stimulating criticism ever since. At home, Sybil, my wife, besides undertaking the many and tedious tasks of secretaryship, has constantly aided and encouraged me in every phase of my studies.

St. George's Day, 1966   Roger Miles
                                                  Trull Green, Somerset

CONTENTS

9

ILLUSTRATIONS

DIAGRAMS

PLANS

12

TABLES

SKETCHES

INTRODUCTION

In the last forty years forestry in England has become a highly controversial subject. If you say 'softwoods' you over-simplify the matter, but — regarded as shorthand — most people will know what you mean. And what *do* you mean? As Roger Miles relates in Part I of this book, the mass-planting of conifers on a national scale did not occur before the 1920's, when the Forestry Commission — set up in 1919 — was launching its campaign to make good the timber losses of the First World War. No one who knew how nearly the German U-Boats had come to starving and crippling this country could criticize the Commission's aims: to create a reserve of native-grown timber against future emergencies, and to generate a new source of wealth and employment in the countryside. Justification — at least of the first aim — came soon enough — too soon in fact for the majority of new plantations, immature for anything but thinning by the time the U-Boats appeared again between 1939 and 1945.

Yet criticism did arise, not of the aims, but of the manner and character of the campaign: notably of the felling of familiar hardwood stands, however over-ripe, and their replacement by softwoods; and of the clothing of bare hillsides, as in the Lake District, or of stretches of level land, as in Breckland, with regiments of conifers. Two parties assembled, massed on either side of a gulf, which so widened and deepened that the idea of 'trees for use' came to be regarded as incompatible with the idea of 'trees for beauty'. It was a case, roughly speaking, of Government foresters, supported by a growing number of private landowners and commercial syndicates, versus a mixed company of naturalists and country lovers (townsmen and countrymen alike), who sought to protect the traditional appearance of the landscape. Both had the backing of Acts of Parliament and powerful organizations, so that

15

disagreement — based on rigidly opposed concepts — became habitual, and hardened into inevitability.

The origins of this division were of course deeper and remoter than any recent and superficial disagreement about conifers, and they are expertly examined in this book. I would mention only the general divorce of use and beauty that affected almost all aspects of English life after the Industrial Revolution. Forestry — once the ideal marriage between the two — was but a late example, because the revival of home timber production was delayed until the twentieth century and had to depend on Government help : by which time, for technical and economic reasons, softwoods had replaced hardwoods as the viable crop. Again, the chances of *rapprochement* were inhibited by acceleration and escalation. The amenity party attracted armies of oddly assorted allies, including some who merely used the conflict as one more means of protesting against the inhumanity and sheer ugliness of urbanized life. Sentiment is a powerful sensation but weak as an argument, especially if the advocates — as so often happened — were weak in knowledge of forestry and, unexpectedly perhaps, of the principles of landscape design. Foresters, for their part, were inclined to shelter behind the dogmas of their profession, and to assume that such modifications as they had been forced to accept in planting techniques, conceded quite enough to beauty; or they shrugged it all off by saying that trees — any trees — became beautiful, simply by growing.

It has been left to new professions and new situations to point to possible solutions, and thus to bring the two sides closer together. For example, there is now a growing realization that because land is short and demand intense, use must be multiple. If land is technically suitable for trees, then forestry must simultaneously create wealth, conserve Nature, and enhance the landscape for the enjoyment of all who seek relief from the pressures of life : especially but not solely in National Parks, such as Exmoor, the subject of study in later pages. We cannot afford any less.

This new situation has advanced the importance of co-ordinators such as the ecologist, whose understanding of the environment, and interdependence of natural phenomena, is at last beginning to be recognized; the landscape architect, long suspect as a kind of garden city planner and no more, now becoming an acceptable team mate for the forester; above all the planner who, though still

16

1. John Evelyn, F.R.S., 1620–1706, drawn and engraved by Robert Nanteuil

2. Coppice: Sweet chestnut about sixteen years old. Challock Forest, Kent.

3. Coppice-with-Standards: Hazel, formerly used for sheep hurdles, now for pea and bean sticks, beneath old oak standards. Polden Hills, Somerset.

short of powers to control land-use in respect of forestry, agriculture and amenity, must in the end have the last word on the interaction of these three fundamentals of landscape. Hitherto, his experience of forestry and amenity disputes has been unsatisfactory. Appealed to as mediator, he has often perpetuated the conflict by regarding it, conventionally, as one involving two separate competitors for the same piece of land, to be divided or awarded intact according to the strength or weakness of the rival claims. There have been few sustained attempts by the parties concerned to integrate their interests.

Indeed, the most notable exercise in this field was undertaken by Roger Miles himself when, at the direction of the Joint Advisory Committee of the National Park, he produced comprehensive surveys of Exmoor for both the afforestation of open land and the treatment of existing woodlands (the latter applying, as a first step, to Somerset only). These reports form the bases, respectively, of Parts II and III — pioneer enterprises of great importance which have encouraged some other National Parks to think along similar lines. The fact that the findings of the reports, even if agreed with the Forestry Commission and private forestry operators, cannot be enforced is highly regrettable; but that does not diminish their value as examples of integrated land-use and landscape planning, which contribute — as all forestry schemes should — to utility and beauty alike.

The advantages of integrated planning are so obvious and overwhelming that the wonder is they have yet to carry the force of law. If this point is still not appreciated, it is worth — at the risk of a little repetition — considering the alternatives : namely some of the arguments advanced by one side or the other, which in isolation may seem quite convincing. Yet two isolated convictions make, not a plan, but a conflict, and that is what has to be resolved.

A forester might say :

'Forestry is not new. Like farming it is a traditional primary industry of the English countryside, and like farming it is active and alters the face of the land. Trees have to be planted, thinned, felled and re-planted; just as arable and grass crops have to be sown, cultivated, harvested and the ground tilled again. Although their cycle is far longer than farm crops, trees are not static, even their beauty waxes and wanes; and there is nothing worse than a derelict and dying woodland. Forestry is a business, as economic as any other, serving trade, giving employment in the woods and mills, and yielding profits — without which it could not exist. If allowed to prosper, it saves foreign currency and acts as a strategic insurance in case of emergency. It has long-term ecological advantages too : for example, when a plantation serves as a wind-break or stabilizes land vulnerable to erosion, or when a forest floor encourages the formation of humus in a thin soil. That soft-woods are replacing hardwoods, with attendant changes in forest practice and aesthetic appearance, is not a tragedy but a challenge. Every tradition, however dear and seemingly immemorial, has a beginning. The traditional English landscape is less than 200 years old, the outcome of the Great Enclosures when the open fields and commons were carved up into separate holdings and fenced with hedges and copses. It caused a great outcry at the time, socially and aesthetically (you only have to read Cobbett) ; but no one with any sense in the 1800's really wanted to revert to the Middle Ages. It was impossible anyway.'

An amenity enthusiast might say :

'There is no softwood tradition in English forestry or landscape, as in other countries. So far as trees are concerned, the countryside derives its beauty from hardwoods — broad-leaved trees raised in copses and plantations of limited size and in hedgerows. Although the industry has been allowed to decay, first-class home-grown hardwood could still be a valuable raw material for our sawmills; and with the advent of new uses, such as the manufacture of chip-board, many other grades of hardwoods have become marketable. In any event the economic value of home-grown softwoods is debatable. The industry is never likely to satisfy more than a modest proportion of the national demand. It would be better business to import virtually all our needs as now, and in England at any rate to concentrate on hardwoods as an amenity rather than economic asset. Remote upland areas should be left to sheep and Nature reservations. Again, in many positions, hardwoods may be no less effective than softwoods as wind-breaks and soil stabilizers, and infinitely superior for areas of beauty and as natural habitats. Softwood plantations are all too often silent and sunless places, with few birds and little botanical interest — factory forests, geometrical hideosities, tree slums.'

18

It would not be difficult, even for an amateur, to fault some of these generalizations and find points of contact and compromise on either side. For example, the suitability of uplands, whether for trees or sheep or anything else, can be technically assessed area by area, having regard to environmental factors such as soil and climate, or to others such as accessibility and recreational demand. In theory at least planning could integrate them all, however numerous and complex the competing interests. An acuter difficulty lies in the application — in making the plan work — for this requires much more than a mere process of adjustment. What is wanted is positive management for an entire region, and this involves both the marriage (where appropriate) of forestry, agriculture, wild life, public enjoyment and amenity — and active after-care to conserve their individual character and vitality. Without this, sterility will surely follow : or, as at present seems to be happening, the destruction of one interest by the unregulated development of another.

There is, however, no need to pursue these deliberations in relation to forestry and landscape, since that is the purpose of this book — being a 'study of the cultivation of trees and their relationship to natural amenity and plantation design'. Amenity, in terms of the attractiveness of individual tree species and the seemliness of their arrangement, may well be a subjective matter about which we differ among ourselves. But, while some prefer one pattern to another, it must be agreed that all patterns worthy of regard must be based upon certain fundamental principles of design. It is essential, therefore, to define a grammar of principles upon which tree selection and arrangement in English landscapes may be based. In this small country, racked with diverse and increasing claims upon diminishing resources of land, there is not enough room for continual skirmishing between sectional interests. Forestry and beauty of landscape have kindred roots in the English countryside and should be joined again in harmony. It is tragic that trees, noblest of all plant life to furnish the earth, should be the cause of such ignoble strife. And it is inconceivable that the science of growing them cannot be married to the art of arranging them, so that a flowering of use and beauty is bequeathed to future generations at a fractional cost compared with other forest values.

Yet, it is no use ending on a pious hope. Nor is there any need, for although we are still handicapped in the matter of powers, there

19

is still much to do by way of preparation — research, informing public opinion, and briefing the planners. That is where this book comes in, for — in a way that exists in no other book that I know of — it fills a vital gap in a critical sector of rural planning. Its value springs from two sources. First, the writer is a true professional, both in forestry and in landscape architecture, and the thesis upon which this book is based gained him his Advanced Degree at Oxford — the university which, perhaps, has trained more British foresters than any other, and is also the seat of the Commonwealth Forestry Institute. But Roger Miles' qualifications extend further than theory. He was living and farming in Exmoor for many years both before and after it became a National Park. At the same time he was accumulating a store of practical experience in local government, involving countless days out in the field, inspecting land, talking to farmers and foresters, and conducting the Exmoor surveys described in this book.

Secondly, the book itself. It is both factual and reflective, analytical and constructive, the one springing out of the other. Thus Part I is a cogent historical essay which provides the background to present problems. As a historian myself, I welcome this, for I believe it is impossible to grasp any subject unless you know what has gone before and originated the situation under study. Then follow the Exmoor Surveys in Part II (afforestation of open land) and Part III (existing woodlands) : each being a technical but readable account of an area in which forestry and amenity interests can meet and clash, with positive and practical suggestions towards solution. It is highly important to realize that whereas the Exmoor Surveys are local undertakings, their application is universal. The lessons to be drawn apply, moreover, not only to all National Parks, but to all land outside National Parks where the integration of forestry and amenity is in question — and that means *everywhere*. The experiment of National Parks has done much to make people aware of the values of wild life and of the beauty of natural landscape, if only to underline the necessity of conserving these areas before it is too late; but it has also encouraged, almost unconsciously, the dangerous assumption that what happens in a National Park is one thing and matters greatly, whereas what happens outside does not matter at all. That idea must be killed at birth, and Roger Miles is a willing and able executioner.

Finally, a few lines about my own interest in this subject and in this book. I make no claims to professionalism in forestry and amenity, but like very many others I care deeply about these matters. I have lived and worked on the edge of Exmoor for the last 20 years, and have served on the statutory committees that administer the National Park, and on the committee of the Exmoor Society, the local branch of the C.P.R.E., including a year's stint as Chairman. My colleagues and I — and indeed hundreds of others who know and love Exmoor — have been deeply concerned at the way in which this wonderful tract of wild country is being diminished by cultivation and enclosure. The loss has been at the rate of nearly a thousand acres a year for the past ten years, so that now barely a quarter of the whole territory remains as moorland, while much less than that is accessible to the public. Exmoor is a national heritage, and we must guard it jealously if the term 'National Park' is to mean anything at all. The immediate difficulty lies in the clash of legitimate interests. Nearly all the land is privately owned. Farmers and foresters, therefore, are legally entitled to exploit their own property by ploughing it or by planting trees, and by enclosing the improved land thereafter. Moreover they are encouraged to do so by grant-aid from the Ministry of Agriculture and the Forestry Commission; and the amenity authorities are powerless to stop them. Here then is a classic case of the need for integrated planning and positive management. If evolved in effective form — to control the relationships of all the competing interests — the new machinery would so knit moorland, trees and farmland together as to conserve and create a harmonious landscape. For this a Master Map would be necessary, based on land use and supported by all the relevant facts about the natural and human resources of the region. The application of the final plan would necessitate new powers, or old ones made effective, to buy out or covenant with landowners and tenants, using compulsion if negotiation failed; and the cost would have to be met out of public funds. But it would be a small price to pay.

What has all this to do with Roger Miles' book? Just this. Not only does he demonstrate how forestry and amenity can be combined as an essential element of regional planning, but he does so at a time when the art of landscape is regaining the recognition and value accorded to it in a previous era — the eighteenth century. But now we have far greater means and superior scope — in the richer variety of our trees, more knowledge and a vast mechanical ability. There is also an infinitely more urgent need to use them. Unless we do so, we shall lose our heritage for ever.

Spring 1967   Victor Bonham-Carter
                                                East Anstey, North Devon

PART I

🔥 Trees and English Landscape since 1670

1 EIGHTEENTH-CENTURY STYLE

a — Evelyn, Enclosure and Enthusiasm

Once before, there was a time when sustained efforts were made to improve our timber resources. Simultaneously then, as now, there was a strong movement to improve the appearance of our landscapes. It began at the end of the seventeenth century when, after a history of almost unrelieved devastation by man, the natural forests of the country had become so depleted that the Navy was threatened by a shortage of suitable home-grown hardwoods needed for the building and repair of warships. At a time when England's position in world affairs was largely dependent upon naval power in the form of wooden ships, the shortage was serious indeed.

The Governments of the period, like those in previous centuries, had failed to take any worthwhile steps to safeguard existing timber supplies or to encourage the planting of new trees for future use. It so happened, however, that the Royal Society had been formed and, in October 1662, the members met to hear John Evelyn, scholar and court official, lecture 'Upon Occasion of certain Quaeries propounded to that illustrious Assembly, by the Honourable the Principal Officers and Commissioners of the Navy'. Two years later Evelyn's book, based upon the lecture, was published under the title of *Silva, or a Discourse of Forest Trees and the propagation of Timber in his Majesty's Dominions*.

The book is a monumental and still valuable treatise upon the culture of trees and contains a plea for afforestation which is well worth recalling again today. Three hundred years ago Evelyn wrote:

'Truly the waste and destruction of our woods has been so universal, that I conceive nothing less than an universal plantation of all the sorts of trees will supply, and well encounter the defect; and therefore I shall here adventure to speak something in general of them all; though I chiefly insist upon the propagation of such only as seem to be most wanting and serviceable to the end proposed.'

The immediate influence of the book upon the wealthy land-owners of the time may be indicated by the fact that only fifteen years later, in his preface to the third edition addressed to Charles II, Evelyn was able to assert that

'. . . many millions of timber-trees, besides infinite others, have been propagated and planted . . . at the instigation and sole direction of this work.'

Long after the author's death in 1706, new editions of *Silva* continued to appear and his work was a major influence upon English forestry techniques for more than two hundred years.

This is not to say that the landowners of his time all devoted themselves to forestry, as Evelyn's rather boastful assertions upon the stimulus of his book might suggest. One Restoration peer is reputed to have said that wood was 'an excrescence of the earth provided by God for the payment of debts'. And there were others who merely followed fashion and, as a result, planted many trees, especially oak, on unsuitable land, laying the foundation of a legacy of indifferent timber which is a problem to this day.

Indeed, the 'Evelyn legend' has been criticized, on strong evidence, by assertions that the large-scale private plantings of oak for both the Navy and the Merchant Navy were due mainly to the exceptionally favourable economic conditions for the production of this timber between 1660 and 1760.[1]

Certainly, Evelyn's teaching had no more than a spasmodic effect upon succeeding Governments. Another writer, describing English forestry prior to the present century, remarks that 'at no time in our history has a concerted public effort to reafforest been sustained long enough to matter'. Of the enthusiastic landowners who shouldered voluntarily most of the burden of supplying the country's needs for timber in times of crisis, he comments, 'the wonder is that unco-ordinated and purely private enterprise accomplished so much'.[2]

At the time of the Restoration there were still sixty-eight Royal Forests in Britain, most of them in England. Many were capable of producing fine timber but their almost continuous neglect became one of the most culpable features of our forest history.

The origin of many Royal Forests is largely a matter for conjecture. Since Saxon days, by royal prerogative tracts of country had been set aside as 'forests' wherein the king had sole right to hunt deer and other game. An 'afforested' area was one in which this prerogative was exercised and the term had only an incidental connection with trees. Indeed, many of the forests were very sparsely wooded. Exmoor Forest in Somerset, for example, was described in 1622 as containing 'noe woods . . . except one oak called Kite Oak'.

In those that were wooded, however, the strict forest laws, designed to protect the game and all that game required in the way of cover and food plants, also, but fortuitously, protected the trees and saplings. These might otherwise have been cleared to prepare the land for agricultural use. Gradually, through the centuries, the Crown's interest in game preservation declined and forests elsewhere were drastically reduced in size. The Royal Forests became more highly prized as sources of timber, particularly oak, for naval purposes. Unfortunately there was no consistent management policy, and successive monarchs could be prudent or irresponsible towards the forests almost at will.

The exploitation of timber by the Crown began with the Tudors. Even so, by early Stuart times, many of the forests, including those as far north as Sherwood and Shotover, Stow and Chopwell, were still supplying much oak for the dockyards. By the time of the Restoration, however, the wholesale disposal of Royal Forests or destruction within them had been carried to such an extent that the main reserves for naval oak were centred upon the Forest of Dean in Gloucestershire and the New and Alice Holt Forests in Hampshire.[3]

The subsequent management of these areas was generally characterized by feverish periods of planting in times of crisis, alternating with long periods of neglect. In 1668, Parliament passed 'An Act for the Increase and Preservation of Timber within the Forest of Dean'. It is recorded that 11,000 acres were later enclosed for planting, these being the first real plantations made by an English Government. In 1698, a similar Act permitted the enclosure of 6,000 acres in the New Forest but, apparently, little more than 1,000 acres were planted. These activities were inspired as much by the drain on supplies occasioned by the Dutch Wars and the Fire of London as upon Evelyn's propaganda. Similarly, another timber shortage occurred during the Seven Years War, in the mid-eighteenth century, and was followed by planting, although this was undertaken only half-heartedly.[4]

In spite of such resurgences of interest, the forests became progressively more depleted, and during the Napoleonic Wars the timber situation was alarming. The condition of our ships by the time of Trafalgar was deplorable.[5] After extraordinary delay, the Government finally adopted an official planting policy in 1808, planning to enclose and plant 100,000 acres of land. By 1816 this programme was well under way chiefly in the Dean and New Forests. But enthusiasm soon waned and, in any event, the oaks then planted matured too late for naval use : by the mid-nineteenth century iron was superseding wood in ship construction, and conifers were becoming more important than hardwoods in the national economy.

There is little doubt that if planting and management in the Royal Forests had been pursued consistently after the Act of 1668, there would always have been sufficient oak for the Navy. As it was, years were rare when more than a tenth part of naval supplies came from the Crown reserves. The parks and woodlands of the private landowners provided most of the remainder and some was imported from the Continent, although it was usually inferior to the harder English material.

Whereas we could grow fine oak in England, especially on the Wealden clays of the South East, we could not produce first-class softwood material for masts and spars. England looked overseas for suitable conifers long before the shortage of oak occurred. Baltic fir (Scots pine) was best and necessitated naval stratagems in war-time to preserve access to the Baltic ports. Neither in England nor in Scotland could we grow Scots pine of just the right flexibility required. American white pine (Weymouth pine) was the next best choice and was longer and lighter; finally spruce from Europe (Norway spruce) was the third choice before 1804, after which all sorts of conifers and hardwoods were used to spin out supplies.[6]

What has since been described as the plantation movement on

private estates during the eighteenth and nineteenth centuries certainly owed something to Evelyn's inspiration. But the wealthy, patriotic landowners, vying with each other in the new fashion, could not have operated on such a huge scale without favourable social and economic conditions. These were largely provided by changes in traditional systems of agricultural land tenure which had already been taking place slowly, but were accelerated during the second half of the eighteenth century.

In western, north-western and south-eastern England a farming pattern had been developed which was composed of scattered farmsteads and hamlets surrounded by small hedged fields. The enclosure of land in parcels in this way had occurred either, in medieval times, direct from the natural forest and waste or, later, particularly in Tudor times, by agreement or otherwise between landlord and peasant farmer. Elsewhere in the country, and especially in the lowlands of Central England, the ancient and hedgeless pattern of open-field farming, surrounding compact villages, still persisted.

It is not necessary to discuss this type of communal peasant agriculture here or to consider in detail the social upheaval which marked its passing in rural England. It is sufficient to point out that, by eighteenth-century standards, open-field farming had become inefficient in face of improvements in cropping and stock breeding. These called for smaller enclosed and sheltered fields and a farming pattern similar to that already in being in western and south-eastern areas.

By means of many local Acts of Enclosure the open fields were redistributed between landowners, freeholders and tenant farmers and enclosed, first with fences, then with hedges, into holdings. Dr. W. G. Hoskins[7] has remarked that 'it was a triumph of planning in so short a time for so complicated a matter, most of it carried through in most places within a year or two years of the passing of the act'. By 1844 a total of rather more than 4 million acres of the old open fields had been divided and hedged around with trees and bushes much as we see them today.

One of the most significant results of this agricultural revolution was that it concentrated the ownership and occupation of land into fewer hands. The landowners in many cases had been able to buy out or compensate the lesser peasant farmers who could not afford to set themselves up in the new independent farms. Furthermore,

29

the new order substituted rents of money for services in labour or goods payable by tenants to landlords. Some of the tenants were reluctant to pay rent for such woodland or waste which they could not foresee being of practical use to them. Such lands therefore were very often retained in the landlord's ownership untrammelled by any of the old communal claims.

The already wealthy squires were thus provided with new sources of land, redundant labour and income which they could employ most fruitfully in agricultural expansion, improvement and afforestation upon their own estates. So far as forestry was concerned these men, inspired by Evelyn and prompted by patriotism and fashion, were strong in resources and a security of tenure, after the Restoration, which enabled them to wait for long-term projects to mature. They were still further assisted by the emergence of foresters, gardeners, nurserymen and agents possessed of skill and experience in the establishment and management of trees and woods. Plant hunters flourished, introducing from abroad many new varieties of trees which were enthusiastically tried out by the landowners. Finally, throughout most of the eighteenth and the early part of the nineteenth centuries, there were the landscape architects. Men like Shenstone and Kent, 'Capability' Brown and Repton, succeeded each other in revolutionizing the design of gardens and parks and influencing the layout of new plantations throughout the country. Horace Walpole said of Kent that 'he leaped the fence and saw that all nature was a garden'. The phrase epitomizes the spirit of the times. This spirit is the pervading genius of the eighteenth century, the catalyst which fused the needs and circumstances of the age to produce the results which we have been able to judge at leisure.

Lord David Cecil has vividly described the elegance, self-assurance and established power of the Whig aristocrats who dominated the country. Passing at least half of each year in their country seats, they took a personal interest in the land from which their wealth had grown and which, with the help of low taxation and further enclosure, they never doubted would remain indefinitely in the ownership of their families. Although they had their town houses and enjoyed a sophisticated social life in club and drawing-room, they were never urban. Robust and earthy in many ways, they were often amateur rather than intellectual in their interests. Immensely active as a governing class, they lived on a scale and with a magnificence appropriate to their position and wealth and yet cultivated the 'sense and taste' which they deemed essential to their art of living. Some of their homes and the settings which they provided for themselves in the countryside are now 'among the most conspicuous monuments of English history'.[8]

In the matter of trees and woods and their fittingness in the landscape, the work of the old planting landlords is held in great esteem. It is regarded now as something traditional. Yet, at the time when it was carried out an earlier but equally traditional pattern was being usurped. A vast rearrangement of the landscape was being attempted for the better production of food and timber. Work of this kind could so easily have been undertaken with a dull and uninspired mechanical monotony. On the contrary, it was planned to take into substantial account a care for the final appearance of the landscape which, particularly in those autocratic days, need not have been considered. The fact that such care was given so generously is the primary reason why the results of the work have since been described variously as 'one of the finest works of functional art in the world' and England's 'primary contribution to the visual arts'.[9, 10]

These are laurels bestowed upon the appearance of English rural scenery, upon the arrangement on the face of the land of field and hedgerow, park and garden, copse, plantation and woodland in what may be popularly termed the eighteenth-century style. For generations such scenery inspired men in all walks of life. Today, after the devastation of world wars and other causes, the relics of that beauty are still an inspiration to many people. What is more these remnants are often defended most bitterly against proposals to change them, and sometimes even blindly and hopelessly against the decaying hands of time itself. Such are the emotions which England's fading beauty can evoke. With what immense conviction and feeling, therefore, must the old landlords have worked in the landscape for the results to have received such overwhelming acclaim and for so long.

b — Species and Methods

There can be no mistake about the economic soundness of eighteenth-century rural planning. Corn and wool prices were falling at the end of the seventeenth century; timber was an attractive investment. The country required timber not only for naval use but, as Evelyn had been careful to point out, for many other purposes. Therefore trees of all available kinds were grown and, under the supervision of skilful gardeners and foresters, they were grown properly. Accounts from the times show that the principles of silviculture were thoroughly understood and that forestry enterprises were usually well founded on knowledge and the economic needs of the period.[11]

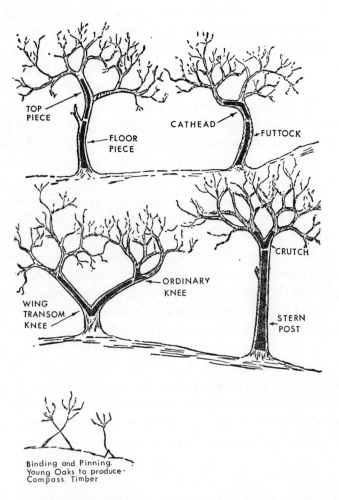

DIAGRAM A: OAKS SUITABLE FOR GREAT AND COMPASS SHIP TIMBER (SHOWING PARTICULAR CUTS)

Based upon a drawing in *Forests and Sea Power* by R. G. Albion, Harvard Univ. Press, 1926.

4. Plantation of hard-
woods : Ash about forty
years old. St. Aubyn,
Cornwall.

5. Plantation of conifers :
Corsican pine about thirty
years old. Dartington,
Devon.

6. John Lancelot 'Capability' Brown, 1716–1783,
painted by Nathaniel Dance

Oak, which had been ubiquitous in the natural forests of this country, was still the most important tree in the national economy. The landlords planted it very extensively. Trees were grown in such a way that they formed rather wide crowns so that in addition to straight timber from the stems, there would be plenty of naturally grown 'bends' and 'knees' in the branches. These provided ready-made the shapes and curves required by the ship-wrights for their intricate work. The sizes and designs of wooden battleships changed very little between 1637 and 1860, being determined, in spite of all the ingenuity of the shipwrights, by the sizes and shapes of the 'great' and 'compass' timber which could be cut from the average oak trees available.[12]

Besides ships, oak was used for beams and trusses in house construction, for heavy duty work of all descriptions, for furniture and barrels, wheel spokes and charcoal and numerous other purposes. The bark was harvested carefully for use in tanning leather goods.

Beech was planted scarcely less extensively than oak. This is surprising because the use of the timber during the period was relatively limited, being confined mostly to interior work and furniture, coachwork and handles. Beech charcoal had already been superseded by coal in the glass industry. Evelyn scorned the wood, which he could hardly bring himself to call timber. Nevertheless, beech suits many of the soils of Southern England and has a special silvicultural value as a tree which will withstand planting in shade. The beauty of the tree also made it extremely popular in the planting of amenity woods and parkland. It was probably for these reasons that so much use was made of the species.

The tough and elastic ash, immensely useful in an age of hand craftsmen requiring tool handles of every description, was widely grown. It was a vital timber in wheel construction, for oars and cart shafts and many other articles in which its special properties were important. Sycamore, which had been introduced to this country as an ornamental species, became very popular for wood-land planting during the eighteenth century. It was also used in the establishment of shelter belts, especially in northern upland country. Elm was not generally planted in woodland, possibly because there was enough occurring naturally and it was springing up in the new hedgerows. Certainly it was prized for the keels of ships, wheel hubs and other uses where its value as a timber which does not split easily could be exploited. Wych elm, however, was planted quite frequently, mostly in the northern counties. Like the common elm, it was used in shipbuilding for certain sections under water near the keel.

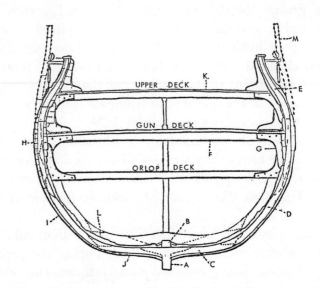

DIAGRAM B: **CROSS-SECTION OF A SEVENTY-FOUR SHOWING TIMBERS USED IN CONSTRUCTION**
A midship section of a 74 gun ship with a deep waist and tumble home sides, as built in His Majesty's dock yards.

KEY A Keel (elm)   I Plank (Baltic oak)
      B Keelson (elm)   J Garboard strakes (elm, beech)
      C Floor piece   K Deck deals (Baltic oak or fir)
      D Futtock   L Ceiling
      E Top piece   M Snodgrass plan for straight sides to save compass timber.
      F Beam (fir)   English oak used in all parts except where substitutes
      G Knee   noted.
      H Thickstuff

Based upon a drawing in *Forests and Sea Power* by R. G. Albion, Harvard Univ. Press, 1926.

Apart from their employment in the formation of new plantations, these principal species were established in considerable numbers in hedges, for these were seen to be potential miniature woodlands. They could produce large timber as well as small poles and other products for local use, while at the same time serving the further purposes of sheltering and enclosing agricultural land.

Poles and other smaller material were grown extensively under a system of woodland management known as coppicing. This system, the first practised in English forestry, was in general use by the fifteenth century and had been known for centuries before that. Coppicing means the periodic cutting of the numerous shoots which grow repeatedly from hardwood stumps, especially oak, sweet chestnut, hazel, ash and alder. For handles, wattle work, hurdles, charcoal, tanbark, firewood and numerous rural uses, areas of coppice from which poles could be cut indefinitely at intervals of twenty years or so, were highly prized.

The planting and management of oak at a wide spacing to encourage the formation of big branching crowns had also been practised long before Evelyn's time, but usually only where material from the natural forests was running short. Coppices were established as an undergrowth below the big trees and this method of woodland management, developed in the sixteenth century, became known as the coppice-with-standards system. Several crops could be taken from the coppice while the oak was growing to the required size. This system, like that of pure coppice, is now out-moded, but examples of both can still be seen throughout the country. Both methods continued to flourish, however, well into the nineteenth century.

In the seventeenth century the plantation system of woodland management was devised and has continued in favour ever since. Under this technique all the trees are allowed to grow to full height and, while many are removed completely during periodic thinnings, the woodland is kept so dense that coppice and side shoots cannot grow properly in the heavy shade. By this method of severe competition the trees grow tall and straight, the weakest are suppressed and cut down and only the very best grow on to form the final crop. Most of the new woods created by the planting landlords were formed in this manner. Conifers which, with one or two minor exceptions, do not throw up coppice shoots from their stumps, do not lend themselves satisfactorily to growth for timber under any method other than the plantation system.

In the eighteenth century, however, nearly all timber require-ments could be served best by the growing of broad-leaved hard-wood trees and these species, particularly those mentioned earlier, were generally well mixed together in the new woods. The actual composition of the mixtures depended upon regional and local conditions of soil and climate and sometimes pure crops were grown where conditions were suitable.

The fact that some trees, described as successor types, need a pioneer species to prepare the way for them, by providing at least shelter from exposure on less favourable sites, was well known. It was common practice to establish oak, for example, in thickets of birch, holly and thorn, these species being gradually reduced as the oak required less nursing in succeeding years. Oak also mixes well with the major species and was often grown with ash, sycamore and beech. The last named tree, because of its shade tolerance, is capable of very late introduction into a wood.

Gradually, during the eighteenth century, it became general practice to employ conifers as nurse trees for hardwoods. Extensive use in this way was made of our native conifer, the Scots pine, especially in the establishment of beech and oak woods, but the tree was also planted for its own value as a timber producer. European larch, an introduced species in the seventeenth century and at first regarded mainly as an ornamental tree, was much used. Norway Spruce, another exotic, destined to become the Christmas Tree of a later age, was the only other conifer to be planted at all widely in the new woods.

Larch received close attention during the last decades of the eighteenth century. Quick-growing on some poorer soils, it did not clash with farming as oak had done with wheat production on the heavier and better lowland soils. Larch was also found to be durable, light in weight, resistant to worm and non-corrosive to iron bolts. It was thought that this timber would be the best substitute for oak in ship-building if supplies of the latter ever failed completely. The Dukes of Atholl planted 14 million larch trees to form 10,000 acres of conifer plantations at Blair and Dunkeld in Scotland between 1764 and 1826.[13] In 1820 the first all-larch frigate was built and launched.[14]

Government aid was actually made available for tree planting in Scotland in 1713 and the Highland Society, founded in 1783, did much to foster an enduring practical interest in Scottish forestry.[15] By contrast, little was done in Wales where there were relatively few large landowners. In England, the London (Royal) Society of Arts awarded a large number of medals for softwood planting from the 1770's to the 1780's, principally for Scots pine, spruce, silver fir and larch.[16] A contemporary writer noted that about three-quarters of all wood used in general construction work at that time was deal (Scots pine).[17] So it may be seen that the use of exotic conifers in English forestry and the demand for softwood timbers were well-established as far back as the eighteenth century.[18]

c — Aesthetic Aspects and Achievements

This short review provides some explanation why certain species of trees came to be chosen, planted in various ways and tended under different systems, for several economic or silvicultural reasons, during the great wave of forestry activity from the end of the seventeenth century until the first quarter or so of the nineteenth.

It has been mentioned that most of the work was done with broadleaved hardwood trees. These when grown appear softer in outline, colour and texture in the landscape than the majority of conifer species. But young hardwood saplings in dense plantation do not appear particularly beautiful and, if planted in harsh patterns out of harmony with the shape of the land, could be disfiguring for many years, particularly on hill sides. Because we can see today the boundaries of their woods and plantations, it is clear that the landlords designed them with considerable care in relation to the landscape as well as to the needs of agriculture and forestry.

Partly this may have been due to the intimate local knowledge and feeling for the country which was a national characteristic when England's economy was a rural one. It was also due to a generally arboricultural attitude to forestry, a regard for the care of each individual tree rather than a mass-production outlook. Evelyn had encouraged this and it is significant that, in the literature of the times, the gardener rather than the forester was an important figure in the creation of the new woods.

Some idea of the sort of care for appearance which was felt so strongly may be gained from extracts taken from a letter by a Mr. Speechly, 'gardener to the Duke of Portland', in which he describes 'the method of forming plantations upon his Grace's estate (Welbeck) in the county of Nottingham'. The full text appears in footnotes in Hunter's 1776 edition of Evelyn's *Silva* and is worthy of study.

'Few noblemen plant more than his Grace the Duke of Portland: and I think I may say, without vanity, none with greater success.

37

. . . The greatest part of our plantation is on that soil which . . . distinguished by the name of Forestland . . . is composed of a mixture of sand and gravel; the hills abound most with the latter. . . . It is on the hilly grounds we make our plantations, which in time will make the valleys of much greater value, on account of the shelter they will afford. . . . We always plant thick, as well as sow plentifully at the same time, provided it be a season in which acorns can be had; so that all our plantations answer in a few years as nurseries to succeeding plantations.

'. . . As to the form of the plantations, they are very irregular: We sometimes follow a chain of hills to a very great distance: so that what we plant in one season, which perhaps is sixty, eighty and sometimes an hundred acres, is no more than part of one great design.

'. . . After the ploughing is finished, we divide the ground into quarters for the planting by ridings. . . . Between the hills, towards the outsides of the plantations, we frequently leave the ridings from sixty to an hundred yards in breadth, and contract them towards the middle of the woods, to the breadth of ten or twelve yards; and on the tops of the hills where there are plains, we frequently leave lawns of an acre or two, which makes pleasing variety.

'In some of them we plant the Cedar of Libanus at good distances, so as to form irregular groves. . . . On the outsides of the woods, next to the ridings, we plant Evergreens as Hollies, Laurels, Yews, Junipers, etc. and these we dispose of in patches sometimes the several sorts entire, at other times we intermix them for variety; but not so as to make a regular screen or edging. Our design in the distribution of these plants, is to make the outsides of the woods appear as if scalloped with Evergreens intermixed sometimes with rare trees. . . . After the ground is laid out into quarters for planting we assign certain parts to Beech, Larch, Spanish Chestnut, etc. These we plant in irregular patches here and there, throughout the plantations, which, when the trees are in leaf, has the most pleasing effect, on account of the diversity of shades . . . we then proceed to the planting in general; Birch is generally the sort of tree we make our beginning with. . . .

'We plant about three or four hundred Birches of the large size on an acre and nearly the same number of the first-sized Oaks; we also plant here and there a Beech, Larch, Spanish Chestnut, etc.

38

exclusive of the patches of the said sorts of trees before planted. We then proceed to plant plentifully of the second and lesser-sized Oaks; and last of all a great number of the small Birches. . . . Of the several sizes of the different kinds of trees, we generally plant upwards of two thousand plants upon an acre of land, all in an irregular manner.

'After the planting is finished we then sow the acorns . . . all over the plantation, except amongst the Beech, Larch, etc. in the aforesaid patches . . .'

Many a modern forester may grow pale at the thought of the difficulties in supervision and management which Mr. Speechly's work would entail today. Nevertheless, the point should be taken that it is an account by a working gardener of day-to-day activities in the woods on a large eighteenth-century estate in the Midlands. It is not written by a fashionable landscape architect but by an ordinary artisan, interpreting his employer's desire that woods, which were being planted primarily for economic reasons, and were not necessarily in full view of the mansion, should still appear seemly in the landscape.

It was, however, in the settings of their houses, and in those portions of the general landscape visible from favoured view points and drives, that the aristocracy spared no expense in the lavish use of trees and woods to beautify the scenery.

There had been parks since very early times, usually enclosures for livestock and deer, allowed by royal assent to surround the manor houses of the lords. Almost invariably house and park occupied some of the best and most sheltered land in their locality. Here the trees and woods, enclosed to harbour and feed the animals, could grow, unmolested by the commoners and nurtured by fertile soils, to magnificent size. In later more peaceful times the park was seen less as a larder and more as an amenity. It provided shelter and privacy, sport and a supply of timber near at hand and of a better quality than could be found easily in the rapidly dwindling natural forests. Gradually its potentiality as a setting to the house became apparent. Woods were planted, often to form a perimeter screen, and avenues became popular parkland ornaments. Until the end of the seventeenth century the design of such work was usually formal, owing much to the French influence upon gardening which was dominated by André Le Nôtre at that time.[19] The mathematical precision of the style is admirably portrayed in many of the drawings or engravings by Kip during the period.

In the eighteenth century, under the influence of landscape gardeners, as they were then significantly termed, existing parks were transformed and often enlarged and many new ones were created. The work proceeded on an astonishing scale. 'Capability' Brown is perhaps the best known exponent, partly because of his nickname but also because of his prodigious output of work.[20] For over forty years he dominated landscape design in England. He had a reputation for ruthlessness and was strongly criticized as a result. Certainly in his passion for natural effects, he swept away many an imposing avenue planted as part of the old formal style which he sought to replace. He designed at great speed and in the grand manner. There is no doubt that he worked to a discernible pattern. His use of the ha-ha and of 'ample lakes', clumps of trees in the parks, outer screens of woodland and serpentine walks, are all very well known and were widely copied. Nevertheless, the designing of 'natural' landscapes in which he specialized is now described by Christopher Hussey as

'an unique English contribution to the arts, and typically English in its union of beauty with use, an art of which our countryside itself constitutes the principal display'.[21]

The perceptive Walpole wrote at the time of Brown's death in 1783,

'Such, however, was the effect of his genius that when he was the happiest man, he will be least remembered; so closely did he copy nature that his works will be mistaken'.

While Hussey may speak for the initiated, Walpole's words more truly describe the reactions to Brownian scenes of the majority of people today.

There were many others who preceded or succeeded Brown and who strongly influenced the landowners in the manner of their plantings.[22] There was the gentle poet Shenstone, who spent twenty years creating the perfect 'Landskip' at The Leasowes near Birmingham. There was Southcote with his ornamented farm in the Thames Valley. From him Brown developed the perimeter woodland screens he used so often in park designs. Kent, influenced by the poet Pope, himself a gardener of some merit, developed the idea of tree clumps in parkland. These were later used frequently by Brown who was virtually trained by Kent. Bridgeman was the first landscaper to use the ha-ha extensively to secure enclosure without interrupting a view. Later came Repton with his Red Books of before-and-after sketches. One of his earliest commissions was at Welbeck where Speechly had already created huge woods. Then there were Price and Knight, two Herefordshire squires who bickered with Repton upon the Principles of Taste in the early years of the nineteenth century. After them the golden age of English landscape began to fade. Parks were still being laid out in the styles these men had set, and the Victorian fashion for planting rare trees in an arboretum or pinetum was to help provide future generations with useful information about exotic species. But the zest and flair of the previous century had gone. The Whig world of wealth and power, based upon a rural economy, crumbled before the pressures of industrialization, heavier taxation and declining agricultural prosperity.

An interesting feature of the creative period in English landscape is the apparent readiness with which the landlords accepted the advice of landscape architects. In their schemes of improvement, the latter invariably caused great upheavals to take place in the immediate neighbourhood of their patrons' homes. That the owners allowed this, and took pleasure in the sight from their windows of so much raw new work, while knowing that they could not live to enjoy the scene in its mature grace, is indicative of something more than the excitement of fashion. Security of tenure and wealth, and even the promise of trees and woods being good investments, do not entirely account for the landowners' extraordinary convictions. Once again the conclusion has to be drawn that these men already possessed either a cultivated or an innate aesthetic sense and therefore the advice of landscape architects fell upon eager ears.[23]

This perceptiveness was something which sprang to life in the age when the word 'taste' first gained a new meaning, when man was, for the first time in England, 'attempting deliberately to organize the landscape as his environment' as Sylvia Crowe has described the essence of the period.[24] That those who paid for all this work were few and autocratic and organized the best landscape around their own homes is immaterial. As has been shown, the same influences permeated their treatment of woods in the countryside at large and, if it cared to do so, the peasant's cat could look at the landscapes of kings.

To return to the economic value of the work, there are plenty of references in the literature upon the late eighteenth and early nineteenth centuries to show that the landlords largely fulfilled Evelyn's objectives. Naval timber was produced in quantity and helped to maintain England's sea power in the wars against the French. Admittedly, at times this supremacy was achieved only by a narrow margin and considerable dependence upon timber imports from the Baltic and elsewhere. Woodworking crafts and industries of every description were generally well supplied from home sources and, as the woodlands matured, so the furniture maker's art became more refined and elegant in the hands of masters such as Chippendale and Hepplewhite.

During the nineteenth century, planting and landscaping on the grand scale began to slacken for several reasons which have yet to be considered in detail. The most important were the effects of the Industrial Revolution and the use of iron for ship-building. Much of the nineteenth century and the early years of the twentieth formed a period of near stagnation in the woods. It so happened that this turned to the country's advantage during the world wars of our own time for, by 1914, there was an enormous stock-pile of matured timber standing in the plantations and amenity woods, the parklands and the hedgerows of England.

H. L. Edlin estimated that the area of woodlands in Great Britain resulting from the enclosure movement was of the order of 2 million acres. That is to say rather more than half of the approximate total of $3\frac{1}{2}$ million acres existing in the country in 1947.[25] In England alone probably not less than 1 million acres may have resulted from enclosure. In addition, there were many thousands of acres of small copses each of under five acres in extent established for shelter, amenity or for sport. Finally, there were the hedge and parkland trees, countless millions of them, for it has been calculated that 180,000 miles of new hedges were made during the enclosures of the eighteenth and nineteenth centuries, apart from those which had been formed earlier.[26] By 1951, after both world wars had drained the country of timber, there were still 73 million of these trees in Great Britain containing one fifth of the standing timber resources left to us.[27] Most of these were in

England and it is due to the presence of row upon row of hedge trees that many counties to this day give a false impression of being well wooded. If we could go back to 1914 when all the woods and copses, parks, plantations and hedgerows were virtually intact and filled with fine timber, the magnitude of the debt we owe to the foresight of earlier generations would be plain for all to see. Now this can only be called to mind with difficulty because no more than the dregs of the storehouse remain.

From this study of eighteenth-century attitudes towards land and landscape, a number of conclusions may be drawn. Firstly, it is clear that the need for change was regarded as a challenge. Until recent times, no greater basic changes, since the destruction of original forest cover, have taken place in English rural patterns than those wrought by the enclosures and the plantation movement. Landscape, which is always changing slowly in response to natural causes and more rapidly in response to the varying needs of man, was then dramatically transformed. New requirements demanded new arrangements upon the face of the land and the challenge was accepted with vigour.

Secondly, planning and design rested upon sound economics. Once the economic reason supporting it disappears, no rural pattern survives in a healthy condition for long. Although it may appear to continue, it is generally degenerating imperceptibly through natural causes. The facts that the planting landlords were so successful with their projects, and that these lasted for so long, are largely due to the soundness of the agricultural economy upon which the schemes were based. Changes in economy mean changes in planning and design and these, in turn, mean changes in the appearance of landscape. These things follow each other inevitably because they are interlocked.

Thirdly, the integration of use and beauty meant harmony not competition. If economic considerations are entirely untempered by aesthetic care, ugliness often results. The need to balance economics with aesthetics was appreciated and changes in the countryside were not made without keen regard for their good appearance. In the old designs use and beauty were joined to provide harmonious scenes while contributing to the country's agricultural and timber requirements. Each was complementary to the other. Beginning with the apportionment of land the designs were completed under a close alliance of technical and aesthetic skills.

43

Fourthly, localized control had certain advantages. While there was no national policy or system to co-ordinate effort, each landlord was strongly influenced by the pervading patriotism, knowledge and taste of his time. But he could interpret these influences to suit local conditions and, being in autocratic control of all interests within his own estate, his decisions were quickly made and were usually final. He was also generally in close continuous contact with all local work and knew the surrounding countryside and its peculiarities intimately. Financially, educationally and socially he was better equipped to integrate the needs of agriculture, forestry and amenity in his locality than any Government agent.

Finally, the planting of exotic conifer species in private woods during this period should be noted. Admittedly, most planting was undertaken with hardwoods and the proportion of softwoods used cannot have been large, in England at least. Nevertheless, the new species were accepted readily by the landlords. It is possible that, had forestry not fallen from economic grace during the following century, softwood planting would have increased gradually, together with knowledge of the silvicultural requirements of the species. In that way another change in landscape composition might have been accomplished — without the abruptness and technical uncertainty which was to characterize the mass introduction of conifer afforestation in the present century.

2 NINETEENTH-CENTURY INDIFFERENCE

a — Changed Circumstances

When the ironclad vessel *Merrimac* sank the wooden ships *Congress* and *Cumberland* in Hampton Roads during the American Civil War, the death knell sounded throughout the world for the importance of oak as a naval timber. With the official acceptance of iron warships after 1862, England was freed from the problem of growing sufficient naval timber which had been a constant worry for more than two hundred years.[1]

Protection from enemy fire was only one of the several advantages which iron possessed over wood for the purposes of general ship construction and these advantages had been known for a number of years. It was not long, therefore, before merchant vessels in appreciable numbers were built of iron. It has been estimated that in 1870 the tonnage of iron ships launched, excluding warships, was more than five times that of wooden craft.[2] The use of timber was still further depressed when, in the 1880's, steel began to supersede iron in the shipyards. Nevertheless, a small proportion of merchant shipping continued to be built of wood and repairs were required for these and for older wooden vessels still kept in service. Such demands for timber as this work made were insufficient to absorb the supplies of oak which were maturing in the English woodlands.

It should have been apparent that, as time passed, an ever-increasing surplus of mature oak, grown specially for ship-building purposes, would accumulate in the woods unless some alternative uses or modifications in management could be devised. Parliament, however, appears to have paid scant attention at the time to the effect which the revolution in ship-building materials was likely to have upon the country's forest economy.

A further reason for the accumulation of mature hardwoods was the peculiar settlement system of land tenure in England, which could prevent tenants for life from felling timber trees.[3] In law, only oak, ash and elm, above specified ages and sizes, were everywhere held to be timber although, in some counties by long custom, a few other species might be included — beech in Buckinghamshire and birch in Yorkshire are two examples. A tenant for life, unless otherwise exempted, was bound to keep the timber trees, like the land, intact as part of the capital of an estate. Similarly, trees planted for ornament or shelter on an estate had to be kept as part of the inheritance.[4]

There were other changes due to industrial developments in the nineteenth century which had repercussions upon woodland management. The coke oven, invented in the eighteenth century, had been improved in efficiency and adopted generally for the smelting of metallic ores, especially iron. As a result, charcoal, which had been used extensively since earliest times as fuel for this purpose, was no longer so important. Other uses for the material continued but, once the major use declined, large areas of coppice from which charcoal had been made became unprofitable. Oak coppice was affected not only by the smaller demand for charcoal but also by changes in the tanning industry. Extracts from foreign trees and chemical substitutes were replacing tan bark in the making of leather. Although oak bark was still employed for the best work, many traditional coppice areas ceased to be worked systematically for this product. The old coppice-with-standards system of silviculture, economically viable until about 1862, thus received a double blow when the main uses for the material produced under it disappeared. The decline in sheep farming also meant that fewer hurdles needed to be woven out of hazel coppice.

As the industrialization of the country progressed, the former agricultural economy fell into a slow decline. With the adoption of the Free Trade Doctrine in the mid-century, it became easier to import cheap food from abroad. During the last quarter of the century, under a flood of corn from the American prairies and frozen meat from South America and Australia, English agriculture collapsed.[5] Forestry practice, already outmoded, neglected and an unattractive investment, depended for its survival upon a healthily balanced agricultural economy and there seemed to be small chance of this recurring in the face of prevailing Parliamentary indifference to rural issues.

Meanwhile, for many landowners, investment in industry was largely providing the wealth required to maintain country estates and to meet increasing taxation. Woodlands, no longer part of a self-sufficient rural economy, came to be prized more and more as pleasure areas for ornament and sport. With the perfection of the central-fire cartridge by Daw in 1861 and the subsequent improvement of breech-loading sporting guns, the success of fashionable shooting parties was usually measured by the numbers of birds slain. The rearing of sufficient birds and their proper presentation to the guns therefore required the services of skilled gamekeepers, and in many estate woodlands their requirements took priority over those of the forester. Gamekeeping, like the preservation of deer in royal forests centuries earlier, helped to conserve the woods but contributed little to their proper management. Although good forestry practice is not incompatible with game preservation and many of the conifer species can provide excellent harbourage for birds,[6] this was not generally appreciated in the nineteenth century. Coppices provide good cover for game and, in some degree, their retention could be justified for sporting reasons. It became common practice to plant shrubs where no coppice existed under standard trees; snowberry, *Leycesteria*, rhododendron and laurel being popular for this purpose.

Those landowners who continued to manage their woodlands with thought for the future, and there were many such in spite of the prevailing mood of the times, were popularly regarded as rich hobbyists. The majority of owners looked upon woodland primarily as an amenity although its traditional role of providing a reserve in case of some financial emergency was not overlooked. By the end of the century, after 'death duties' had been extended in 1894, this role acquired a new and ominous significance, particularly for those who had been improvident in the management of their woods.

Under all the social and economic circumstances of the period, it is not surprising that forestry practice in this country was almost wholly unprepared for the tremendous demand for softwood timbers which developed during the nineteenth century. The belief is not uncommon that this demand arose only during the present century. In fact, it has been increasing, and hardwood requirements have been decreasing, progressively for more than one hundred years. The enormous growth in population and the rapid and widespread industrialization of the country resulted in calls for more and more cheap, easily worked timber for a whole range of new purposes. English woodlands simply did not contain the varieties or the volume of the timbers required.

As the country led the world in industrial manufacture and the products found ready markets abroad, a favourable balance of trade enabled the importation of foreign softwood timber to be financed without difficulty. It may be argued, on the grounds of the economic concept of comparative advantage, that we were correct in selling those manufactures in which we then excelled and in importing those materials which we lacked, while we could do so at cheap rates. Short-sighted although this policy may appear now, there were then seemingly endless supplies of timber readily available from those regions where natural and extensive coniferous forests existed, such as America, Russia and the Scandinavian lands. By the end of the century about nine-tenths of all timber and forest products used in this country were imported.[7] Between the years of approximately 1850 and 1910 importations increased fivefold and were predominantly of pine and fir.[8] Such was the stagnation of English forestry and the *laissez-faire* attitude of Parliament towards it that, it has been claimed, a generation of woodworking tradesmen and manufacturers arose who believed that good softwood timbers must invariably be imported.[9]

b — Pressure to Revive Forestry

Fortunately, some landowners were not lulled into complacency by industrial prosperity and easy foreign timber supplies. They were not satisfied that areas of nearly unmarketable coppice and coppice-with-standards should have no future other than as game preserves, ornament or sources of just enough timber to pay debts or taxes or to satisfy a few local rural uses. They knew that, without proper management, these residual values would also deteriorate in time. They felt that the woods should be replanted with commercially attractive species and foresaw that, if home supplies of softwood were to meet only a proportion of the new

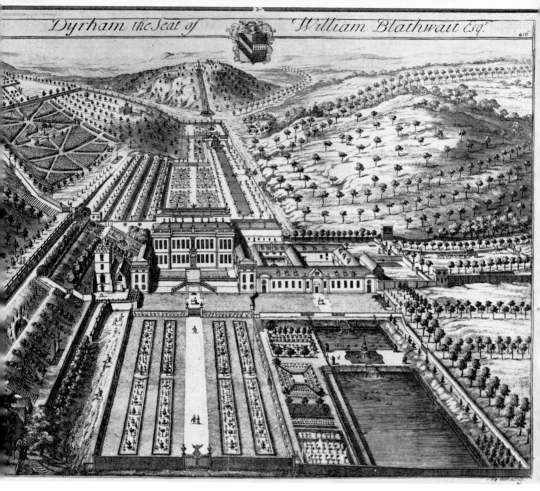

7. Dyrham Park, Gloucestershire: The extreme formality of seventeenth century parkland planting, from a drawing by Kip.

8. Blenheim Palace, Oxfordshire: The park, landscaped by Brown, contains characteristic lakes, woodland belts, curving patterns and tree clumps; these are related to a formal Grand Avenue—originally representing the battle-plan of Blenheim.

9. Corndon Hill from the Long Mynd, Shropshire : Small woods and hedgerow trees of all ages—a fine example of traditional English lowland scenery.

10. Epping Forest, London : These beech used to be pollarded regularly—like coppice, but at a height beyond the reach of browsing animals. The area is due for management to ensure the regeneration of amenity woodland.

demands, the afforestation of large areas of new land with conifers was a further requirement in this country. They believed that national as well as private action was necessary. They were dismayed by the apparent indifference with which Parliament viewed the degeneration of an activity which should have formed part of a healthy agricultural background to the country's industrial strength. To add to their concern, they were aware that, unlike England, most other European countries, especially Germany, were paying considerable attention to the conservation of valuable timber supplies and were developing forestry as a science in tune with contemporary demands.[10]

Much of the information gained during the second half of the nineteenth century about the performance of conifers under varied English conditions of soil and climate, may be attributed to the practical work of these men. They tried out new ideas in the management of woods, employing already well-known softwoods, such as the Scots and Corsican pines, Norway spruce and European larch, on a much more extensive scale than in the past. Many experimental plantings of freshly discovered conifers were also made. Trees were constantly being introduced from abroad throughout the century by plant hunters such as David Douglas and John Veitch.[11] Those species destined to become foremost in importance to forestry in this country included Douglas fir, introduced in 1827, Sitka spruce, which arrived in 1831 and Japanese larch, the seeds of which were first imported in 1861.

Some landowners liked to add specimens of the new conifers to their parklands. One of the most popular trees for this purpose was the Giant *Sequoia* or *Wellingtonia*, probably because of the accounts received from America of the great age and enormous size which it can attain. The species was first introduced to England in 1853. It also became fashionable to plant collections of many species of conifers together to form a pinetum or, if hardwoods were represented as well, an arboretum. A particularly fine example of the latter may be seen at Westonbirt in Gloucestershire. Established initially in 1829, it has been constantly maintained and extended, especially since 1892, and is now managed for the nation by the Forestry Commission.[12]

In these several ways sample groups and specimens of a large variety of softwood trees were established throughout the country. When the twentieth century forester was faced with the task of restoring England's timber resources as rapidly as possible with fast-growing conifers, valuable examples of the performance of different species under numerous geographical conditions were already available. Many of the conifers had become acclimatized to English conditions, but the failures were as instructive as the successes.

As well as practising what they preached, the landowners helped to form, in 1881, the Royal Arboricultural (now Forestry) Society in England as a counterpart to one which had been founded in Scotland in 1854. The Society, besides facilitating the exchange of ideas between members and promoting forestry generally, played an important part in persuading Parliament to consider seriously the adoption of a national forest policy. In 1885 the Government was impressed sufficiently to set up a Select Committee on Forestry to enquire into the matter.

It took most of twenty-five years, however, for successive Governments to consider the state of English forestry and to take the first cautious steps towards remedying its defects. The leisurely investigations and tardy action have not escaped criticism. A number of reports were issued by the Select Committee of 1885–87 and a Departmental Committee of the Board of Agriculture in 1902.

In the first two years of the present century some areas of land and woods at Dymock in Gloucestershire and Tintern in the Wye Valley were acquired by the Office of Woods, Forests and Land Revenues. These were the first fresh areas in England, outside the old Royal Forests, to come under State control for forestry purposes. A year or two later, in 1904, a school was established at Parkend in the Forest of Dean for the training of foresters.

In the matter of education, however, as in practical forestry, private enterprise was ahead of the State. In 1885, Dr. (later Sir William) Schlich, a German, generally recognized as a leading exponent of scientific forestry, and previously Inspector-General of Forests in India, opened a school of forestry at Cooper's Hill in Surrey. In 1905 this was transferred to Oxford University where it has since become the most important centre of forestry knowledge in England and the Commonwealth countries.

At last, in 1909, some more effective action seemed likely on the part of the Government. In that year a massive report was issued by the Royal Commission on Coast Erosion and Afforestation.

This recommended two alternative plans for State afforestation. The rate of land acquisition and planting was to be either 150,000 acres per year for 60 years, making a total of 9 million acres of new forest, or 75,000 acres per year for 80 years making a total of 6 million acres. Neither scheme was entirely realistic because technical knowledge of softwood forestry under English conditions was not sufficiently advanced at the time to cope with such large undertakings. It has also been said that the approach to the problem was rather from the newer angle of employment than of timber production.[13] Nevertheless, attention had been drawn to the importance of afforestation in the national economy. The Development Commission, which was set up in 1909, was provided with powers and funds to promote forestry in this country, although that was only one of its duties.

Wisely, this Commission recognized that a better understanding of where and how new forests should be established, and the improvement of facilities for training staff, were essential before extensive State afforestation projects could be undertaken with any hope of success. Accordingly, funds were expended with caution. Some useful experimental work was initiated, the overhaul of management systems in old Crown forests was commenced and educational arrangements were extended. A small Advisory Service was set up to help the owners of private woodlands. As yet, however, there was no clear national forest policy.

c — Awakening Public Interest in the Countryside

Until the early decades of the nineteenth century the population of this country, like the size of most towns, remained relatively small and evenly distributed, and the national economy was predominantly an agricultural one. Interest in the countryside for recreation, including the enjoyment of its beauty, could be satisfied locally by most people, who had neither the means nor the need to travel far from their homes. In 1800 the population was about $10\frac{1}{2}$ millions and mainly rural; by 1850 it had reached almost 21 millions; by 1900, it had nearly doubled again to 37 millions and had become mainly urban.

The early phases of the industrial revolution, centred on the coalfields and the cotton and wool towns of the North, the Midlands and South Wales, were assisted first by the building of canals and later by the railways. By the mid-nineteenth century half the population of the country had been attracted to and concentrated in those regions. The growth of the industrial towns was even more dramatic than that of the population, especially after 1850 when the decline in agriculture further accelerated the migration of people into the towns to find work in the factories.

Dr. W. G. Hoskins has described how much of the factory development began on low-lying flat land near rivers or canals, along which raw materials and products could be easily transported.[14] In the same areas, houses and tenements were constructed quickly, cheaply and densely, so that large numbers of workers could be accommodated within walking distance of the factories. There was little care for standards of building construction or sanitation and, on the ill-drained sites, living conditions soon became appallingly squalid. The word slum, first used in the 1820's to describe such an area of housing, is derived from slump, meaning a wet mire. Serious outbreaks of cholera and typhoid occurred in the 'thirties and 'forties. As land for building developed a scarcity value in some of the older towns, the open spaces within them vanished rapidly. Few places managed to save their commons or the large gardens and orchards of the previous century, which disappeared under bricks and mortar. Such countryside as remained between many of the towns in the industrial regions became blighted with chimney dirt, overlaid with waste heaps and pockmarked with subsidence.

Urban Reforms

The first tentative steps to remedy some of the evils were taken during the 1840's when the Government, alarmed by the increasing occurrence of disease, instituted enquiries into the causes of a rising death rate. From the resulting reports of a Royal Commission on the Health of Towns stemmed a series of Acts of Parliament, which laid the first permanent statutory restrictions upon the freedom of landowners to build as they pleased, and became the foundations of the modern system of planning.[15]

The Public Health Act of 1848 enabled local health boards to ensure that both new and existing houses in certain areas were provided with water and drainage. The Nuisance Removal and Disease Prevention Act of the same year applied throughout the country and made it an offence to build a new house to drain into an open ditch. Progress was very slow but powers to improve urban living conditions were extended gradually, often by means of local Acts petitioned for by the more energetic boroughs. The Public Health Act of 1875 consolidated the provisions of earlier general and local Acts giving national application to most of them.

Further Acts included a sweeping reform of the structure of local government which, outside the boroughs, had been left to a hotch-potch of authorities. These were replaced by the establishment of County Councils in 1888 and Urban and Rural District Councils in 1894. Thus by the end of the century, so far as urban planning was concerned, an effective system of local government had been created with considerable powers to control public health and housing.

These reforms, with others affecting education and working hours and conditions, vital though they were to the well-being of industrial communities, still left an unbalance which the dreary uniformity of bye-law housing and better sanitation could not correct. This missing factor was not defined officially until 1909, when the first Act of Parliament to recognize Town Planning as a specialist field described it as 'amenity and convenience' and provided for planning schemes to be prepared for suburban land. The provisions of this Act owed much to the example of enlightened industrialists, who had created such places as Bournville and Port Sunlight, and to Ebenezer Howard's garden city movement which had inspired work to be commenced at Letchworth in 1903. In 1913 the Town Planning Institute was founded and henceforward planning became accepted as a distinct profession.

Fight for the Commons

More than half a century earlier, however, the powerful and fundamental need of people for refreshment of mind and body in fresh air and sunshine and in contact with natural things, within or near to their environment, had begun to make itself felt. In the 1840's public parks came in as an adjunct to urban life and the provision of open spaces in towns became a popular form of benefaction among industrialists. In most manufacturing towns, however, these parks were few and small in relation to the great populations which they served. Attention became focussed upon the commons, especially those which had not yet been built upon, near the towns.

The enclosure of the old open fields for more intensive agricultural use had been virtually completed by the beginning of Victoria's reign. The enclosure of commons still continued and was stimulated by the General Enclosure Act of 1845. G. M. Trevelyan observes that

'it was characteristic of the altered balance of society that enclosure of commons was ultimately stopped in the decade between 1865 and 1875 by the protest not of the rural peasantry, but of the urban population, who objected to exclusion from its holiday playgrounds and rural breathing spaces.'[16]

Although by present standards working hours were long, they had been shortened sufficiently to provide some leisure time for recreation further afield than the local park. Holidays had already become a regular feature of middle-class life and often involved railway travel to seaside resorts and inland areas such as the Lake District.[17] More free time was sought as a condition of work in the factories. Carried through Parliament by Sir John Lubbock, the Bank Holiday Act of 1871 specified four days compulsory holiday each year in place of the old, more frequent, religious holy days, the observance of which had lapsed.

Opposition to the enclosure of commons all over the country was effectively organized by the Commons, Open Spaces and Footpaths Preservation Society which was formed in 1865 with the primary object of resisting encroachment upon commons in the London area. The Society was supported by many prominent and wealthy people, fought numerous legal battles and obtained judgments of the highest importance in the protection of the commons.[18] Partly as a result of the Society's activities, the passing of the Metropolitan Commons Act in 1866 excluded from enclosure any common of which all or part was situated within the Metropolitan Police District. Ten years later came the Commons Act of 1876 and further legislation followed concerning what is described as the regulation of commons, or their organized use for pasturage by specified persons rather than their enclosure.

In the vicinity of London, the Royal Parks were already administered for public use by the Crown.[19] The protection of additional areas such as Hampstead Heath, Blackheath and commons at Clapham, Wandsworth, Tooting and Wimbledon proved of immense benefit when the urban population increased still further. Elsewhere in the country similar action was taken and places such as the Malvern Hills and Ashdown Forest were protected.

New Trends

During this time, public attitudes towards amenity developed certain marked characteristics. Firstly, there was the emphasis placed upon access. The need to secure space for people to enjoy physical recreation was made a major feature of the case for the protection of the commons. The still popular belief that common land is public property, open to everyone, is erroneous because much of that type of land has been in private hands for centuries and most of it is still in that category. Permissive access has now become more widespread and the Law of Property Act, 1925, and the Rights of Way Act, 1932, have helped to extend legal right of access over some commons and footpaths.

Secondly, the word preservation in the title of the Commons Society indicates an attitude towards the countryside which was to develop strongly during later years. The preservation of rural scenery in the second half of the nineteenth century was no doubt regarded as an antidote to the rising flood of ugliness in the towns. But the need to manage recreational land to keep its special features does not seem to have been fully appreciated. Preservation, as applied to the maintenance of inanimate buildings, was apparently considered equally suitable for living landscape.

Lastly, the half-century is notable for an increase in the public ownership of land expressly for the enjoyment of the people. Many of the legal battles over the commons had the effect of establishing that recreational use was more important than any other use of the land concerned. The owners, thereby prevented from realizing a profit from development, were also faced with the problem of looking after the land for public benefit without any worthwhile financial recompense. The acquisition of such areas by public authorities offered a solution to the problem. With acquisition, the positive management of the land for amenity purposes, as opposed to simple and vaguely negative preservation, was usually secured. For instance, the Epping Forest Act of 1878, which followed litigation and public purchase, appointed the

Corporation of the City of London as Conservators with specific management functions, including the duty 'as far as possible to preserve the natural aspect of the Forest'.[20]

A little later came attempts to open up more remote countryside for public enjoyment. In 1884 James Bryce (later Lord Bryce) a prominent member of the Commons Society, introduced before Parliament his first Access to Mountains (Scotland) Bill. During the following six or seven years he introduced, equally unsuccessfully, six more such Bills. In 1892 a Parliamentary debate took place upon the need to secure free access to uncultivated mountains and moorlands, especially in Scotland, at which Bryce spoke persuasively but without success. In succeeding years more Bills were introduced by Bryce and others but nothing was accomplished at that time. Resistance to the proposals seems to have been based chiefly upon fear of damage, and the disturbance of sporting and gamekeeping interests.

The National Trust

In the closing years of the century, however, a plan was conceived to set up a body of responsible private citizens who would act for the nation to acquire land and buildings worthy of permanent preservation. They would hold such properties as trustees, protecting them from destruction or disfigurement and enabling people to enjoy them in perpetuity. So, in 1895, the National Trust for Places of Historic Interest or Natural Beauty was founded by Miss Octavia Hill, Canon Rawnsley and Sir Robert Hunter. The founders were already associated with other amenity movements in relation to the Lake District, the Commons or Garden Cities.

The success of the National Trust is well known. From modest beginnings it now owns over 400,000 acres in more than 1,000 separate properties scattered throughout the country. It has also accepted many covenants which protect further areas of beautiful land or buildings. The public are given free access to the Trust's open spaces, subject to the requirements of farming, forestry and the protection of nature. Land management forms an important feature of National Trust control, but a balance between productive and amenity management is observed. Where the latter is considered of over-riding importance, it is scrupulously and generously maintained. So, while there are many fully productive farms and woodlands in the Trust's ownership, there are also extensive areas of moorland, common, hill, down and wood capable of more productive use, but which are left undeveloped for public enjoyment.

Although national in name, the Trust is independent of the State and is not a Government Department. But successive Governments have given it valuable assistance, particularly in relief from taxation, although its main sources of revenue are gifts and subscriptions from more than 150,000 members. As long ago as 1907 a National Trust Act allowed for land and buildings held for the nation's benefit to be inalienable. Such land cannot be sold or mortgaged by the Trust or be acquired compulsorily without special Parliamentary authority, and money tied to the land is now exempt from death duties.

The National Trust only accepts properties when genuine historic, architectural or aesthetic values are involved, and the property is or can be made to be self-supporting. This business-like selectivity, applied to what may be described broadly as amenity management, has in a large measure helped to ensure the survival of the Trust. Its objective attitude to these matters has also helped over the years to establish the need to appreciate the cost of amenity. In this way the Trust may be said to have set an example to some of the later preservation societies whose demands have sometimes been founded more upon emotion and sentiment than upon objective appraisal.

In conclusion, although the title of this chapter suggests that indifference was the chief characteristic of nineteenth-century attitudes towards forestry, planning and amenity, the period also anticipated the revival of interest in the twentieth century. Much of what may now be regarded as indifference was caused by far-reaching social and economic upheavals.

Temporarily as is now known, but permanently as it must have seemed then, forestry lost its economic importance, becoming mainly an adjunct to sport, private amenity or the payment of debts. The localized planning of small towns and villages, largely the prerogative of the landowners and usually exercised beneficiently by them, was overwhelmed in the mushroom growth of new industrial areas where speculation and greed could flourish without much restraint. The provision of recreation for a swollen and overcrowded urban population, cut off from the rural surroundings and pursuits of their forbears, presented entirely new problems for which solutions had yet to be found.

Work, pleasure and reasonably healthy living conditions, instead of being combined in one environment under an agricultural economy, were split apart for most people in a newly urbanized and industrialized society. In the towns there was, as yet, no substitute for the landowners as co-ordinators of the various needs of the community. In the processes of social reorganization which characterized the second half of the century, each need attracted its champions who clamoured for the Government's attention. And there was little co-ordination between these rivals for Parliamentary time. The rapidly increasing complexity of affairs was itself an encouragement to the sectionalization of interests, and the age of the specialist was foreshadowed. The recognition which each pressure-group might obtain was to depend for many years upon the energy and persistence of those who supported it.

Of the groups considered here, the foresters were preoccupied with gaining recognition for the new role they could play in the country's economy. Amenity values in the modern sense of the term, did not greatly concern them. That matter was gradually absorbed into the province of the self-styled preservationists, then busy securing rural playgrounds for the urban masses. The planners, not yet involved with the countryside, were absorbed with the improvement of basic living conditions in industrial towns. Creativeness in relation to amenity generally was at a very low ebb.

3 TWENTIETH-CENTURY REVIVAL

a — The First World War and the Forestry Commission's Early Years

At the outbreak of war with Germany in 1914, England was dependent upon imported timber, mostly softwood, to the extent of about 93% of total requirements. Little more than 5% of the land surface was under woodland and that was mostly of hardwood species. Germany possessed ample reserves of all kinds of timbers and her forests, which covered about 26% of the land surface, had been under continuous systematic management for many years.[1] Timber, recognized by Germany as an essential munition of war, is also one of the most bulky of ship's cargoes. An immense strain was placed upon British shipping when it became harassed by submarine warfare and yet had to maintain a flow of timber imports as well as food and other vital commodities.

Somehow, by means of rationing, substituting home grown hardwoods for imported softwoods whenever possible and arranging for the Army in France to use French supplies, timber imports were cut drastically and war-time requirements were met. It was estimated in 1924 that, during the war and the immediate post-war years, almost 450,000 acres of woods were felled in this country (out of the probable 3 million acres standing in 1914) and the volume of timber used was approximately one-third of the total volume standing in 1914.[2] Table 1, page 60, shows the distribution of the various types of British woods as they were in 1924, and the preponderance of the hardwood categories, especially in England, should be noted.

The German submarine campaign precipitated Government

action regarding British forestry. In 1916 a Ministry of Recon-struction Sub-Committee, under the Chairmanship of Mr. F. D. (later Sir Francis) Acland, M.P., was appointed to consider and report upon the conservation and development of forestry resources in the United Kingdom. The Acland Report which resulted was presented in 1917 and, among other recommenda-tions, proposed the afforestation with softwood species of 2

TABLE 1

DISTRIBUTION OF ALL BRITISH WOODLANDS
BY CATEGORIES IN 1924

	England	Wales	Scotland	Great Britain	% of total Woodland Area
	Acres	Acres	Acres	Acres	
ECONOMIC OR POTENTIALLY PRODUCTIVE High Forest—					
Conifers	195,231	46,940	429,670	671,841	
Hardwoods	338,456	43,957	60,941	443,354	
Mxd. Confrs. & Hwds.	220,390	22,106	59,199	301,695	
Total High Forest	754,077	113,003	549,810	1,416,890	47·9
Coppice and Coppice-with-Standards	485,229	35,331	8,120	528,680	17·9
Scrub	87,410	34,934	208,359	330,703	11·2
Felled or Devastated	194,742	62,182	221,182	478,106	16·1
Total Scrub and Felled or Devastated	282,152	97,116	429,541	808,809	27·3
UNECONOMIC (including amenity woods & shelter belts)	109,529	8,011	86,753	204,293	6·9
GRAND TOTAL	1,630,987	253,461	1,074,224	2,958,672	100·0

NOTE : When the total land area of Great Britain (approximately 56·2 million acres) is compared with the woodland acreages above, the average proportion of the whole country under woodland is 5·3% (England 5·1, Wales 5·0 and Scotland 5·6).
SOURCE : F.C. *Census of Woodlands*, 1924, pages 7–8.

million acres of rough grazing land. The bulk of this programme was to be undertaken within eighty years, mostly by the State, through a new central Forest Authority, but partly by private landowners. The latter were also expected, optimistically as it turned out, to restore their existing woods after wartime fellings and to improve the productivity of those which had been ill-attended for many years. Limited grant-aid for private planting and replanting was to be advanced.[3] In 1918, the Acland Report was accepted by the Cabinet and the first Forestry Commissioners were appointed under the Forestry Act of 1919.

For twenty years the Forestry Commissioners struggled against financial checks and policy changes to satisfy their strategic role and grow as much softwood timber, especially pit props, as quickly and cheaply as possible.[4] By September 1939, they had fulfilled about 88% of the land acquisition and 75% of the planting programmes set by the Acland Committee for the first twenty years, and the Commission had become the largest landowner in the country with well over 1 million acres in hand (Table 2, page 62).

The Commission also suffered from a lack of technical know-ledge as to the best way of undertaking a softwood afforestation programme of the scale envisaged. Research and forest education had somehow to keep pace with an industry which was started with borrowed experience, mostly German, and the Commis-sioners themselves were not unaware that, under these circum-stances, technical mistakes were almost certain to occur.[5] That aesthetic mistakes might also happen was not considered at that time, and there was nothing whatever in the Forestry Commis-sion's brief about amenity. In an atmosphere of urgency the Act of 1919, based upon the experience of one war and a scarcely veiled intention to prepare for the next, invited the application of mass-production methods to achieve a limited objective. The divorce between art and science in forestry was effectively sanctioned.

Sir George Stapledon criticized the weaknesses of the Com-missioners' brief, claiming that their very success in a too limited field emphasized the need for co-ordination between all aspects of land utilization. He would have liked the restoration of existing woods to have been their first concern in spite of the inconvenience and expense of dealing with numerous small parcels of land. He pleaded for a better integration between the long-term interests of agriculture and forestry in afforestation plans. He criticized the neglect of aesthetics in forestry and regarded this aspect as inseparable from all matters concerning land use.[6]

TABLE 2

LAND UTILIZATION OF FORESTRY COMMISSION'S
ESTATE AT 30TH SEPTEMBER, 1939

	England and Wales	Scotland	Total
	Acres	Acres	Acres
Forest land :			
Planted :			
Acquired plantations	61,000	12,000	73,000
Planted by F.C.	224,500	136,500	361,000*
Under plantations	285,500	148,500	434,000
To be planted	153,000	127,000	280,000
Ultimate forest area	438,500	275,500	714,000
Nurseries	600	400	1,000
Forest Workers' Holdings (including outrun)	13,000	3,000	16,000
Agricultural	26,300	16,700	43,000
Unplantable and Misc.	122,100	247,900	370,000
Total area	600,500	543,500	1,144,000
Number of Forest Units	130	111	241

* The total area planted, including replanting of plantations destroyed by fire, was 368,878 acres.
NOTE : The above figures include the Crown Woods transferred to the Commissioners under the Transfer of Woods Act, 1923, extending to about 120,000 acres, of which approximately 60,000 acres are plantable.
SOURCE : F.C. *Post-War Forest Policy Report*, 1943, Cmd. 6447, page 93.

There was, however, little competition for land in those years; while agriculture remained depressed, large compact areas could be obtained fairly cheaply for afforestation and could be managed more economically than numerous scattered woods. But it was not long before the Commissioners found it necessary to acquire old woodlands if they hoped to get them replanted. Later, after another war, the need for a closer integration of forestry and agricultural interests was acknowledged and, later still, forest aesthetics achieved a place in national policy.

By 1939, softwood afforestation by the Forestry Commission

had become a prominent feature in many types of English landscape. New forest units were scattered throughout the country, with Kielder on the Border and Thetford in East Anglia well on the way to becoming two of the largest individual forests in the whole of Britain. The widespread use of Sitka spruce in planting poor high-lying land in the wetter western side of the country was a development in English forestry almost entirely attributable to the Commission's work.[7] Even at that time there were indications that the species might one day replace the oak as the dominant forest tree in this country. In the drier eastern side of England the pines proved most suitable, while the larches were more generally distributed, and Douglas fir occupied better sites in association with the spruces.

So far as the cultivation of hardwoods was concerned, the activities of the Commission were much less noticeable. In 1923, the former Crown Forests were transferred to the Commission's control.[8] Large portions of these forests were already predominantly composed of hardwoods and continued to be managed with a bias in favour of these species. Such maintenance of established traditional woods was not remarkable enough to attract attention. In addition, by 1939, the Commission had planted, or regenerated by natural means, about 28,000 acres of hardwoods, mostly oak and beech. This area represented an average annual proportion of only about 8% of all Commission planting. Although most of these hardwoods were established in the southern counties of England and Wales, the proportion concentrated in those regions was still far outweighed by the amount of softwood planting.

The Landowners' Problems

There was another event which served to isolate and emphasize the Forestry Commission's softwood afforestation activities. This was the general failure of private landowners either to take part in afforestation or to restock their woods to the extent which had been expected of them. The circumstances which led to this situation seem to have been appreciated by the Forestry Commissioners but not by the Acland Committee.

The progressive impoverishment of landed estates only began with the protracted agricultural depression of the eighteen-eighties. It was sustained by the cumulative effects of reduced receipts from rents, rising maintenance cost, restrictions upon landlords' freedom of action in the system of land tenure, and high taxation, including death duties. Many estates were split into smaller units in efforts to curtail expense or effect financial recovery. Forestry suffered because timber felling was accelerated to raise revenue and planting slowed down owing to lack of capital for such long-term investment. Standards of private woodland management were already declining, therefore, before the 1914–18 fellings took an extra toll.[9]

In 1907, landowners formed a Central Land Association, later re-named the Country Landowners' Association, to combat more effectively the threat of further measures likely to be detrimental to estate management. The Association, now known as the C.L.A., has since become spokesman for rural landowners throughout the country. It helped to bring about the de-rating of agricultural land and buildings in 1929, and to stave off increases in death duties on agricultural property.

W. E. Hiley believed that these concessions, together with the Forestry Commission's planting grants and the tax remissions already available to landowners who cared to run their woods on business-like lines, strongly favoured private forestry ventures.[10] Generally, however, the inducements proved insufficient to attract those who had little faith in being able to keep their lands intact for their successors. The break-up of estates continued and tenants, who had purchased their farms on the proceeds of wartime prosperity from landlords who were prevented from raising rents, had little capital to spare for forestry when agriculture became depressed again in the nineteen-twenties and 'thirties. The new owner-occupiers extended their control of agricultural land area in this country from 9·5% in 1914 to 32% in 1940, while landed estates of the old style declined from 86% to 57% in the same period and State control of land rose from 3% to 8%.[11] This changing pattern of land tenure tended, except in the case of the State, to disperse control over private woods without releasing money for investment in them.

The Forestry Commissioners provided some technical advice upon woodland management, and joined with the Forestry Societies and the Landowners' Association to study marketing and other problems. As a result, several reports were published.[12] It was only on the eve of the Second World War that some progress

11. Kielder Forest, Northumberland : Part of the Border Forest Park, showing the forest road by the Lewis Burn and spruce plantations at Mounces.

12. Thetford Forest, Norfolk : Corsican pine on Rendlesham Heath, planted in 1919 by the Forestry Commission, photographed in 1959.

13. Thetford Forest, Norfolk: Three examples of roadside treatment in flat country to add interest to plantation edges. Line of poplars (top); groups of mixed species (middle); picnic place under old trees (bottom).

was made towards a new policy, based upon more liberal financial support for good management and firmer State action towards neglect in private forestry.[13] So marked was this neglect that planting by landowners scarcely counterbalanced fellings between 1919 and 1939. Indeed, most of what was accomplished towards restoring the felled areas of the First World War was due to the Forestry Commission at the expense of the main afforestation programme. By 1939, there was scarcely as much mature timber in the country as there had been in 1919.[14]

The statistics in Table 1, page 60, show that at the Census of 1924, there were higher proportions in England than elsewhere of the woodland categories in which hardwoods generally predominate. These are hardwood and mixed high forest, coppice with or without standards and uneconomic woods, including amenity areas. The indications are, therefore, that regardless of timber quality, hardwood species and their foliage effects were continuing to dominate English woodland landscapes. Indeed, fellings undertaken both before, during and after the 1914–18 war, had helped to accentuate this bias because, owing to the demand for softwoods, the cutting of mature conifers had been favoured and these had not been replaced. On the other hand, while much of the best ash and oak had also been removed, coppice shoots and other regrowth soon filled the gaps with foliage, thereby helping to heal scars in the landscape. Unfortunately, the material, although traditional in appearance, was for the most part unlikely to provide valuable timber in the future.

Up to 1939 this pattern in private woods was sustained chiefly by the continuation of adverse economic circumstances affecting management. Moreover, those landowners who did replant, generally established a proportion of young hardwoods which was roughly double that being planted by the State. The average annual proportion by area during 1919–39 was about 16% compared with 8% in Forestry Commission properties.[15] The often fertile woodland sites, especially in England, which landowners planted were usually more suitable for the cultivation of a higher proportion of hardwoods than the poor open land then being afforested by the State.

Circumstances affecting private woods between the world wars therefore combined to maintain fortuitously the old hardwood patterns in English landscapes for a further period of years, well beyond that attributable to the general stagnation of forestry in the nineteenth century. During those years the amenity movement was gathering strength, increasingly anxious to protect the beauty of the countryside and adversely comparing the appearance of the Commission's softwood plantations with that of the old broad-leaved woods. It would seem that the circumstances which post-poned the replenishment of private woods also helped to per-petuate the image of the purely broadleaved woodland, however neglected it might be in a technical sense, as a criterion of forest beauty in the public mind.

b — Forestry in conflict with Amenity and Recreational Planning

Throughout the 1920's the demands of the urban population for more access to the countryside rose steeply. They included the plea that the character and appearance of many areas should be preserved or protected from change. There was no general legislation to support these ideas. As a result pressure-groups, often with only localized interests, were formed throughout the country. In 1926, the Council for the Preservation of Rural England, referred to usually as the C.P.R.E., was founded as a co-ordinating organization for these interests, and became spokes-man for the amenity movement as a whole.

Meanwhile, the Forestry Commission had attracted consider-able criticism on the grounds of seeming insensitive to amenity interests. The appearance of many of the new softwood plantations in the countryside antagonized public opinion for aesthetic reasons, and the restrictions imposed upon access through planted land aroused added opposition.

Large rectangular blocks of conifers, often of one species un-relieved by mixture with another, an apparent exclusion of hard-woods and a grid-iron pattern of fire breaks and rides intersecting newly afforested areas, seemed typical of the Commission's work. Where such geometry was fully displayed on hillsides, as in some parts of the Lake District, criticism became particularly strong. The large scale of many plantations and the obliteration of subtle natural contours by their rigid patterns, the sombre colours and the sharp outlines of the young trees, all conflicted with popular conceptions of woodland beauty. The even age, dense planting, suppression of undergrowth and exclusion of sunlight in many plantations, caused further aggravation. Feelings ran high enough for the Commission to be accused of creating tree slums.

The immature conifer plantations were persistently and unfavourably compared with mature if often neglected hardwood glades. The delicate colouring, informal arrangement and spreading crowns of the latter had long satisfied English taste in these matters. Whereas most people, consciously or unconsciously, accepted constantly changing agricultural patterns, usually small in scale and short in term, many were unable to accept seemingly revolutionary changes, large in scale and of long term effect, in the appearance of woodland. English people were accustomed to the gradual evolution of farming and were imbued with an agricultural tradition. Unlike many Continental countries, especially Germany, there was no comparable forest tradition in England. It seems that when sweeping changes were presented abruptly and with a Teutonic precision after a long spell of inactivity in forestry, the innate conservatism of taste was profoundly offended.

Furthermore to reduce the chances of accidental fires and also to keep out rabbits, the Commission found it necessary to surround the planted areas with wire netting fences and locked gates. This sometimes meant that owing to the positioning of plantations, access to open land beyond them was debarred or made more difficult.

The growing concern of the public for the protection of amenity interests was not without its champions in Parliament. Sir Charles Trevelyan, who had taken over Bryce's Access to Mountains Bill, constantly introduced similar Bills, one of which reached Committee stage before disappearing. Other Members joined in the fight with a succession of motions during the 1930's and, finally, Royal Assent was given to the Access to Mountains Act of 1939. Ironically, the Second World War began two months later and this statute was never used. In any event, it was very complex and was repealed by the National Parks and Access to the Countryside Act of 1949, sixty-five years after Bryce introduced his first Bill.

National Parks and Planning

Until the late 1920's the idea of National Parks in this country had not received official attention, but their success in other countries, especially America, had excited much interest.[16] In 1929 the C.P.R.E. submitted a memorandum to the Prime Minister on the subject. This led to the appointment of a committee of enquiry under the chairmanship of Dr. Christopher (later Lord) Addison. The Addison Report of the National Park Committee was published in 1931 but a financial crisis diverted Parliamentary attention from its favourable recommendations.[17] The campaign was continued largely through the efforts of the C.P.R.E. which formed, in 1935, a Standing Committee on National Parks under the chairmanship of the late Lord Birkett. Pressure was brought to bear constantly upon the Government to consider the matter further during the remaining years before the Second World War. The official view taken, however, was that many of the aims contained in the Addison Report could be accomplished by local authorities under existing planning legislation.[18]

Planning during the 'twenties had still been confined to urban and suburban areas, but was expanded to include the countryside under the first Town and Country Planning Act in 1932, and aided by the Restriction of Ribbon Development Act of 1935. The pressures which brought about this extension of powers in the 'thirties were due basically to the still rising population, the development of motor transport and the increasing use of electricity. Industry, no longer tied to the coalfields, canals and railways, could be sited in entirely new areas and workers could live further away from their jobs. There was a general movement towards living standards requiring more space. So, building rapidly encroached upon the countryside, especially along the newly widened roads. Moreover, the motor car had revolutionized holiday habits, enabling larger numbers of people to reach areas previously considered remote; this often resulted in the disfigurement of countryside and coastline with ill-designed development of all kinds.

Incidentally, the Act of 1932 was the first to contain specific provisions for protecting trees and woods from felling. The extension of these powers, in later years, provided one reason for developing a consultation procedure upon amenity between the Forestry Commission and planning authorities. But the main aim of planning was to stop the worst features of the new spread of urbanization. In this field some substantial successes were achieved. Unfortunately, the legislation was soon found to be too negative in concept and parochial in administration to deal effectively with

68

major national problems. The regrouping of industry and population, and the positive control of land-use, as distinct from local amenity and environment, were beyond its scope. The Government's belief that the recommendations of the Addison Committee had been catered for was therefore misplaced — and a measure of its apathy towards the future of the English countryside.

c — Attempts to Reconcile Forestry and Amenity Interests

The circumstances outlined in the previous section of this chapter provided the Forestry Commissioners with an excellent opportunity to regain some of the public approval which they had lost during the 1920's. In their first decade the Commissioners had had little time to spare from their struggle for survival to answer their critics in amenity matters which, in any event, must have appeared to be largely outside their terms of reference. At first the Commissioners attempted only to justify the need for softwood afforestation on economic and silvicultural grounds, regardless of the appearance of the new plantations.[19] In the early 'thirties, however, at about the time of the Addison Report, they began to consider seriously ways and means of integrating public access and recreational facilities within their forests, and of mitigating some of the visual effects which their work was having in the countryside.[20]

Hiking, cycling and camping had increased greatly in popularity especially among younger people from the cities to whom, perhaps, aesthetic aspects of forestry were of less concern than opportunities for energetic holidays in the open air. The National Park movement had come to a standstill but the Forestry Commissioners already owned large tracts of wild elevated land which was unplantable, but which they had had to acquire in order to secure other more suitable areas. Although access through plantations might still have to be restricted until the trees had grown sufficiently to be less susceptible to fire risks, the Commissioners were empowered under the Forestry Act of 1927 to make bye-laws to control public behaviour on all their lands.[21]

National Forest Parks

The possibility of admitting people to the more open areas was tested cautiously in 1931 and succeeding years. Facilities were

69

granted on a small scale at first to members of the then recently formed Youth Hostels Association; by 1934 there were twelve hostels on Commission land and the experiments were considered successful. Meanwhile the Commissioners, observing the popularity of the New Forest in Hampshire, felt that this forest conformed more nearly to the ideal of a national park than any other area in Britain. It was unique in that unenclosed stretches of 'ancient and ornamental' woods were already protected by statute. This old Royal Forest also contained large enclosed plantations for timber production and stretches of open heath. It was a model for the combination of forestry and recreation upon which the design of modern forests might be based. At Kielder in Northumberland, on what had been almost treeless hills typical of the Border Country, a huge forest was then being created by the Commission. It was to be predominantly composed of the spruces, but pines, larch and, on the better soils, mixed conifers and hardwoods, were also to be planted. The Commissioners envisaged the area being developed in an irregular pattern of forest and open unplantable highland, which would provide for the integration of timber production and public recreation in a similar fashion to the New Forest.

So the idea of forming National Forest Parks was evolved and, in 1935, the Forestry Commissioners set up a Committee to report upon the suitability of a group of their Scottish forests in Argyll for this purpose. The report was favourable, financial support from the Government was sanctioned and the Argyll park was opened unofficially in 1936. Following the same procedure, a second park was established in Snowdonia in 1937 and a third in the Forest of Dean in 1938. After the Second World War, five more were formed. Three were in Scotland and two in England; the last to be opened, in 1955, being the Border which includes the forest of Kielder. The Hardknott forest park in the Lake District was discontinued in 1959 for reasons which will be discussed later; thus the Border and the Dean remain the only two examples in England.

The forests within these two parks contrast markedly with each other. The Border, in the north, is modern and almost entirely coniferous, as yet the immature product of twentieth-century State afforestation superimposed upon an older landscape of wide and rolling hills. The large size of the forested area is in keeping with

70

the scale of the surrounding scenery, and the park provides an important example of the dual use of land in an entirely contemporary manner, combining intensive softwood production with opportunities for recreation. The Dean, in the south, is an ancient and valuable hardwood region, to be maintained as such under State control, while conifers are introduced mainly on the poorer soils with the effect of adding a new but not dominant chapter in the forest's history.[22] The area is more compact than the Border, there is less open space and the scale of the surrounding countryside is smaller and more intimate. The forest has performed a treble role in that timber production and public recreation have been combined with considerable mining activity.

Since 1955, no further forest parks have been designated and Commission policy has developed towards the provision of recreational facilities in all State forests wherever such arrangements seem desirable and practicable.[23] There is no doubt about the success of the forest park movement. Since 1960, well over a quarter of a million people have stayed overnight each year in the designated areas, apart from uncounted day-visitors, and the numbers continue to rise. Through the parks the Commissioners have managed to improve their relations with the public; while the public, subconsciously perhaps, has acquired some appreciation of the forester's skills and difficulties. Valuable experience has been gained of the requirements of people on holiday in remote rural areas, including such diverse items as car parks, lavatories, camp sites, hostels, litter collection, the marking of forest trails, water points and picnic areas. The Commission has also set an exceptionally high standard in the production of guide books for the forest parks and other regions of special interest.[24]

The New Forest

The New Forest — although the prototype — has not been designated as a park. Instead, it is administered by the Commission as a State forest under a series of special Acts of Parliament. It receives almost as many visitors as all the national forest parks put together although, in size, it amounts to less than one-sixth of the area covered by them. This intensive recreational use seems to be due mainly to the New Forest being easily accessible to the heavily populated south of England. It is also an area where woodland beauty has been consciously appreciated for more than a century, and it stands high in public esteem on that account.

In the late eighteenth century, William Gilpin, champion of the picturesque in Lakeland scenery, retired to the New Forest and was inspired to spend ten years writing a fascinating analysis of woodland beauty in all its forms.[25] In the Forest, after the last rush of oak planting following the Napoleonic Wars of the early nineteenth century, activity lapsed for a number of years. The amenity value of certain areas of old hardwood trees seems to have been publicly recognized as early as 1845, when the Southampton and Dorchester Railway Act was passed and the track was constructed to avoid disturbing ornamental woods.[26] Later, when it was found that, under the Deer Removal Act of 1851, the power of the Crown to enclose and plant new areas could be extended indefinitely, the public became concerned lest restriction upon access and large-scale planting of conifers, notably Scots pine, should impair the amenities of the Forest.[27]

The New Forest Act of 1877 contained the first statutory provisions for maintaining the visual amenities of the area. The Crown's right of enclosure was limited and within the enclosures there were specific instructions to have 'regard to the ornamental as well as the profitable use of the ground' (Sec. 6). Furthermore, the Act stated that 'the ancient and ornamental woods shall be preserved and . . . shall remain open and uninclosed' (Sec. 8). Although the Act also provided for planting in the enclosures with trees of any kind 'which may be thought expedient' (Sec. 7), the general effect of this legislation was to bring silvicultural activity, except for the tending of established plantations, to a halt.[28]

Felling in the enclosures during the First World War was carried out without much care for the appearance of the Forest. When it was realized that the Act of 1877 provided plenty of scope for replanting with softwoods, the post-war restoration of the woods was also pursued with small regard for amenity. Public antagonism was aroused once more and not allayed until 1928 when Lord Clinton, then Chairman of the Forestry Commission, declared in the House of Lords that the amenity of the Forest should be the chief object of management.[29] Shortly afterwards an Advisory Committee was appointed to guide the Commissioners in this matter.

The new policy led to an improvement in the appearance of the enclosed woods, especially after the appointment of D. W. Young

14. New Forest, Hampshire: Ancient and ornamental woods of beech and oak in the Denny Forest Nature Reserve.

15. Ullswater, Lake District: All the admired elements of Lakeland scenery—and afforestation is prevented by agreement.

16. Hodder's Combe, Somerset : Oak woods, subject to a Tree Preservation Order, in a popular part of the Quantock Hills Area of Outstanding Natural Beauty.

17. Exe Valley, Somers Overgrown oak coppice thinned out and Dougla fir planted in the resulti 'dappled shade', Anothe thinning is due.

18. Weasenham, Norfolk: Northern edge of New Wood showing irregular effect of several species and age-groups of hardwoods and softwoods grown together.

19. Weasenham, Norfolk: Inside New Wood—mixed species, ages and natural regeneration are more typical of a Continental 'selection' forest than a modern English woodland.

20. The Brendon Hills: Part of the Forestry Commission's Brendon Forest at Croydon Hill, and the orderly agricultural pattern.

21. The Brendon Hills: On the ridge road looking west to Langham Hill plantations (centre) and Dunkery Beacon (in distance, right). Keeping young beech hedgerow trees is unusual in this part of Exmoor.

as Deputy Surveyor in 1931. At a time when foresters generally were regarding their plantations like farm crops to be evenly grown and cut in a single harvest, Young was a pioneer in attempting to build up uneven-aged crops, through a combination of natural regeneration and planting, and the felling only of selected trees or groups of trees at any one time.[30] These methods of management seldom involve extensive clearances and aim to include all age-groups of trees, often of mixed species, intermingled on the ground instead of being arranged in even-aged blocks. Visually, they provide much more interest and variety than conventional methods. They are more applicable, however, to the management of established woods than in the afforestation of new land.

During the Second World War, nearly twice as much timber was felled as in 1914–18 but, largely as a result of Young's supervision, far less damage was done to the amenities of the Forest. In 1946 a New Forest Committee, which included members of the C.P.R.E., was appointed to study and report upon the condition of the area for the Forestry Commissioners. Based upon the recommendations of this Committee, the New Forest Act of 1949 provided for an improvement in land utilization, including an extension to the area of enclosed productive woods. Significantly perhaps, it did not repeal Section 6 of the 1877 Act under which care for appearances in the enclosures is still required.

The 1949 Act also contains special provisions for the 'ancient and ornamental' woods. After 1877, succeeding managers of the New Forest had virtually no power to take any steps to secure the perpetuation of these woods. Cutting was confined in effect to dead or dangerous trees, and enclosure was forbidden. Cattle and ponies were able to enter and browse young seedling trees which might otherwise have been encouraged to grow and replace the veterans. In these circumstances, which lasted over seventy years, the amenity woods deteriorated both in appearance and quality. Since 1949 the Forestry Commissioners have been permitted to enclose sections of the ornamental woods, not exceeding twenty acres in one place, and reafforest them with hardwood species. Once the trees have been established the enclosures have to be removed. By 1962 about 400 acres were under treatment, but results were not promising except in the younger and better stocked areas which need little more than thinning to encourage growth. In the older, most dilapidated parts, soil conditions do not always favour regeneration. The requirement, supposedly for the sake of amenity, that conifers must not be used to nurse the hardwoods, has been hampering the work of restoration, often in places where it is most needed. The small size and scattered location of plots under treatment add to the difficulties and cost of management.

Although the New Forest Act of 1964 now appears to facilitate the creation of new ornamental woods, the old areas may still serve as a warning in considering Tree Preservation Orders.[31] They demonstrate the deterioration in amenity values which may result from prolonged statutory preservation, without adequate provisions for amenity management — and the aesthetic difficulties which can arise when such management is introduced at a very late stage in the life of the trees.

Visual Amenity

Aesthetic matters raise far more complications, both in established woods and newly afforested areas, than the provision of access and facilities for physical recreation. Nevertheless, when the Forestry Commissioners launched the idea of national forest parks, they also began to study the problems of visual amenity.

A substantial section of their 15th Annual Report in 1934 is devoted to the subject under the title of 'Hardwoods, Conifers and Amenity'. From this it is clear that the Commissioners were prepared to concede that however expedient the growing of conifers might be, something could be done to improve the appearance of the plantations in the landscape. This was a major policy decision marking another step towards a more liberal interpretation of the role of forestry in relation to national life.

The Commissioners suggested some simple improvements, including:

1. Planting hardwood belts along roadsides in flat country and other suitable positions (already being carried out in their East Anglian pine forests).
2. Avoiding straight outlines to plantations.
3. Laying out roads and rides with care for the country.
4. Introducing variety by changes of species within the plantations.

Had these ideas been put into practice with imagination in all

74

forestry projects during the last thirty years or so, a great improvement in plantation design would now be noticeable throughout the country. Unfortunately, they were applied in limited areas only, and then sometimes with a sparing and mechanical diligence exasperating in its lack of feeling for the character of local landscape.[32]

Also in the early 1930's, to assist them in relating beauty and silviculture, the Commissioners formed a joint informal Committee with members of the C.P.R.E. This was important because liaison between the Commission and public opinion in amenity matters had not previously existed. In subsequent years the new Committee proffered advice upon ways of improving the appearance of plantations in a number of districts including Breckland, Dartmoor, Savernake and the Sussex Downs.[33]

The Lake District

The Committee's most notable work was a study of the Lake District where the Commission's planting activities had aroused strong opposition. Following detailed consultations, a White Paper was published in 1936 which recorded the Commissioners' agreement not to acquire land for planting within an area covering 300 square miles of central Lakeland. This area, outlined in black on Plan A, page 76, amounts to more than one-third of the total land contained in the Lake District National Park which was designated fifteen years later in 1951. It was also agreed that in an additional area in southern Lakeland, hatched vertically on Plan A, each proposed land acquisition should be considered on its merits, and consultations undertaken through the Joint Committee before planting started.

The Agreement of 1936 was amended in 1954, but only to enable the Forestry Commissioners to acquire woodland areas already under timber trees within the central reservation in 1936. Such acquisitions might be agreed provided their main objective was to sustain hardwood crops characteristic of the district, and the use of conifers as nurse-trees was kept to a minimum. Private landowners in the area were also to be encouraged to manage their woods in accordance with the Joint Committee's plan. The Agreement and Amendment were published as a combined report in 1955.

This is an important document in the history of English forestry

75

in relation to landscape. It records, in effect, the first attempt in modern times to correlate afforestation with the conservation of existing scenic beauty on a regional scale. It is remarkable that the original agreement was reached at a time when rural planning was in its infancy and the formation of national parks was still many years ahead. It seems clear that the Forestry Commissioners were prepared to hold back in the Lake District because of its exceptionally high place in public esteem. No other region in England has quite such a strong general appeal.

Norman Nicholson has described how the beauty of the mountains and lakes has captured the imagination of Englishmen for generations.[34] Reported upon by seventeenth- and eighteenth-century travellers, idealized by William Gilpin and others during the cult of the picturesque, romanticized by the Lakeland poets, the

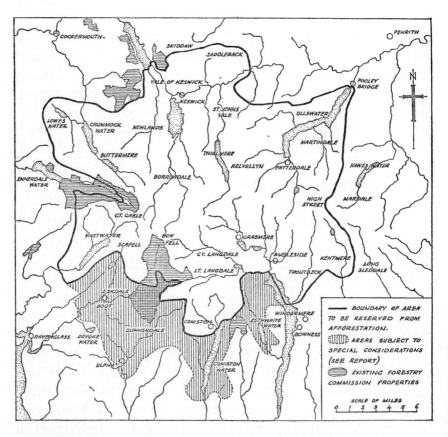

PLAN A: Lake District Afforestation Agreement, 1936/55.

SOURCE: F.C. *Agreements on Afforestation in the Lake District*, 1955.

area was already catering for tourists in Wordsworth's time. His *Guide through the District of the Lakes*, which reached a fifth edition in 1835, contained the claim that the region should be deemed 'a sort of national property'. This has since been regarded by John Dower and others as the first shot in the campaign for British National Parks.[35] Wordsworth helped to pave the way for the moderns : the field naturalists, the ramblers and, finally, those who sought to conserve the beauty of the scenery for public enjoyment for all time.

The continuing strength of public feeling and the able manner in which it has been organized to resist change in the landscapes of the Lake District are illustrated by the reaffirmation of the Agreement in 1954 and the stringent examination which planting proposals still receive, especially within the southern part of the region. A notable example is provided in Eskdale and Dunnerdale where, following the Agreement of 1936, the Forestry Commissioners were voluntarily bought out from an area of land already acquired for planting. The money was raised by public subscription and the land transferred to the National Trust. Later, in 1943, the Commissioners designated the remaining land, mostly in Dunnerdale, as the Hardknott national forest park and, mindful of their general agreement with the C.P.R.E., they set up a special Committee to advise upon this matter.

The Hardknott Report in 1944 contained recommendations which showed far greater sensitivity to the character of the local landscape than the generalized ideas of the Commissioners ten years earlier. They included :

1. Using species to achieve as natural an effect as possible.
2. Following contours in the outline of plantations wherever possible.
3. Leaving viewpoints unplanted and enough land to keep the views clear when the trees have grown.
4. Protecting skylines by not planting too close to them.
5. Keeping planting well back from the sides of certain roads and becks.
6. Leaving notable rock formations and stream banks free of trees.
7. Preserving the sylvan element at the dale-head.
8. Carrying out further close study and consultation on the ground.

Unfortunately, these ideas were never tested properly, because public pressure against afforestation of any kind resulted in a further sale of unplanted land to the National Trust and the closure of the forest park in 1959. The remaining forest area was insufficient to justify the title.[36]

That the members of the Hardknott Committee were thwarted in their attempt to integrate use and beauty in no way detracted from the significance of their observations. The original Lakeland plan of 1936 was based primarily upon the division of land between plantation and open fell, as if between workshop and playground. The Hardknott Committee evidently regarded their problem as one of multiple land-use in which positive regard for landscape design should play an important part. On these grounds, the Report may be regarded as remarkably forward-looking.

Landscape Architects and Planning

At that time, planning was still too ill-equipped to play a significant part in rural and recreational matters. Moreover, the profession of landscape architecture was less well known than that of planning. The development of landscape architecture as a separate specialty, sharing responsibility for environmental design with architecture and engineering, had already occurred in Germany and the U.S.A. in the nineteenth century. It was marked in this country by the foundation of the Institute of Landscape Architects in 1929. A professional course in the subject was established at Reading University at about the same time, but it was several years before its value as an aid to planning was accepted.

Planning, being concerned with the integration of all land uses and interests in the best possible way to ensure a good environment for national life, is a co-ordinating science, involving the gathering and assessment of information upon the whole range of human activity. As such, it is dependent upon specialist advice in many fields whether artistic or scientific. In matters of design it relies principally upon the architect, especially in urban and suburban areas where attention to design was at first most needed. The increased complexity of the problems involved led to a division of responsibility in design between architect, concerned primarily with structures and linked with the engineer, and landscape architect, concerned primarily with organic form and linked with the biological sciences.

78

There is a truism that landscape reflects national life because it is always changing in response to human needs. It has also been said that there is a saturation point of human use for every type of landscape — beyond which it will deteriorate if not redesigned to accommodate larger numbers or more intensive use.[37] The urban squalor and rural spoliation of the nineteenth century were extreme examples of such deterioration caused by a total disregard for environmental design.

Moreover, for a long time the belief persisted that use and beauty in relation to landscape could be kept in separate compartments — the towns being improved by professional planning and sections of unspoiled countryside being reserved by preservation. During the present century a great increase and variety of demand upon limited land resources has occurred. There has been further growth in population, and some undertakings, including conifer forests, are of enormous size compared with the scale of their surroundings. Gradually it has become clear that a separatist attitude towards visual amenity in rural areas cannot always be satisfactorily maintained. Often, the landscape has to play a multiple role, becoming a combination of workshop, playground and environment.

A building, designed for a special need, cannot always be modified to suit another, but has to be redesigned. Similarly, landscape may sometimes have to be re-created if it is to remain visually attractive and satisfy modern demands. There are also occasions when a new project, rather than its setting, requires to be redesigned so that it will harmonize with its surroundings. Generally, almost any type of development which is based upon expediency alone, untempered by some aesthetic care, may appear ugly. This is as true of a rural industry as of an urban enterprise. Forestry in its modern form, when it first appeared in the English countryside, displayed many of the characteristics of expediency.

The economic, political and technical uncertainties surrounding the State afforestation programme in the 'twenties were themselves discouragements to aesthetics. There is also evidence in Forestry Commission Annual Reports to suggest that many foresters were convinced that, because the materials in which they worked were living trees, beauty and harmony would develop through growth regardless of the arrangement of the trees in the landscape. Thus, regrettably, many people came to equate conifers with ugliness,

79

when in fact it was the *arrangement* rather than the *species* which upset them.

In the 'thirties, neither the foresters, who were then prepared to make some fringe concessions to amenity in their plantations, nor the amenity organizations, whose chief tactics involved the preservation of existing scenery, appear to have considered that the key to their problems might be in the hands of the landscape architect. The role of the latter was greatly misunderstood and he was regarded rather as a cosmetician, busy ornamenting urban and suburban areas. The deeper significance of his work, for the countryside as well as the town, was still not properly appreciated.

In fact, by 1939, although the separate interests of forestry, amenity and planning in the English countryside had been strengthened, the need to integrate them was not yet fully comprehended. A national forest policy was established but set within narrow limits. It had largely failed so far as private forestry was concerned and could be co-ordinated with other interests only with some difficulty. Planning had been extended to include the countryside but was regulatory rather than positive and creative in effect. Furthermore, it was not obligatory and less than three-quarters of the land area of England was subject to planning schemes. Urban and suburban problems left little time for rural matters, especially those requiring regional rather than localized attention.

While forestry and planning were being administered by professional specialists, amenity interests remained largely dependent for recognition upon the activities of private organizations — such as the National Trust and the C.P.R.E. These bodies represented amenity in the widest sense of the term, including not only the physical and aesthetic aspects of recreation and nature conservation, but also care for the design of all sorts of development. Indeed, they managed to exercise a quasi-planning function in rural affairs, although their legislative support was meagre, and their success could be measured more in terms of preservation than of creative design. Nevertheless, they helped to span a gap while professional planning, landscape architecture and other specialties were developing the ability to play a more significant role in the changing English countryside.

As specialization increases in the separate branches of a subject, there is a risk that co-ordination between departments may be

80

weakened or even overlooked. The English countryside, following the decline of the landowners as co-ordinators, the development of sectional interests and the emergence of professional administration, was liable to suffer from this cause. The Forestry Commissioners, pursuing a narrow specialist course, quickly discovered the unbalance of interests which resulted from their own activities. The inadequacies of their policy in relation to the restoration of private woods became a subject for consultation with landowners. With the help of the C.P.R.E., amenity interests were studied. The formation of forest parks was a great success and some progress was made towards improving the appearance of plantations.

In planning circles also, inadequacies were being questioned, not least where the countryside was concerned. And the problem of National Parks remained unsettled. It was the Second World War which precipitated a stringent review of both forestry and planning policies and paved the way towards a better integration of these interests in the countryside.

4 TOWARDS MULTIPLE LAND-USE

a — The Second World War and New Legislation

Forestry

In 1939 this country was rather more dependent upon imported softwood timber than it had been in 1913. State reserves of timber lay chiefly in the former Crown forests and blocks of existing woodland acquired by the Forestry Commission. The latter's new plantations were too young to supply much more than thinnings. For the second time within a generation it was clear that private woods, still mainly composed of broadleaved species and not properly restored from the fellings of the previous war, would have to be the main sources of supply for the country's needs during the Second World War.

By 1943, home production was meeting 65% of our total needs in timber. But the drain upon resources continued for several years after hostilities because, by then, some of the exporting countries had reconstruction problems of their own and it was some time before foreign supplies of softwood became reliable.[1] The Forestry Commission's Census of Woodlands of five acres or more in extent made in 1947–49, revealed the measure of the sacrifice. During the eight years 1939–47, some 373,000 acres of woods had been clear-felled and a further 151,000 acres devastated by the removal of better trees from among those of inferior type (Table 3, page 83). During the actual war years alone, more than one-third of the volume of all timber standing at the outbreak of war was consumed.[2] Although practically all of this came from private woods, the significant contribution of softwood timber supplied by the Forestry Commission justified the strategic role it had been given in 1919.

82

TABLE 3

DISTRIBUTION OF ALL BRITISH WOODLANDS BY TYPES AND SUB-TYPES IN 1947

Type	England Acres	%*	Scotland Acres	%*	Wales Acres	%*	Great Britain Acres	%*
HIGH FOREST								
Conifer	331,275	18	439,084	34	97,438	31	867,797	25
Mixed	117,996	6	37,235	3	10,835	3	166,066	5
Hwds.	580,286	31	97,017	8	77,633	25	754,936	22
Total High Forest	1,029,557	55	573,336	45	185,906	59	1,788,799	52
COPPICE								
With Stds.	227,423	12	89	—	2,276	1	229,788	7
Coppice only	102,637	6	487	—	17,082	5	120,206	3
Total Coppice	330,060	18	576	—	19,358	6	349,994	10
SCRUB	200,040	10	256,683	20	40,228	13	496,951	15
DEVASTATED	105,415	6	33,636	3	12,013	4	151,064	4
FELLED								
Before 9/39	33,492	2	233,433	18	21,578	7	288,503	8
Since 9/39	166,482	9	169,174	14	37,395	11	373,051	11
Total Felled	199,974	11	402,607	32	58,973	18	661,554	19
Total, All Types	1,865,046	100	1,266,838	100	316,478	100	3,448,362	100

* Percentage of total woodland area in each country.
SOURCE: F.C. *Census of Woodlands*, 1947–49, page 41.

In effect, all and more of the new area afforested in the years between the wars was cancelled out by these clearances, and a particularly serious feature was the loss of many thousands of acres of immature conifers which had had to be used. Most of the best hardwoods were felled and certain categories, such as prime ash and veneer beech, were virtually exhausted. To some extent this was offset by the use made of large areas of inferior timbers, which would normally have been almost unsaleable. However, many woods were only 'picked over' and a great surplus of second and third quality material, especially oak, remained after the war. Finally, any semblance of an orderly arrangement of age-classes in British woods, never a satisfactory feature of their structure, but necessary to proper management and supply, was completely disrupted by war-time inroads.

The Census also revealed that there were still about 289,000 acres of woodland which had been felled before 1939 and had not been replanted. Although the total area of woods of all kinds had risen since the 1924 Census to more than $3\frac{1}{3}$ million acres, the increase was due mainly to State afforestation on new land. Only just over half the total area could be regarded as productive in 1947. As more than 80% of all woods were still in private hands, and included most of the unproductive categories, it was clear that the restoration of these would require urgent attention.

A comparative study of productivity in British woods at 1913, 1924, 1938 and 1947 is contained in the Census Report (Diagram C, page 84). This confirms that the domination of broadleaved trees in the countryside was emphasized after the First World War. The fellings of the second war, by cutting still deeper into slender reserves of softwoods, accentuated the trend and the Forestry Commissioners concluded, in 1947, that 'broadleaved trees must now be more prominent and conifers less prominent over large stretches of the British landscape than at any time during the last three-quarters of a century'.

That this effect was more noticeable in England than in Scotland

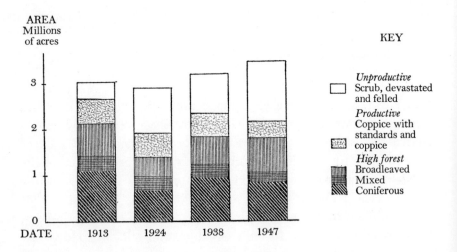

DIAGRAM C: CHANGES IN PRODUCTIVITY 1913-1947
All woodlands

SOURCE: F.C. *Census of Woodlands*, 1947-49, page 258.

or Wales is borne out by the Census statistics for each country (Table 3, page 83, and Diagrams D and E, pages 85, 86). These show that the proportions of most of the woodland categories in which hardwoods predominate were much higher in English woods than elsewhere. Once again, circumstances had led to the survival

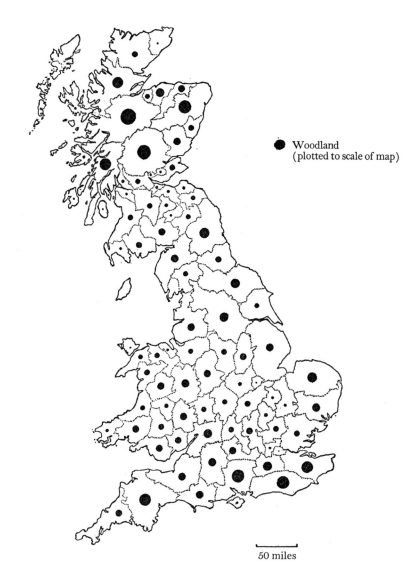

● Woodland
(plotted to scale of map)

50 miles

DIAGRAM D: TOTAL WOODLAND AREA IN RELATION TO TOTAL LAND AREA BY COUNTIES
All woodlands

SOURCE: F.C. *Census of Woodlands*, 1947–49, page 239.

85

of a preponderance of broadleaved trees in English landscapes but this time, beneath the abundance of foliage, there were probably more aged or inferior trees than ever before. A detail regarding the scrub category, of particular interest here, is that at the time of the Census, Somerset contained more oak scrub than any other county and Devon was second in that respect. The Exmoor National Park,

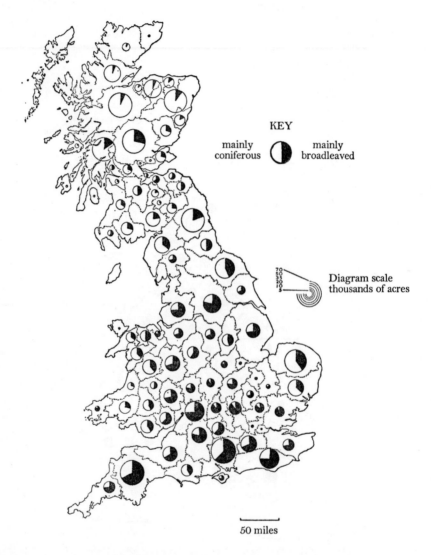

KEY

mainly
coniferous   mainly
                broadleaved

70
50
35
20
10
5
Diagram scale
thousands of acres

50 miles

DIAGRAM E: CLASSIFICATION OF HIGH FOREST AS MAINLY CONIFEROUS OR MAINLY BROADLEAVED
All woodlands

SOURCE: F.C. *Census of Woodlands*, 1947–49, page 243.

which is shared between these counties, is the subject of a special survey regarding amenity and the restocking of existing woods in Part III of this text.

The war had scarcely begun before the Forestry Commissioners started to prepare plans in readiness for a post-war expansion of afforestation and the restocking of exhausted private woods. As a result of their studies, two White Papers were published, namely Post-War Forest Policy in 1943 and Post-War Forest Policy: Private Woodlands in 1944.[3]

The overall proposals aimed at securing an ultimate total of 5 million acres of fully stocked, well-managed and productive woodland in Britain during the half-century after the conclusion of the Second World War. It was expected that, of this total, 2 million acres would be obtained through the proper management of existing woods by landowners, adequately supported and encouraged by the State, and 3 million acres through new afforestation undertaken by the Commission. Impressive targets of land acquisition, from the rough grazing land of the country, and of planting and replanting were set. Corresponding expansions in other branches, including research, education, roads, housing and forest parks, were envisaged.

Most of the proposals had a direct bearing upon the future appearance of English landscapes. For instance, for economic reasons, the Commissioners had in mind the development of forest regions containing both State forests and private woods and characterized by relatively few tree species, mostly coniferous in type. The Border Country was quoted as an example, already developing and dominated by spruce which would be increasingly required for pulp production. Regional characterization through the dominance of conifers, may appear, in the light of modern timber requirements, to be a logical sequel to the domination of hardwoods, which for centuries have distinguished various parts of the country while serving national needs. For example, pine associated with the drier eastern counties, or spruce in the west, could become no less characteristic of those regions than the long-standing associations of oak with south-eastern districts, or beech with chalk and limestone areas. Nevertheless, characterization of this kind is not necessarily synonymous with a pleasing appearance; and whether the new forestry plans would enhance or spoil the acknowledged beauty and richness of effects in the English

87

countryside would depend entirely upon the design of such schemes.

In the development of forest regions it was expected that only about two-thirds of existing private woodland would be in large enough parcels for economic management. Their owners were to be asked to dedicate the land voluntarily, and in perpetuity, for forestry purposes under agreed management plans supported by more acceptable forms of financial assistance than had been available before the war. Failure to dedicate might result in the compulsory acquisition of the land by the State. Of course, some quite small woods might be included in dedication schemes or swallowed up in the creation of larger units. Altogether, however, 'small woods, amenity, shelter belts, beauty spots and so on', as they were described, totalled an estimated 1 million acres. And the majority of these were written off as being individually of an uneconomic size and unsuitable for inclusion in the master plan — or for grant aid for replanting.

These small areas, together with parkland and hedgerow trees, contained a volume of timber the size and value of which could only be guessed in 1943. In spite of their apparent lack of concern for the future development of these sources, the Commissioners recommended that this 'reserve of timber' should be subject, like other categories, to continued felling control by means of the licensing system first introduced during the war. At the same time, following the revival of agriculture in response to war-time needs, hedgerow trees were being regarded with disfavour in farming circles, especially in arable districts. The upkeep of parkland had already declined as a result of the reduced wealth of the land-owners, much of it being put to more intensive agricultural use; and this often involved the removal of trees. These influences, augmented by the Forestry Commissioners' intended policy towards countless small woodland features in the countryside, suggested that, in the future, large stretches of lowland scenery would be gradually stripped of trees.

Finally, the post-war proposals for forestry envisaged the eclipse of broadleaved woods as strong features in most of our landscapes, and the domination of conifers in forests and large woods within a half-century — all for the first time in recorded history. It was considered that hardwood species including oak, beech, ash, sycamore, poplar and a few others would be required in the future but only in prime condition and in relatively limited quantities. The growing of such hardwoods could therefore be confined to sites capable of producing best quality material. The ground occupied by near-useless lower grades, of which there was far too much, could be better employed under conifers.

The magnitude of the changes in the appearance of our landscapes implied by the Commissioners' proposals was greater than that undertaken by the landowners of the eighteenth century. No less a project than the massive substitution of new types of trees and forest patterns for traditional woods and timbering was envisaged. Many landscapes, whether of bare hills or wooded lowlands, were likely to be altered dramatically in character, partly because of the scale, pace and manner in which conifers were to be distributed; and also because the forms, colours and textures of these species are markedly different. Unless design was to be taken into account in the new reorganization of forestry as in the old, the reconciliation of economics and visual amenity would be left to chance.

Ironically, the Commissioners stated in a chapter devoted to amenity and recreational facilities in their Report that 'it is almost a truism that in these small islands it is necessary to reconcile the claims of amenity and economic utilization; if they are kept in watertight compartments there will not be enough land to go round'.[4] And yet, while other auxiliary branches of the main undertaking were to be strengthened to match enlarged forestry plans, no provision was made for a correspondingly larger organization to take care of the greater number of aesthetic problems which might be expected to arise. Only the continuation of the Joint Informal Committee, which included members of the C.P.R.E., was recommended as an advisory body upon amenity. The possibility that that committee, lacking its own specialist field officers, might be overwhelmed by extra work was apparently overlooked.

It seems now that the Commissioners were very short-sighted at that time about the importance of visual amenity. They were already empowered and equipped to alter the appearance of landscape on a substantial scale and had attracted much adverse criticism as a result of their activities in that respect. When they sought to enlarge the scope of their work still further, it would have been both logical and good tactics to have recommended that

89

forest expansion should include care for landscape design. Appropriate staff could have been appointed, or training in design could have been added in forestry education. The nature and range of a Forest Authority's basic work and experience are such that landscaping is a natural extension of its duties. Such suggestions would have stood a good chance of acceptance in the 1940's, because Parliament was already committed to fresh planning legislation, including wide measures to protect the beauty of the countryside.

As it was, the opportunity for the Forestry Commissioners to become leading exponents of landscaping techniques in rural areas was missed. The visual aspects of amenity in relation to forestry were to be kept for a further period in just the kind of watertight compartment which the Commissioners had deplored. Professor A. G. Tansley, the ecologist, argued in favour of a much broader mandate for the Forestry Commission strengthened on the scientific and aesthetic sides to ensure a better balance.[5] His views were remarkably similar to those expressed by Sir George Stapledon, the agriculturalist, ten years earlier.

In succeeding years, the Commissioners' plans became modified considerably as a result of various pressures from other interests, changing circumstances and new demands upon land. Almost immediately upon receipt of the 1943 Report, the Government advised further consultation with landowners, many of whom were not satisfied with proposed arrangements for private wood-land, including detail in the Dedication Scheme and lack of grant aid for small woods. These matters were corrected sufficiently for the Forestry Act of 1945 to be passed, the Forestry Commission in England being placed under the responsibility of the Minister of Agriculture. This arrangement had not been favoured in the Commissioners' Report, but it was thought that it would strengthen their statutory position in face of post-war demands for land which might involve using powers of compulsory acquisition on a wide scale.

Later, Parliament approved the Commissioners' first five-year programme, the retention of felling licence control was agreed and the Dedication Scheme accepted in principle. Commitment to the full programme was withheld for further investigations, including consultations with the Minister of Town and Country Planning. The Forestry Act of 1947, necessary to enable dedication to operate, was not passed without strong objection to the omission of any middle course between dedication and State acquisition of private woods.[6] The amendment failed and the interest of landowners in the Scheme became lukewarm, necessitating more consultations. These paved the way to the development of an acceptable alternative known as the Approved Woods Scheme in 1952 : involving woodland management according to a plan approved by the Forestry Commission but without the covenant which is a feature of dedication. The Dedication Scheme itself was amended continually, and it was not until 1956 that arrangements were settled to the general satisfaction of landowners.

Meanwhile, the Woodland Census of 1947–49 confirmed the Commissioners' belief that control over felling should be maintained. So, further legislation was required, because emergency wartime controls were unsuitable for permanent use. Accordingly, the third post-war Forestry Act was passed in 1951. But lengthy debate in both Houses had produced some amendments to the kind of overbearing control proposed in the original draft.[7] The provisions of the Act are wide, enabling the Commissioners to regulate the utilization of home-grown timber with considerable precision ranging, according to circumstance, from stockpiling to compulsory felling. There are certain exemptions from control such as garden, orchard and dangerous trees, those under specified small diameters and a licence-free allowance of 825 cu. ft. per quarter for estate use. New features introduced into British forest law include the power to grant felling licences subject to replanting conditions and to make felling directions.

The Act of 1951 contains the first specific references to amenity to be found in any general Forestry Act. The Commissioners are empowered to refuse a licence or grant a conditional licence if it appears to them to be expedient to do so in the interests of 'the amenities of the district'. These interests, in Section 3 (2), are given equal status with the interests of good forestry or agriculture and, like them, may be the subject of advice from Regional Advisory Committees. Amenity must also be taken into account under certain circumstances before felling directions are made under Section 7 (1).

Section 13 of the Act lays down procedure in the event of an owner wishing to fell trees which are subject to a Tree Preserva-

TABLE 4

LAND UTILIZATION OF FORESTRY COMMISSION'S ESTATE AT 30TH SEPTEMBER, 1951
(Given in thousands of acres)

	Great Britain	England	Scotland	Wales
Total acquired	1,781·5	574·2	973·8	233·5
Forest Land : Total	1,074·2	432·3	468·1	173·8
Acquired plantations	76·4	52·2	19·5	4·7
Planted by F.C.	660·6*	268·1	269·8	122·7
To be planted	337·2	112·0	178·8	46·4
Other Land : Total	707·3	141·9	505·7	59·7
Nurseries	2·1	·8	·9	·4
Rough grazing/Agr. land	410·5	57·7	306·2	46·6
Forest Workers' Holdings	12·9	5·8	3·2	3·9
Unplantable & Misc.	281·8	77·6	195·4	8·8

* Net Total : losses from fire, wind, felling etc. = 36,301 acres making gross planting total of 696,901 acres.
SOURCE : 32nd F.C. *Annual Report*, 1951, pages 22 and 28.

tion Order made under planning legislation. The section seeks to integrate the functions of the Forestry Commissioners and planning authorities but has caused a certain amount of resentment on both sides. The final decision lies with the Minister responsible for planning but some foresters and landowners feel that planners should not have so much power to interfere in the management of woodlands.[8] However, planning authorities were advised soon after the war to equip themselves with the necessary knowledge to deal with forestry matters.[9] No parallel advice appears to have been given to the Forestry Commissioners to secure technical assistance upon landscaping problems. At all events, those portions of the 1951 Act concerning amenity and preservation have prompted the development of systems of liaison between the Forestry Commission and planning authorities which, when successful, have helped both parties to reach a better understanding.

Planning

In planning, as in forestry, the need to review national policy and legislation was discernible before the Second World War and was precipitated by that event. Public opinion, already noticeably concerned about unregulated urban growth and rural disfigurement, was sharpened by enemy bombing in 1940–41. The Government was led to undertake that, after the war, finer towns should be built or rebuilt and prosperity maintained in the countryside.

In the early years of the war three remarkable Reports were published containing the findings of Special Committees appointed to examine various aspects of national planning — the Barlow, Uthwatt and Scott Reports.[10] Of these, the Scott Report dealt particularly with the utilization of land in rural areas, with special emphasis upon the safeguarding of agriculture, and the preservation of the countryside as a source of amenity and opportunity for recreation. Among the Scott Committee's many recommendations and suggestions, the demarcation of National Parks and nature reserves was advocated, together with positive action to improve public access in the countryside, and to preserve and enhance natural beauty.

Legislation suited to the positive and regulatory control of land-use generally could not be worked out at once, but certain steps needed to be taken immediately to improve the basis of planning and to deal with specific urban problems. As a result, between 1943 and 1946, there was a spate of Parliamentary Acts concerned with planning. A new and separate Ministry was established, but the main scheme of overall control was embodied in the Town and Country Planning Act of 1947.[11]

Although the Act of 1947 did not set up a central planning authority, the Minister was given very strong powers; and local administration was strengthened by the transference of responsibility to the larger authorities, normally county councils or county borough councils. These authorities were required to prepare, and review from time to time, development plans based upon complete physical, social and economic surveys of their areas, thereby providing frameworks or patterns of land-use against which day-to-day development could be considered. All development, with certain exceptions including forestry, was brought under control by making it subject to the permission of a local planning authority or of central government. Certain provisions were re-enacted and others added to deal with specific amenity problems such as the preservation of trees and woods. Financial arrangements were designed to solve the complicated problems raised by national planning. At the same time the powers of public authorities to acquire and develop land for planning purposes, together with the scale and scope of grant-aid for these activities, were extended.[12]

The protection or enhancement of amenity, in the widest sense of that word, underlies the whole concept of planning within the provisions of the 1947 Act. Amenity has been described as 'that element in the appearance and layout of town and country which makes for a comfortable and pleasant life rather than a mere existence'.[13] The 'interests of amenity', although referred to only four times in the Act in respect of specific problems, therefore cover a very wide field. They must be considered by planning authorities equally with all other relevant factors so as to secure the use of land in the best interests of the community at large. Any proposal affecting 'the appearance and layout of town and country' may thus come within the scope of planning, whether it is put forward by a private individual, a statutory undertaking or a Government Department. Day-to-day development control en- sures consideration in the majority of cases and there are special procedures for consultation regarding Government development which, since it is carried out on behalf of the Crown, does not require planning permission in the normal way.[14]

The entry of planning authorities into the field of forestry stems as much from the implications of the basic concept of planning as from the two sections of the 1947 Act which refer directly to the subject. In Section 12 (2) (e) the use of land for forestry, as for agriculture, receives special recognition in that it is not regarded as development in the ordinary sense. The felling and planting of trees therefore do not require planning permission. At the same time, the amenity values of trees and woods, as distinct from their economic values, are recognized in Section 28. That provides for the making of Tree Preservation Orders, although not upon areas already subject to a dedication covenant, or for which a grant has been made towards upkeep by the Forestry Commission.

Thus, two apparent extremes arose, namely the exclusion of forestry from conventional planning control on the one hand, and stringent planning powers to intervene in woodland management on the other. These have since been interpreted in a variety of ways and have caused much controversy. But some intricate systems of liaison between landowners, planners, foresters and amenity organizations have been devised and are referred to later. If a planning authority is to fulfil its wider duties properly, it can neither exclude forestry from consideration nor make Tree Preservation Orders without discrimination. Forestry is an important land-use and the requirements of the industry have to be studied carefully within the main framework of development plans. Amenity values in the countryside depend frequently upon the presence or absence of trees, and the planner cannot do justice to this aspect of his work if there are no means of knowing about proposals for felling, replanting or the afforestation of fresh land. Thus, in a large measure, the Act of 1947 left the integration of planning and forestry interests to be achieved by means of consultation.

The need for consultation had been anticipated before the passing of the Act. During most of the war and until the end of 1949, the Board of Trade was responsible for controlling the felling of timber; and arrangements had been agreed with the Ministry of Planning for mutual consultation upon applications for felling licences. When the Forestry Commission became the licensing authority in 1950 these arrangements continued. Because it was thought that too many applications were being received, it was agreed that the Ministry and the appropriate planning authority should be notified only under certain specific circumstances. Consultation was confined to those applications which were either connected with the sale or break-up of estates, or involved more than 25,000 cu. ft. of timber, or affected a locality where the Forestry Commission was aware that an important amenity interest might be involved. The Forestry Commission could not know which timbered features came within the last category until planning authorities had surveyed their areas and listed those features. Afforestation projects, on the other hand, were then being undertaken almost exclusively by the State and, as a Government Department, the Forestry Commission consulted with the Ministry of Planning which, in turn, notified the appropriate planning authority. The Ministry of Agriculture might also be involved if farming interests were likely to be affected.

National Parks Established

The major planning problems associated with National Parks, public access, nature reserves and ancillary recreational matters, were not dealt with specifically in the Act of 1947. In 1944, the Ministry of Planning requested John Dower to make a special study of these problems in England and Wales and to report upon them.

The Dower Report was published in 1945.[15] This penetrating and sensitive exposition upon the form and management of National Parks in Britain laid the foundation of all later policy. On the subject of forestry, the author recognized it as an integral part of overall husbandry, but stressed the need for 'care for landscape effect at every stage'. While admiring the facilities for recreation provided in national forest parks, Dower was careful to distinguish between such areas, where economic forestry is the dominant consideration, and National Parks, where the conservation and improvement of characteristic landscape beauty and provision for recreation in the widest sense should predominate. He also foresaw the possibility of conflict between afforestation and National Parks in the upland areas of the country which were best suited to both purposes. Nevertheless, he believed that such rival claims could be resolved satisfactorily through full and early consultation which should lead, preferably, to the agreement of detailed and long-term plans for integration.

Later in 1945, the Minister of Planning appointed a Committee under the Chairmanship of Sir Arthur Hobhouse to consider more fully the findings of the Dower Report and to carry out further preliminary work. This Committee, sub-divided and aided in the study of special problems, presented three reports in 1947. These are the Hobhouse Report, chiefly concerned with the demarcation, administration and financing of National Parks; the Huxley Report, on the conservation of nature in the countryside generally; and a third, on footpaths and access, which also applied to the whole country.[16] The recommendations in these reports formed the basis of the National Parks and Access to the Countryside Act of 1949, although the passing into law of the 1947 Planning Act had overtaken the Hobhouse Committee's recommendations in many respects. The new administrative structure for planning, based upon local authorities, could scarcely be altered radically and so soon. Moreover, these authorities were already provided with powers to prepare development plans, to control development — although not to the extent considered desirable by the National Parks Committee — and to deal with such matters as the prevention of disfigurement in the countryside and tree preservation. The findings of the Hobhouse Committee were therefore fitted into the existing planning structure.

22. East-Central Exmoor: Contrasting scenery from Ley Hill looking south across Horner Valley woods, farmland and the Dunkery heather moors.

23. East Central Exmoor: From the slopes of heather moor below Dunkery looking south-eastwards to the Exe Valley and the Brendons.

24. Exmoor Forest: Pinkworthy Pond and the grass moorland of The Chains to the north. The highest, wettest and most remote part of the former Royal Forest.

The 1949 Act provided for a National Parks Commission to be appointed under the general direction of the Ministry of Planning with the duties of selecting and designating National Parks, of protecting and enhancing their natural beauty and of promoting within them open-air recreation and the study of nature. But the Commission is almost entirely an advisory body. Executive powers are left to local planning authorities, reinforced by the appointment, to the special board or committee concerned, of members nominated by the Minister of Planning, and responsible to the Minister himself. The Commission is financed nationally and special grant-aid is available to local planning authorities for certain positive works in National Parks, including land acquisition and tree-planting, but most of the cost of running the Parks falls entirely on local rates. In these respects the provisions of the Act are markedly different from the recommendations of the Hobhouse Committee. It had been envisaged that both central and local executive authorities would be set up and financed from central funds — including sums drawn from a National Land Fund set aside by the Chancellor of the Exchequer in 1947 as a nest-egg, partly with future expenditure upon National Parks in mind.[17]

The National Parks Commission is also empowered to select, for designation as Areas of Outstanding Natural Beauty, stretches of attractive countryside which, mainly on account of their smaller size, do not rank as Parks. The establishment of long distance footpaths is another responsibility of the Commission. In both matters, however, subsequent administration, maintenance and ancillary works are the concern of local authorities exercising their powers, chiefly under the Act of 1947, in consultation with the Commission and assisted partly by grant-aid under the Act of 1949. Local authorities were also made responsible for sorting out the problems of public access in the countryside as a whole. They were required to prepare surveys of open land and of paths and bridleways in their areas and enabled to create, divert or extinguish pathways. Finally, the Act gave other powers to the Nature Conservancy, a body established by Royal Charter earlier in 1949, so that land could be acquired and managed for nature reserves, and local planning authorities notified about sites of special scientific interest.

The scope of the National Parks Act of 1949 is therefore very wide, but it is designed to reinforce the provisions of the 1947

G

Planning Act rather than to stand on its own. Thus, the two statutes have to be considered together in order to understand the machinery of amenity planning in rural areas. Although the Act of 1949 stiffens planning powers to safeguard landscape beauty, access and scientific amenity and to promote public recreation in the countryside, it makes it clear that these matters have to be considered carefully in relation to the basic life and economy of the areas concerned. Section 84 of the Act requires that the National Parks Commission, the Nature Conservancy and local authorities, in exercising their functions, shall have 'due regard' for the needs of agriculture and forestry.

By the early 1950's, therefore, forestry, planning and amenity interests had been equipped with new legislation, and several new statutory organizations had been established. Official recognition of the status of these matters was more evenly balanced; but it was also apparent that their satisfactory integration would largely depend upon still further consultations between the departments concerned.

b — The 'Fifties as a Test Period

By the beginning of the 1950's, two new trends had already become apparent which were to influence the pattern of forestry development in the countryside. Firstly, land had not been so readily available for planting as the Commissioners had hoped; by 1951, they had acquired less than one-quarter of the target they had set themselves for the first five years after the war.[18] Secondly, there had been a striking revival of interest in private forestry in spite of rising wages, price controls, shortage of plants, uncertainties surrounding the Dedication Scheme and the possibility of land nationalization.[19]

The Land Problem

Despite the difficulty of obtaining new land, the Commissioners, for some years, managed to achieve a progressive annual increase in the area planted, but only by eating into their reserves of unplanted land which was not replenished by further acquisitions. By 1955, when the total area planted by the Forestry Commission since 1919 passed the million-acre mark, the Commissioners had finally accepted that a decline in the future rate of afforestation had to be faced. The situation has been explained by the fact that competition for hill land between forestry and agriculture was no longer being resolved by the price mechanism, as in the period between the wars, but was being planned by the Minister of Agriculture under whose authority the Forestry Commission had been placed in 1945. Food production rather than forestry was favoured by this process. Although there were some attempts at first to create large forest units with the aid of the Minister's compulsory purchase powers, these were not successful. After the famous case of Crichel Down, hope of planning hill land-use by such means was abandoned, and the idea of developing large-scale forestry in England appears to have been jettisoned.[20]

With the publication of the Zuckerman Report in 1957, a policy of careful integration between afforestation and agriculture was adopted by the Government: the purpose being the arrest of depopulation and the spread of marginal farming in upland areas.[21] These problems were particularly acute in parts of mid-Wales and the crofting areas of Scotland, but the Zuckerman principle of integration was accepted for all similar land in the United Kingdom.[22] So long as the location of forestry was to be governed more by political and social considerations than by purely economic principles, the Forestry Commission's expansion programme would have to be curtailed.[23]

Nevertheless, as was stated at the time, resources are seldom allocated to alternative uses on economic grounds alone, especially if the matter is the concern of Government. Economic, strategic, social and, sometimes, ecological factors all influence the decision. Although agricultural interests constituted the earliest and strongest influence upon the supply of land for forestry purposes during the 1950's, demands upon the countryside for public recreation and amenity were still increasing rapidly. These, too, had become the concern of Government. The Forestry Commission was expected to consult with planning authorities about them, especially in the new National Parks, and other areas of special interest then being designated. These areas often coincided substantially with the type of highland where forestry was already finding it difficult to secure a place. Although other land-uses, such as Service Training areas, were sometimes involved, the competition for hill and marginal land, especially in England where the supply was limited, became principally a three-cornered one between agriculture, forestry and recreation. It was, however, the influence of agricultural policies, more than amenity, which first steered the Forestry Commission away from the acquisition of land, and the development of forest regions, on the scale envisaged in the Policy Report of 1943.

Private Forestry Revives

In contrast to the difficulties encountered by the State programme, the progress made by private forestry was much more encouraging. Following the removal of most of the uncertainties about the Dedication Scheme, the annual rate of private planting rose steadily during the 'fifties. The Forestry Commissioners did much to help this renaissance. The Approved Woodlands Scheme was started and offered owners an alternative to Dedication. Financial grants under both these schemes, and for planting in small woods, were increased from time to time in tune with rising costs. Plants were supplied and special grants for thinning, scrub clearance and poplar planting were made available, as well as capital loans for private and co-operative ventures. In 1954, a Departmental Committee, under the Chairmanship of Mr. Hugh Watson, was set up to study and report upon ways and means of improving the private marketing of forest produce. The Watson Report in 1956 contained recommendations which included further increases in grant-aid and the formation of an effective association of private growers comparable in knowledge, status and negotiating power to the National Farmers' Union.[24]

By 1958, the Forestry Commissioners were able to announce, with considerable satisfaction, that over a million acres of privately owned land were under active forestry management.[25] This total included the areas within, or being considered for, Dedication and Approved Schemes as well as those known to be well-managed outside the schemes. The magnitude of this achievement may be measured by the statement in the Census of 1947–49 that the total area of private woodland in the country then considered suitable for economic management was 2·3 million acres. The revival of private forestry had occurred without the compulsion which had seemed to be threatened in the 'forties; instead, more and more concessions had been made to woodland owners and the 'fifties were characterized by a strengthening of co-operation between owners and the Commission's officers.

100

Effects Upon Landscape

Both the Zuckerman and Watson Committees commented upon some trends in the utilization of forest produce which developed during the 'fifties. Like all such shifts in demand, these could be expected, sooner or later, to influence woodland patterns in the landscape, by reason either of the species required or the manner of their growth or time of harvesting. For instance, the use of soft-wood pitprops was declining and there was a contraction in the market for hardwoods for railway wagon construction. But there were also increases in demand for good quality hardwoods for domestic furniture, and potentially dramatic developments in the use of both hardwoods and softwoods for chipping and pulping for the manufacture of paper and many forms of board. The new mills being established were expected to provide outlets for large quantities of round, small-sized, hardwood thinnings, branchwood, coppice and scrub unsuitable for higher grade uses and otherwise difficult to market, as well as small softwood thinnings, especially spruce.[26]

These trends were not then sufficiently advanced to have noticeable effects; but planting statistics show broadly some changes in landscape which could be expected as a result of post-war forestry developments already established. The proportion of hardwoods planted as pure crops since the Second World War, both by the Forestry Commission and private owners, rose steadily to reach a peak in the mid-fifties, after which it gradually declined. In reverse of the pattern established between the wars, however, the proportion planted by the Commission was consistently higher than that established privately, the final annual averages for the decade 1947–56 being respectively $8\frac{1}{2}\%$ and $5\frac{1}{2}\%$ (Comparative Table 1, page 102). On the other hand, unlike the State, private owners, with generally more fertile and sheltered woodland sites in their possession, were able to maintain a strong preference for mixed planting, much of which would lead to final crops of pure hardwoods. The annual average proportion in this category was 26%. So private planters were establishing little more than two-thirds of their woodlands under pure conifer crops, compared with $91\frac{1}{2}\%$ by the Forestry Commission.

When a similar comparison is made for England only, the differences are even more striking. (Comparative Table 2, page

101

COMPARATIVE TABLE 1

Types of Planting in GREAT BRITAIN undertaken by the State
compared with those carried out by grant-aided private owners, 1947–56

STATE PLANTING IN GREAT BRITAIN

Year	Total acres planted	Conifer acres	Hard-wood acres	Mixed Cnfr. & Hwd. acres	% Cnfr. by area	% Hwd. by area	% Mixed by area
1947	26,356	24,914	1,442		94½%	5½%	
1948	36,404	33,379	3,025		91¾%	8¼%	
1949	43,886	41,164	2,722		93¾%	6¼%	
1950	53,737	49,564	4,173		92¼%	7¾%	
1951	57,164	52,246	4,918		91½%	8½%	
1952	61,632	56,132	5,500		91%	9%	
1953	67,610	60,661	6,949		89¾%	10¼%	
1954	70,437	63,084	7,353		89½%	10½%	
1955	67,906	61,714	6,192		91%	9%	
1956	62,400	56,316	6,084		90¼%	9¾%	
10 yr. total	547,532	499,174	48,358		91½%	8½%	

Approx. Av. % per Yr.

PRIVATE (GRANT-AIDED ONLY) IN GREAT BRITAIN

Year	Total acres planted	Conifer acres	Hard-wood acres	Mixed Cnfr. & Hwd. acres	% Cnfr. by area	% Hwd. by area	% Mixed by area
1947	7,600	5,425	344	1,831	72½%	4%	23½%
1948*	10,184	7,203	380	2,601	70¾%	3¾%	25½%
1949	10,959	7,928	313	2,718	72¼%	3%	24¾%
1950	15,256	9,346	589	5,321	61½%	3¾%	34¾%
1951	5,713	4,082	340	1,291	71¼%	6%	22¾%
1952†	10,249	7,195	651	2,403	70¼%	6¼%	23½%
1953	18,160	11,789	1,267	5,104	65%	7%	28%
1954	16,824	10,738	1,179	4,907	64%	7%	29%
1955	21,321	14,338	1,509	5,474	67¼%	7%	25¾%
1956	24,735	17,339	1,673	5,723	70¼%	6¾%	23%
10 yr. total	141,001‡	95,383	8,245	37,373	68½%	5½%	26%

Approx. Av. % per Yr.

* First Dedication Covenant completed.
† Approved Woods Scheme introduced.
‡ In addition an estimated (but not subdivided) 31,900 acres were planted
without grant aid.
SOURCES: 28th–37th F.C. *Annual Reports*, 1947–56.

103). Again the State maintained its lead in hardwood planting
with a peak of 24% in 1953 and an annual average of 20¾% by
area, compared with which private hardwoods averaged 10¼%
each year.[27] In the same period private mixed planting rose to
53% in 1950 and averaged 46% over the decade. Only in 1947
did the planting of pure conifer crops rise above 50%, the average

being $43\frac{3}{4}\%$, and in nearly all years the acreages of mixed and hardwood crops accounted for more than 50% of all private land planted. In parallel, conifer planting by the Commission was much less than the average for Britain, being $79\frac{1}{4}\%$, which further indicated the favourable treatment accorded to England so far as hardwood planting was concerned. Comparisons for Wales and Scotland only emphasize that the bulk of all broadleaved and mixed planting was taking place in England.

COMPARATIVE TABLE 2

Types of Planting in ENGLAND undertaken by the State compared with those carried out by grant-aided private owners, 1947–56

STATE PLANTING IN ENGLAND

Year	Total acres planted	Conifer acres	Hard-wood acres	Mixed Cnfr. & Hwd. acres	% Cnfr. by area	% Hwd. by area	% Mixed by area
1947	8,891	7,686	1,205		$86\frac{1}{2}\%$	$13\frac{1}{2}\%$	
1948	14,125	11,250	2,875		$79\frac{3}{4}\%$	$20\frac{1}{4}\%$	
1949	15,286	12,815	2,471		84%	16%	
1950	17,728	14,162	3,566		80%	20%	
1951	17,491	13,590	3,901		$77\frac{3}{4}\%$	$22\frac{1}{4}\%$	
1952	18,055	13,898	4,157		77%	23%	
1953	21,508	16,307	5,201		76%	24%	
1954	22,994	17,512	5,482		$76\frac{1}{4}\%$	$23\frac{3}{4}\%$	
1955	21,222	16,483	4,739		$77\frac{3}{4}\%$	$22\frac{1}{4}\%$	
1956	20,822	16,025	4,797		77%	23%	
10 yr. total	178,122	139,728	38,394		$79\frac{1}{4}\%$	$20\frac{3}{4}\%$ Approx. Av. % per Yr.	

PRIVATE (GRANT-AIDED ONLY) IN ENGLAND

Year	Total acres planted	Conifer acres	Hard-wood acres	Mixed Cnfr. & Hwd. acres	% Cnfr. by area	% Hwd. by area	% Mixed by area
1947	4,421	2,557	267	1,597	59%	6%	35%
1948*	5,235	2,504	335	2,396	48%	6%	46%
1949	5,387	2,557	269	2,561	47%	5%	48%
1950	9,185	3,771	526	4,888	41%	6%	53%
1951	2,149	921	236	992	43%	11%	46%
1952†	3,960	1,518	584	1,858	39%	15%	46%
1953	9,455	4,204	1,057	4,194	44%	11%	45%
1954	8,019	2,882	1,045	4,092	36%	13%	51%
1955	9,237	3,423	1,343	4,471	37%	15%	48%
1956	11,156	4,925	1,476	4,755	44%	13%	43%
10 yr. total	68,204	29,262	7,138	31,804	$43\frac{3}{4}\%$	$10\frac{1}{4}\%$	46% Approx. Av. % per Yr.

* First Dedication Covenant completed.
† Approved Woods Scheme introduced.
SOURCES: 28th–37th F.C. *Annual Reports,* 1947–56.

Oak and beech were the principal hardwood species employed in both State and private planting but sycamore, ash, poplar, birch, elm and sweet chestnut were also used in variable amounts. The most popular conifer species in private woods was Scots pine, followed generally by Japanese larch and Douglas fir; Sitka spruce was much less favoured than in the State forests where it continued to hold pride of place. Scots pine came second in the Commission's work but, collectively, the planting of all pine species exceeded the numbers of spruces in several of the later years. This was chiefly because major technical developments in the ploughing and preparation of land were enabling more exposed and difficult sites to be afforested. There was a marked increase in the use of lodgepole pine as a tough pioneer and nurse species in some of these areas.

In Scotland, where conifer species dominated planting programmes and where the original birch and pine woodland communities of the highlands had been facets of what is known ecologically as the Northern Coniferous Forest of Europe, a softwood tradition had been persistent through the centuries. The widespread planting of conifers was no new development and the expansion of this activity was unlikely to appear as unfamiliar as in lowland England.[28]

In contrast, most of England, except perhaps for some upland and northern areas and the pine forests of East Anglia, was at the beginning of historical time ecologically within the Summer-Green Deciduous Forest of Western Europe. A hardwood tradition had persisted although intensive agricultural use and later urban development had fragmented the forest cover and established a pattern of innumerable small features. The dominance of the hardwood tree had been retained with the aid of parkland and hedgerow, and forestry had been integrated on a scale commensurate with the intimate structure of the overall pattern and the generally undramatic lowland scenery. The introduction of large-scale afforestation projects with coniferous trees even in the upland areas of England, themselves relatively small in scale and seldom rugged in appearance, continued throughout the 'fifties to arouse frequent opposition on aesthetic grounds. However, the development of forest regions as envisaged in the Policy Report of 1943 made little headway, mainly for agricultural reasons already discussed. Thus, increases in Forestry Commission land continued to be scattered geographically and variable in size. Although such acquisitions were often controversial, especially in planting design, their random distribution and smaller scale were, in spite of certain economic disadvantages, more or less in keeping with the basic patterns of English landscapes.

The restocking of private woods in England could take place with less impact upon landscape than afforestation. In arrangement, shape and size, the woods already formed part of accepted rural scenes, and landowners could therefore avoid initial difficulties associated with the selection of fresh ground for forestry purposes. As the bulk of the most fertile hardwood sites were situated among these woods, it was ecologically as well as economically sound to practise mixed cropping where conditions allowed, and to re-establish pure hardwoods on exceptionally favourable sites, confining coniferous crops to the least fertile sections. As a result, the changeover to predominantly softwood forestry was being accomplished generally in a varied and unobtrusive manner, apparently gradual in pace and small in scale, softened by the presence of hardwood trees and assisted by the frequent use of the indigenous Scots pine and the deciduous larches — i.e. the conifers most acceptable in amenity circles. Usually, it was only when such projects seemed likely to affect prominent woods or those near popular beauty spots that opposition became aroused, and planning authorities were expected to make preservation orders. The effects of such restrictions are considered later. In the main, as the recorded progress of private forestry shows, the restocking of woodland went forward without undue conflict. A further helpful factor was the continuing presence of hedgerow and parkland trees and small coverts or spinneys, mostly of broad-leaved species. In many counties, especially in the south, these provided a widespread and dominant network of traditional timbering within which the restocking of the larger woods was often scarcely noticeable.

One estimate, made during the 'fifties, of the likely result of these subtle changes in private woodland management, was that between one-third and two-thirds of the existing broadleaved woods would eventually be converted to coniferous cropping.[29] The final new balance would probably take a century to attain and the process would therefore be gradual. It was thought that certain hardwood areas of poor quality might have to remain unchanged for amenity reasons, but the trend in private forestry towards mixed cropping might increase rather than decrease the aesthetic appeal of the woods. It would also provide more varied, interesting and challenging silvicultural opportunities than those offered by softwood production alone. The need to keep the traditional appearance of much of the English scenery through the growing of hedgerow and parkland trees was also stressed.

Hedgerow Trees and Their Replacement

Apart from amenity value, the amount of timber contained in hedgerow trees had not been fully appreciated until the publication in 1953 of the Forestry Commission's Second Census Report.[30] At that time one-fifth of the national reserve of growing timber was contained in hedgerows and parks and, when the volume standing in small woods was added, more than one-quarter of all our timber resources was to be found in those two categories. England contained the bulk of these trees, their density being greatest in the counties south of the Thames; and, in order of frequency and volume, the species were oak, elm, ash, beech, sycamore and Scots pine.

In 1953 a Departmental Committee under the Chairmanship of Lord Merthyr was set up to examine the compatibility of hedgerow timber production with agricultural interests, and to make recommendations upon future policy. Later, the scope of the Committee's enquiry was expanded to include small woods, parks, roadside trees and shelter belts, and the interests of amenity as well as those of agriculture and forestry. The Committee undertook multiple consultation with representatives of other land-uses and interests, and the Merthyr Report is remarkable for an exceptionally wide range of investigations and recommendations.[31]

It was estimated that over a quarter of a million acres of land would be required to contain the volume of hardwoods then in the hedgerows and parks, and that these trees would continue for some years as a chief source of supply for the largest sizes of saw timber. While there was often a good case for the removal of hedgerows in arable areas, this was not always advisable, and there was much less justification for removal on grass farms or upland areas. The Committee thought that much more attention should be paid to the establishment of shelter belts. At the same time, steps should be taken to foster young trees in hedges and

106

mechanical cutters should be used more discriminately. The planting of hardwoods in small waste areas of all kinds, especially in southern England and Wales, also needed encouraging. Particular attention was paid to amenity. It was stressed that the peculiar charm afforded by hedgerow timbering in much of the landscape possessed an economic value, in terms of attracting overseas tourists, which should not be lightly dismissed. But a healthy as well as a sensitive attitude towards amenity was intended, based upon good management and the blending of diverse rural needs with an understanding of the many variations of landscape character.

Response to the recommendations of the Merthyr Committee has varied considerably. The attainment of one of the chief objectives of the Report, namely an increase in young hardwood trees in hedgerows and small groups, has been undermined by administrative and financial difficulties. But specific problems such as the planting of industrial waste land and the establishment of shelter belts have been studied.[32] Also technical advice and grant-aid have continued to be available from the Ministry of Agriculture and the Forestry Commission for larger projects as well as the planting or replanting of small woods and belts of more than one acre in size. The recommendation to extend planting grants to help the establishment of groups and single trees has not been accepted, however, and the only forestry grant of that nature then available, for poplar planting, was terminated in 1958. Furthermore, the Commission has found it impracticable to make replanting conditions upon the issue of felling licences for trees in hedgerow and parkland categories.

There is no doubt that hedgerow trees are being removed faster than they are being replaced, and replacement, if it occurs at all, is likely to be in a new pattern of shelter belts or small coverts. However, responsibility for replenishing the timbered character of English landscapes does not fall entirely upon the Forestry Commission and the Ministry of Agriculture. The Merthyr Report indicated that several departments, authorities and statutory undertakers were involved, and pointed out that planning powers to control felling and subsidize planting in hedgerow categories in the interests of amenity were more complete than those of the Forestry Commission.

The making of Tree Preservation Orders upon groups and

single trees was undertaken by planning authorities during the 'fifties, but the trees concerned were usually in prominent positions and related to development, road routes, established beauty spots or landmarks rather than the countryside in general. The fact that a larger number of Orders was made in London and South-East England than in any other region suggests that one of the main stimuli to the making of Orders was the spread of urban development.[33] A principal deterrent to the use of this control upon scattered hedgerow trees in rural areas has been the basic planning principle of favouring agricultural interests.[34] In addition, there have been administrative costs and time to be considered, especially in well-timbered counties, and the possibility of claims for compensation which might place a burden upon local rates.

Similarly, planning authorities refrained generally in the 'fifties from using their powers, under Section 89 of the National Parks Act of 1949, to plant trees in the countryside except in special places such as National Parks or Areas of Outstanding Natural Beauty, when a substantial part of the cost would be borne by the Exchequer. The Essex County Council provided a notable exception and used Section 89, strengthened by a Local Act, to embark upon an annual programme of tree planting based upon formal Agreements with landowners.[35] Most local authorities, however, already owned or were responsible for some trees on roadside verges and small holdings, in school grounds and other institutions. They became more aware of the need to maintain or replace these features.[36] Some authorities, especially in industrial counties such as Lancashire, where the amount of derelict land presented serious problems, began substantial reclamation schemes which often included tree planting.[37]

By far the biggest contribution to tree planting attributable to planning has been obtained through the making, in appropriate cases, of planting conditions upon the issue of permission for development. This process has helped to increase the numbers of hardwoods in the younger age classes throughout the country, although it will take some years for the effects to be noticeable in the landscape. Much of this planting has been done in urban areas and with small decorative species suited to confined spaces, but forest trees have also been planted where space allows. And the larger species, in keeping with rural surroundings, have usually been planted near development in the countryside.

108

Tree Preservation Orders

It is often held by those interested in amenity that planning powers to preserve and plant trees in rural areas have not been employed widely enough. But there is an equally strong feeling in forestry circles that Tree Preservation Orders have been made too liberally upon woodlands without sufficient regard for silvicultural and financial repercussions. Over 90% of all Orders so far made are in England where, by the end of 1963, a total of 4,069 Orders covering 56,471 acres were in force.[38]

Although the effect of a Tree Preservation Order is now widely regarded as stultifying to good forestry practice, this was not the original intention when the inappropriately named form of control was evolved. The Ministry of Planning made it clear in the Memorandum of 1949 that mere preservation applied to trees leads eventually to decay and so defeats its own ends.[39] It was reiterated in the Ministry's Progress Report of 1951 that, while an Order may only be made in the interests of amenity, its proper use is not to sterilize woods but to control felling and ensure regeneration, so that the woods continue to flourish. An essential part of the successful administration of an Order is that permission should be given periodically for felling and replanting to take place.[40] Subsequent amendments affecting Tree Preservation Orders have been matters of detail.[41] Basic policy has remained unaltered, although it was stated in 1953 that the Memorandum was under revision[42] (See Postscript, page 245).

Much of the theory contained in the Memorandum about the use of Orders has proved unrealistic. Most woods possessing amenity values which can be satisfactorily safeguarded in plans of operations, agreed between all parties including the appropriate planning authority, have no need of preservation control. Indeed, this situation was foreseen in the Memorandum, where it is stated that the Minister would normally expect an Order to be amended or revoked if the woodland concerned became the subject of dedication proposals or of advances under the Forestry Acts.[43] Those woods which possess amenity value of a kind which cannot be sustained in economic plans of management, cannot be managed any more successfully under an Order. In fact under such circumstances the provisions of an Order may make management of any kind almost impossible.

The majority of woods rated by planning authorities as of 'outstanding amenity value' are usually composed of broadleaved species. Frequently, such woods are of a poor site quality, better suited to growing softwoods. If they are to be managed for timber production, therefore, the keeping of enough hardwoods to satisfy amenity may not be economic. In the Memorandum, it was foreseen that a conflict of interests on this particular issue might arise, but it was expected, optimistically, that a compromise could usually be found.[44]

In practice, payment of compensation to the owner is normally allowed under an Order for loss of timber value due to refusal or postponement of consent to fell trees. However, such interference on amenity grounds with normal felling routine tends to make subsequent management more complicated and costly, for which there is no compensation. Where, as is not uncommon, there is little marketable material in a broadleaved wood, the amount of compensation is likely to be small. And if it can be shown that the trees form part of a feature which was established originally for amenity reasons, compensation may be altogether withheld. Furthermore, replanting, the manner of which may be prescribed by a planning authority, is not subject to compensation although, in order to maintain the special character of a woodland, it may need to be of a more expensive type than usual.

The reaction of many landowners to Tree Preservation Orders has been to abandon the affected woods as unworkable, because they consider that the financial provisions neither adequately nor fairly meet the costs of the unprofitable type of amenity management which is usually required. Orders have thus proved generally negative in effect, and the best that can be said is that they help to keep up certain woodland features for a generation or so until decline sets in through age and neglect. As a means of securing the perpetuation of such features through positive management, preservation control has been markedly unsuccessful.

Planning authorities have often been criticized in forestry circles for continuing to make Orders in spite of the known inadequacies. It has to be borne in mind, however, that an Order is still the only statutory means available for the payment of some compensation in order to safeguard important amenity woods. The alternative of purchase and subsequent amenity management is usually far more expensive. In recent years this alternative has been tested on a limited scale by some authorities with the agreement of land-owners, mostly in National Parks, where such action has received encouragement from the Ministry and the National Parks Commission.[45]

Some Intricacies of Consultation

In general, the 1950's formed an exploratory period during which strengths and weaknesses were investigated in the mass of new legislation affecting forestry and landscape introduced during the 'forties. A complex of consultative procedures developed gradually for the exchange of views and co-ordination of interests. Among the earliest of these arrangements were those between the Forestry Commission and planning authorities to discuss applications for felling and replanting affecting private woods of amenity value, and to consider the amenity aspects of proposals to acquire land for afforestation by the State. On the whole, the arrangements proved satisfactory although, in the early years, some authorities, mistrusting the informal nature of consultations, were inclined to be precipitate in making Tree Preservation Orders.

On average about 20% of all felling licence applications through-out the country were considered. In some counties such as Somerset, where reliance was placed upon detailed negotiations rather than preservation control, the proportion, measured by the acreage of land involved, was two or three times higher.[46] The Forestry Commissioners found that although planning consultations caused some delay, they usually resulted in the successful reconciliation of forestry and amenity interests. Very few cases needed referring to the Minister of Planning.[47]

Consultations about impending Dedication and Approved Woods Schemes went less well because the Forestry Commission claimed that it had a duty to respect the confidence of clients. Although the Dedication Scheme did not exclude consideration for amenity aspects in woodland management,[48] planning authorities were not automatically consulted upon detail as in the case of felling licence applications. The owner was advised by the Commission of any planning interest in the woods concerned, but he was in no way bound to consult the local authority which might, therefore, know nothing until work started in the woods. By then, it was difficult to secure modifications, for amenity reasons, to the

111

long term plans of operations already agreed between the owner and the Commission. Some authorities felt that the wider use of Tree Preservation Orders was therefore justified as a means of ensuring full consultation in case dedication proposals were made affecting classified woods; the Minister of Planning upheld this view. In the South-West, however, a special arrangement was eventually agreed and local authorities were told when an owner became interested in dedication. The Forestry Commission's final agreement to plans and grant payments might then be withheld until planning consultations had been completed.[49]

At national level, consultation procedures also became increasingly intricate. Between 1950 and 1957 the designation of National Parks and arrangements for their administration proceeded rapidly and ten Parks, seven in England and three in Wales, were formed covering 5,258 square miles, mostly highland, in the north and west of the country. A start was also made upon the designation of beautiful but generally less wild parts of the country as Areas of Outstanding Natural Beauty. Many of these included hills, forest land and heaths and a few, chiefly in Southern England, were larger than some of the Parks. By 1966, these Areas totalled 21, mostly in England, and covering 3,678 square miles (Plan B, page 113).

The emphasis upon landscape values in these areas, and the need to integrate them with ordinary development, gave rise to standing arrangements for liaison between the National Parks Commission and all the numerous statutory and private interests concerned. As the designation of each Park and Area of Outstanding Natural Beauty was confirmed, the Forestry Commission agreed that, within such areas, consultation with planning authorities would be extended to include all felling licence applications. The Parks Commission as well as the Ministry of Planning would be notified of State afforestation proposals. Although as much as 15,000 acres of land for afforestation were sometimes investigated in one year, the results were generally satisfactory. The Forestry Commission co-operated closely and met many of the objections raised, even withdrawing altogether if opposition to afforestation of any kind proved exceptionally strong. Relatively few projects were abandoned entirely, but the cessation of planting at Hardknott in the Lake District is a case in point, and there were some in Exmoor which will be referred to

25. Exmoor Forest: Warren Farm, and beech shelter belts above Exe Cleave. This land was enclosed and the farmstead built by the Knight family in the 1840's.

26. View from Simonsbath, old administrative centre of the Forest, southwards along the Barle Valley. The beech wood on the left is Birch Cleave, planted before 1840 and now under a Tree Preservation Order.

27. Exmoor Coast in Somerset: Bossington beach and the alluvial levels, with the coastal woods at Porlock Weir in the background.

28. Exmoor Coast in Devon: Woody Bay in the foreground, with Lee Bay beyond and the Valley of Rocks in the distance.

later. In 1955, to try and find some general principles for the reconciliation of afforestation and landscape interests, members of the two Commissions combined to survey the North York Moors Park and worked out a policy intended to help the case-by-case consideration of future planting proposals.[50]

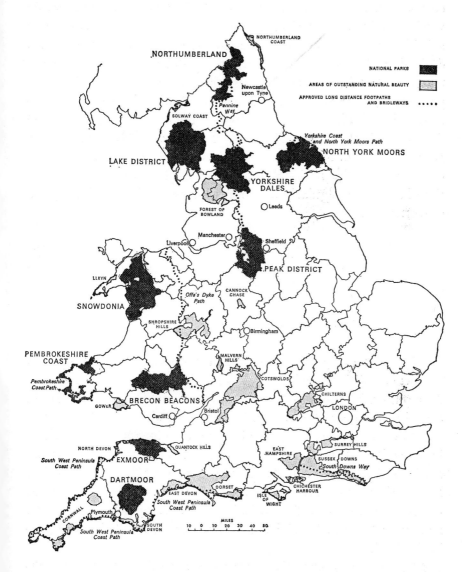

PLAN B: THE NATIONAL PARKS, AREAS OF OUTSTANDING NATURAL BEAUTY AND APPROVED LONG DISTANCE FOOTPATHS AND BRIDLEWAYS AT SEPTEMBER 30, 1966

SOURCE: 17th N.P.C. *Annual Report*, 1966.

Private forestry in National Parks was still mostly concerned with the restocking of existing woods. Compared with negotiations over State afforestation plans, it proved more difficult to agree modifications for amenity purposes in private woods. The chief reason was usually financial, the owner finding that the extra cost, or loss of potential profit, was sufficient to upset the economic working of his enterprise. The Forestry Commission could not subsidize private amenity management to the extent sometimes desired, and local planning authorities did not always have the resources to take over and manage the areas concerned.[51] In 1956, proposals prepared jointly between the National Parks Commission and Park Planning Authorities for the amendment of the 1949 Act were sent to the Minister. These largely concerned the strengthening of financial arrangements. Since then, however, the difficulties of the national economy and lack of Parliamentary time have been regularly advanced as reasons for inaction by the Government.

The Nature Conservancy

Meanwhile, the Nature Conservancy, granted wide executive power under the 1949 Act, had set up regional offices and started the immense tasks of selecting, demarcating and securing by purchase, lease or agreement, National Nature Reserves throughout the country. Arrangements were made for the positive management of these areas so that the flora, fauna, geology and physical conditions could be either studied or preserved or both.[52] Altogether, by 1965, there were 111 National Reserves in Britain covering over 228,000 acres. There were also Forest Reserves and Local Reserves, the latter being set up by county authorities in consultation with the Conservancy. England contained 54 National Reserves, and 16 in the Forest or Local categories. Lesser sites or potential reserves notified by the Conservancy to planning authorities for inclusion in development plans, and known as Sites of Special Scientific Interest, totalled over 2,000 in England.[53]

Many of the Forest Reserves were agreed between the Conservancy and the Forestry Commission on land belonging to the latter. Close co-operation developed between the two departments, especially in matters of research. The claims of visual amenity have often had the strong support of scientific interest; certain wood-

114

lands, heaths and moors being excluded from intensive economic management to avoid disturbing special habitats. Thus the activities of the Nature Conservancy also influenced forestry and landscape, and the scientific aspects of amenity gradually became integrated with rural planning.

Modifications to Forest Policy

The exchange of ideas between foresters and rural planners was further facilitated after the mid-'fifties by courses on Forestry and Country Planning, organized each year by the Forestry Commission at their study centre in the New Forest. Among themselves, professional foresters gave an increasing amount of attention to the visual aspects of their work, deciding that three guiding principles, namely naturalness, gradualness and reasonableness could be applied in State forestry to help achieve better visual effects.[54] The need for greater attention to beauty also appears to have been more widely accepted within the Forestry Commission itself.[55]

In 1957, the Government decided to re-examine forest policy in relation to agriculture, private woods and social, economic and amenity factors; strategic values were also reconsidered in view of changing concepts of warfare. The decisions taken were announced in 1958 and had the immediate effect of releasing the Forestry Commission from the post-war target of securing an estate of 5 million acres within fifty years. This would enable the Commission to give more attention to the management of existing forests, many of which were rapidly reaching the stage when 'second generation' crops would need to be introduced. At the same time, land acquisition and planting were expected to continue at about the pace found practicable in the 'fifties, but with emphasis on the uplands of Wales and Scotland, since forestry was most needed there for social reasons. Increases in grant-aid for private forestry were made conditional upon the formation of an effective woodland owners' association, as recommended in the Watson Report, and some relaxations in the general system of felling licence control were to be allowed.

In terms of effect upon English landscapes and rural planning these policy changes meant that pressure upon upland areas for State afforestation was relieved, and some improvement in the appearance of older established State forests could be expected as diversification of cropping increased. Relaxations in felling licence control had repercussions upon planning authorities, because the Forestry Commission no longer pressed an owner to replant under circumstances where they would not do so themselves. Small woods of uneconomic size or shape, difficult of access or otherwise unattractive in view of the new policy, might be granted licences with no replanting conditions. The replacement of such features if required for amenity reasons therefore became, like the perpetuation of hedgerow timbering, a matter of more concern for planning authorities. Many of them were once more tempted to extend the use of Tree Preservation Orders. Finally, the owners of private woodlands wasted no time in forming the new organization required as a condition upon increased grant-aid. The Timber Growers' Organization, now well-known as the T.G.O., sprang from the existing Forestry Committee of the Country Landowners' Association. By 1966, it had attracted more than 1,900 members owning over half a million acres of woodland, mostly in England. The T.G.O. has an effective voice in forestry affairs and, in more recent years, has played a large part in discussions with planning authorities upon the amenity aspects of private afforestation in National Parks.

The likelihood that the appearance of State forests would improve in the future was strengthened when, in 1959, the Forestry Commissioners prepared a revised declaration of policy incorporating the changes indicated by the Government.[56] For the first time an assurance was given that attention to the aesthetic role of the forest would be henceforth one of the aims of State forest policy in Britain. It was a great step forward — after forty years.

c — The Countryside in 1970

Syndicated Forestry

As the Forestry Commission relaxed its demands upon the English uplands, so private organizations began to move in. The tax concessions and other benefits enjoyed by woodland owners for a number of years had attracted the attention of business men keen to invest their profits in trees.[57] The Forestry Commission first remarked upon the entry of 'financial syndicates' into private forestry as an interesting new development in 1958.[58] Although syndicated forestry was a perfectly legal arrangement, fears among traditional landowners that fiscal advantages might be abused, were not allayed until the Finance Act of 1960 curbed the possibility of excessive tax diversion through 'hobby woodlands', while allowing the welcome infusion of fresh funds into the industry.

Unfortunately, the organizations seemed likely to make the same aesthetic errors in the scale and arrangement of their planting plans which the Forestry Commission had made in the past. Immediate public disapproval was aroused, particularly in the South-West where Exmoor, Dartmoor and Bodmin Moor were believed to be favoured for planting.[59] The new agencies, well staffed by professional foresters and land agents, and equipped for large scale commercial forestry, were supported by the T.G.O. and the Forestry Commission. As private concerns, they had no need to consider amenity, and discussions with planning authorities, if carried out at all, might not occur until after land had been acquired for planting. There appeared to be grave danger, especially in National Parks, that extensive planting might go ahead without the consultation procedure observed in State proposals.

The Voluntary Scheme for Afforestation

The C.P.R.E. decided that the situation called for a national campaign against excessive afforestation, similar to that organized in the Lake District twenty-five years previously. In 1960, a case for afforestation to be placed under full planning control was strongly pressed.[60] Meanwhile, in 1958, the Exmoor National Park Planning Authority had encouraged the author to undertake a survey of the Park with a view to determining where and how planting might be done, and yet work in with the interests of landscape, recreation, agriculture and other land uses. This survey became a subject for discussions with the National Parks and Forestry Commissions.[61] In 1961 the Minister of Housing and Local Government (formerly Planning) announced that no change in legislation affecting forestry would be contemplated until all other avenues for voluntary agreement had been tested. A Voluntary Scheme for consultation upon afforestation proposals in National Parks had been agreed between the Minister, the two

117

Commissions and private forestry interests and the terms were circulated (Appendix 1). This was the first national attempt to secure agreement to long-term plans for integration, the need for which had been foreseen by John Dower in 1945.

Briefly, Park Authorities were advised to carry out surveys, similar to that undertaken already in Exmoor, and to allocate land in three categories indicating whether afforestation would be acceptable, unconditionally or conditionally, or unacceptable. The basis of the scheme was therefore similar to that of the Lake District Agreement of 1936, namely the division of land with little or no regard for design. A consultation map at 1″ scale was required but, without an explanatory report, only the siting and extent of possible areas for afforestation could be shown, rather vaguely, at such small scale; the detail of plantation design would have to be settled, presumably, by piecemeal methods. Unless all parties could agree a grammar of fundamental design principles, the voluntary scheme represented only a partial solution of what John Dower had called 'care for landscape effect at every stage'. Furthermore, the scheme was confined to National Parks, and omitted other areas of landscape value and the countryside generally, while the restocking of existing woodlands was specifically excluded.[62]

Pending completion of the surveys and consultations, the C.L.A. and the T.G.O. advised their members to consult with Park Authorities upon afforestation proposals. In some areas, however, the new syndicates, while awaiting the outcome of the voluntary scheme, concentrated on acquiring and restocking old woods excluded under the scheme. Consultation procedure broke down again and some authorities fell back once more on Tree Preservation Orders to ensure that proper discussions took place. In Exmoor, a second survey was put in hand to study amenity problems arising from the restoration of management in existing woods.[63] Meanwhile, although a measure of agreement has been reached upon the working of a voluntary scheme for afforestation in some National Parks, the idea has been rejected in others.[64] The process of reaching agreement seems to have been slowed down and complicated by financial implications and the lack of a common language between the parties concerned regarding the principles of design.

The Changing Balance between Hardwoods and Softwoods

In State forestry, the influence of the new national policy soon became apparent. By 1962, the easing of pressure upon England for afforestation and the increase of planting in Scotland and Wales had made a substantial difference to the distribution of the Forestry Commission's estate (Table 5, page 119). The integration of forestry and agriculture in upland areas appeared to be working smoothly, and had led in some cases to the planning of forest patterns of smaller scale and greater irregularity, often more in keeping with landscape values than many of the larger afforestation projects. There was an interesting similarity between plans for linking forestry and hill farming, put forward in the late 'fifties in Scotland, and others being suggested to marry forestry and amenity in Exmoor.[65] This coincidence suggested that, as in the eighteenth century, real care taken over fitting interests together in the landscape could still lead to better visual effects. When amenity is of special importance, however, the choice and arrangement of species has to be thought out as well as the shaping of plantations.

Also by 1962, it had been estimated that the total area under woodland in Britain had risen to about 4 million acres or 7% of the total land area, still a small proportion compared with some

TABLE 5

COMPARISON OF STATE FOREST LAND IN 1958 AND 1962
REFLECTING SHIFT IN PLANTING POLICY TO FAVOUR
SCOTLAND AND WALES
(Areas in thousands of acres)

	England	Scotland	Wales	Great Britain
1958				
Acquired Woods	51·2	25·2	6·1	
Planted by F.C.	402·9	481·7	205·1	1,498·4
To be planted	96·1	169·0	61·1	
1962				
Acquired Woods	52·5	25·0	6·0	
Planted by F.C.	462·1	602·2	250·9	1,715·5
To be planted	87·5	179·6	49·7	

NOTE: Total Forest Estate, including all types of land, was 2,361·4 in Sept. 1958 and 2,584·5 in Sept. 1962.
SOURCES: 39th and 43rd F.C. *Annual Reports*, 1958 and 1962.

European countries but 1·5% higher than in 1919. Excluding parkland and hedgerow categories, over a million acres were under hardwoods, nearly 1¾ million acres under conifers and ¼ million acres under mixed crops. The balance of about a million acres were coppice or unproductive areas of various kinds. In terms of total volume in the country, softwoods accounted for about two-fifths, and hardwoods for about three-fifths, inclusive of hedgerow and parkland trees. Owing to the preponderance of younger age-classes among the softwoods and their fast growth-rates, it was clear that the softwood volume would soon overtake that of hardwood, the more so as the majority of broadleaved trees were old or ageing. Only about 5% of the hardwoods were under twenty years of age and 11% were less than forty years old. As the concentration of old trees became less year by year and relatively little broadleaved planting had been done during the present century, a sharp contraction in this type of woodland and in the supply of hardwood timber could be expected.[66]

The effects upon the appearance of landscape may not be as drastic as these estimates suggest. Other calculations have indicated that at the average annual rate of hardwood felling in the early 'sixties, it would take more than a century to dispose of the trees which are over eighty years of age. By trebling the rate of cut, however, the old trees could be cleared in less than a quarter of a century.[67] One deterrent to heavier felling still appears to be the difficulty of marketing the generally poor type of timber involved. Paradoxically, the apparent abundance of hardwood trees, especially oak, in southern counties is a major problem from both the forestry and amenity points of view. Supplies of prime oak do not reach our requirements and first quality timber of some other species is becoming scarce. Most of the suitable sites for growing them have been taken for farming and the acute shortage of younger age-classes suggests that a further deterioration in supplies is inevitable. Even if they are not felled, the ageing hardwoods will become increasingly dilapidated, often to the detriment of the landscape. The lack of young replacements is as serious to amenity as to timber supplies.

Most of the State forests are not suited to good quality hardwood growth but in the period 1952–62 the average annual area planted was 8,000 acres, principally in the re-stocking of old woods.[68] Nevertheless, the proportion planted each year has

120

declined steadily, as in private forestry, and future hardwood supplies appear to depend primarily upon the continued plantings of mixed crops in existing woods by landowners. Woodland owners and farmers are most likely to possess suitable sites and soils, and would be well advised to make some long-term investments in good quality hardwood production.[69] Similarly, the discriminate management of the estimated half-million miles of hedgerow in this country has not yet received the attention it deserves.[70] The increase in post-and-rail or wire fencing in rural districts, estimated to amount to 192,000 miles, while providing a surprisingly large outlet for forest produce, appears ominous in relation to hedgerow timber production and landscape considerations.[71]

The continuing and overwhelming demand for softwood timber and products and the consequent emphasis upon conifer planting remain inescapable. At the beginning of the 'sixties Britain was still importing 90% of all softwoods required, as well as large quantities of pulp and two-thirds of the hardwood requirement, including foreign timbers such as teak and the mahoganies, at an annual cost of about £450 millions. Home production of softwoods was beginning to assume some significance and by 1980 it is expected to have increased three-fold from State forests and two-fold from private woods.[72] Even so, the annual contribution will remain relatively modest by comparison with the massive overall requirement, although reserves will have been built up in case of emergencies and the social values of forestry re-established.

The demand for pit props has continued to decline, but the increasing use of timber for pulping and chipping, the most striking development in recent years, is expected to absorb much of the surplus mining timber. Softwoods are mostly needed in the new mills, but the development has had some effects upon hardwood areas by enabling certain types of scrub and coppice to be used, and reviving the possibility of working economic coppice rotations with suitable species.[73]

The progress of private forestry has continued to be satisfactory. In the first thirteen years after the Second World War, landowners planted more than double the area established privately during the twenty years between the wars. After a peak of 36,900 acres in 1960, planting has been maintained at more than 30,000 acres annually. England has now taken the lead from Scotland and with rather more bias in favour of softwoods than in the 'fifties; both these features are due, in all probability, to the activities of forestry syndicates and a higher proportion of afforestation in private work. The appearance of conversion operations in existing woods has been improved in some cases by the employment of the 'dappled shade technique', a flexible shelterwood system developed by the Forestry Commission.[74] Where practicable, it helps the change in woodland composition to be accomplished more gradually, and with greater benefit to the young trees, than by clear felling and full replanting. On the other hand, improvements in machinery and the use of fertilizers have meant that higher and more hostile uplands can be afforested with conifers. Nevertheless, in afforestation generally, more attention is being paid to variation in the species planted to suit local changes in soil and climate, and to the contouring of roads and boundaries. This has helped to meet some aesthetic objections to new planting.

Altogether, although less has been done to increase the woodland acreage of Britain than was hoped for in 1943, what has been done is impressive.[75] It has been calculated that in recent years the annual increase in woodland area has been practically the same as that of the urban area in Britain. Afforestation in the uplands and the repair of lowland woods has resulted in a more even distribution of woodland, which is now larger in total area than at any time during this century. Largely, the species planted have been coniferous except in eastern, south-eastern and south-western England where most planting has been replanting in which broad-leaved trees have played a large part. The main concentration of afforestation in England is still in the Border Country and the pattern of forestry development has continued on a smaller individual scale in England than elsewhere. Some regional characterization with softwood species is nevertheless to be seen, principally through the use of spruce in the north and west, and pine in the east. The statement in the Census of 1947 about the shortage of conifers in the countryside, is no longer true. New plantations of these species have become a most striking feature over large tracts of the British uplands. In English landscapes, however, their establishment has been less widespread or obtrusive than seemed likely in the 'forties. (Diagram F, page 123.)

The revolution in woodland composition in this country is now substantially advanced. And the once apparent threat of general harshness and incongruity has been dispelled in some degree through shifts in policy, consultation procedures and other influences. Even so, the subject of visual amenity in relation to forestry remains controversial. The means by which landscape values can be safeguarded are not well based aesthetically, administratively or financially. Probably the principal influence of planning upon forestry development in England has been to steer

DIAGRAM F: THE LARGER COMMISSION FORESTS OF ENGLAND
(over 2,000 acres)

SOURCE: F.C. Booklet *Forestry in England*, 1963.

afforestation and restocking towards the least controversial areas. Gradually, however, with the continuing reduction of hardwood hedgerow trees and small coverts, the growing conifers will become more exposed in the landscape. Forest enterprises will make increasing demands upon land and existing woodlands of more critical amenity value. A new wave of controversy may therefore break out between amenity and commercial forestry. One of the biggest hindrances to the settlement of such controversies during the past forty years has been the lack of a mutually agreed code of practice in forest design. A guide on this subject seems to be urgently required.

Tourism and Amenity

With the 'sixties, the public demand for recreation in the countryside has reached an unprecedented level, due to a new expansion of population, better education and increasing affluence, mobility and leisure time. These factors are expected to grow even more dramatically during the remainder of the present century.[76] Moreover, tourism has become a major national industry, the estimated annual income from overseas visitors alone being currently in the region of £300 million, or probably not less than half our import bill for timber and the largest 'dollar spinner' in the British economy. It has been calculated that two-thirds of this income is attracted by England where the beauty of the countryside is rated by overseas visitors as second only to the fascination of London.[77] These tourists, as the Merthyr Committee pointed out, hope to find and enjoy a special individual character and freshness in English rural scenes not afforded by their own lands. Care for visual amenity is therefore a real investment and pays high dividends.

Problems associated with amenity are not peculiar to forestry, and may arise in connection with many other aspects of national life. In planning during the 'fifties, as a result of the need for optimum development, the value of employing the special skills of landscape architects in environmental design received wider recognition. By the early 'sixties, the acceptance of landscape architects as members of design teams undertaking private or public works had become general. Some organizations, such as Electricity Authorities and the Ministry of Transport, employed specialist sections to deal exclusively with the amenity aspects of their projects. In forestry circles, however, the admission of landscape architects continued to be stoutly resisted,[78] although the renaissance of forestry may be regarded as representing the most massive attempt at landscape work ever embarked upon in this country.[79]

Conferences and New Ideas

A feature of the early 'sixties has been the proliferation of conferences, discussions and writings upon matters directly concerning woodland beauty. The Forestry Commissioners, in preparation for their new policy regarding amenity, had much to say about the subject in their 40th Annual Report in 1959. It has since been pursued by senior forest officers, planners, conservationists, preservationists and many others. All that has been said or written possesses the ring of sincerity and many sound ideas have emerged; but much of it is characterized by assertiveness and generalization more than objective reasoning. While there have been a number of references to criteria in matters of visual amenity, there have been few attempts to define them.[80]

Among foresters there has been a tendency to claim, on the strength of examples where forest designs are in harmony with landscape, that all new forests will develop with equally pleasing results. The ugliness of the earlier stages of much forest development has been written off as either inevitable or the unfortunate result of past mistakes. For the older forests, reliance has been placed upon the increased variety which will follow more irregular cropping as plantations mature; and the broad assumption has been made that public opinion is fast changing in favour of modern forestry patterns.

The concept of multiple land-use, already recognized in planning, also attracted the attention of foresters. The wider application of this principle was urged for National Parks in order to provide more land for planting. The national forest parks were quoted as examples of long-standing multiple use in which the claims of recreation had not been disregarded. While the basis of this argument is acceptable, in any form of multiple use there has to be priority and, if forestry is justifiably the dominant use in a forest park,[81] consideration for landscape values and public recreation in the widest sense are valid priorities in National Parks. Multiple use in any area, if untempered by careful overall planning and attention to landscape design, may have visually disastrous results.[82] In National Parks attempts to expand the amount of land for forestry by piecemeal methods had already proved unsatisfactory. This had led to the Voluntary Scheme, which at least recognized the need for careful basic surveys.

Some attention was given by foresters and others to the concept of the natural forest. This seemed to offer certain silvicultural advantages as well as appearing attractive on amenity grounds, by reason of irregularity in mixture of species and age-classes. The success of very complex systems of selection management practised in parts of Germany and Switzerland was quoted, and attention drawn to the few examples where management along similar lines is practised by private landowners in this country.[83] Young's work in the New Forest had also been based upon these ideas. But there were risks in adopting the concept as a general basis for British silviculture.[84] The apparent advantages of soil improvement, reduction of disease and increased wind firmness of trees were not entirely proven. And, even if they were, it was thought that they would not necessarily outweigh the economic advantage of simplicity in treatment and management obtainable with blocks of pure species. Irregular methods of management are extremely demanding in supervision, and in Switzerland, for example, the number of officers required for a given area of forest is about four times as many as in Britain.[85] Nevertheless, irregular forestry, being more suited to the improvement of existing old woods than to the afforestation of bare land, does appear to be worth consideration in the public management of important amenity areas.

Gradually it became clear that much closer co-ordination was necessary if competing claims upon the countryside were ever to be satisfactorily resolved by means of properly integrated and well designed long-term plans.[86] Although we had been one of the first countries to accept overall town and country planning, and National Parks and Nature Reserves had been established for a number of years, there was still no national land policy.[87] Meanwhile, far-reaching work had been done in America upon the problems of multiple use and design.[88] By comparison, British country planning techniques appeared superficial. But criteria used in the selection of areas of landscape value had already been questioned.[89] And when a map of England and Wales was published showing that nearly 40% of all land had been designated or classified in one amenity category or another, by central or local planning authorities, the need to undertake more detailed work was made plain[90] (Plan C, page 128). Less supposition and more information seemed to be required upon actual public tastes regarding recreation and amenity in the countryside.[91] Furthermore, few studies had yet been undertaken to measure amenity values in economic terms so that a better idea of justifiable expenditure upon them might be obtained.[92]

But whatever part forestry might finally play in areas of fine landscape, the need for better design in the siting and layout of plantations was at last accepted. Indeed, the Forestry Commissioners claimed that students at forestry schools were already being taught how to combine use and beauty.[93] The Royal Forestry Society, however, went further, and asked that 'bold landscape planning' should be applied to forestry in National Parks.[94] The C.P.R.E. expressed similar views and, with the Society of Foresters, regretted the fast disappearance of hedgerow trees in the country.[95] Later, in 1962, a revised policy for the New Forest was outlined by the Forestry Commission, allowing still more attention to amenity and recreation in that area.[96] Then, in the following year, a statement by the Director-General gave hope that all State forests would be laid out in future with more care for landscape.[97]

Another Revision of Forest Policy

By July 1963, five years had passed since the last important statement by the Minister of Agriculture upon forest policy, and the quinquennial review which had been promised in 1958 was due. The new statement confirmed that forest expansion and restoration was expected to continue at about the rate set in 1958. It also contained two important announcements affecting woodland amenity.[98] Firstly, the Forestry Commission would continue to concentrate upon the uplands of Wales and Scotland in particular, but would be able to acquire land elsewhere either for economic reasons or 'where planting can maintain or improve the beauty of the landscape'. Secondly, the Commission, in preparing its future programmes, would 'devote more attention to increasing the beauty of the landscape'. A question was asked in the House about consultation arrangements between forestry and amenity

127

interests. The Minister replied that such consultations were inherent to the new policy and that the Commission would be 'employing a landscape architect to assist in that respect'. Thus,

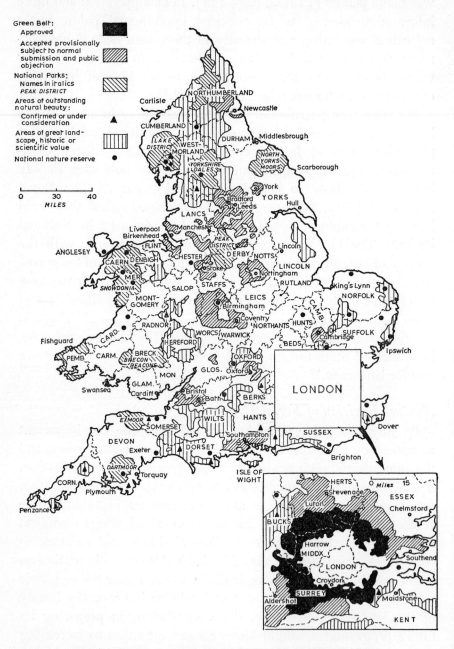

PLAN C: PROTECTED LAND IN ENGLAND AND WALES

Based on a map in the *Daily Telegraph*, 14 July 1960.

29. Webber's Post car park, Dunkery: Showing informal rough surfacing and how scattered, self-sown pine outliers from nearby plantations help to screen cars from the open moor.

30. Barle Valley, near Tarr Steps: Characteristic scrub and coppice woodland containing some hardwood standards on a fertile and sheltered site of great amenity value.

31. Watersmeet, near Lynmouth: Oak scrub and coppice clothes the steep sides of the valleys of the East and West Lyn Rivers.

32. Horner Valley: Seen from Webber's Post, the contrast in growth and texture between trees on sheltered, north-facing slopes and those on exposed, southerly aspects is sharply marked.

some support was given to the Commissioners' policy statement of 1959 regarding the aesthetic role of forestry.

Preparing for the Future

Another important event in 1963 which involved every aspect of rural planning, was a national study conference called *The Countryside in 1970*. This was organized by the Nature Conservancy and presided over by H.R.H. The Duke of Edinburgh. A huge range of subjects was covered and the main theme, based upon conservation and creation rather than preservation, was defined by the Duke as 'the total management of the rural areas of this country for the fair and equal benefit of all groups'.

Never before had so many representatives of departments and organizations concerned with the use of the countryside been brought together. The entire structure of rural planning, legislation and administration, including systems of consultation, came under examination in relation to all human impacts upon the countryside.[99] The need for even closer co-ordination of interests and more research into relevant problems, possibly through a new Central Natural Resources Research Council, received general agreement.[100] More effective legislation, financial aid and positive action regarding amenity, especially the wider use of landscape planning, were also called for. Multiple land-use was acknowledged as desirable. The Institute of Landscape Architects made the important proviso that 'conscious design, based on scientific and aesthetic principles, must take the place of piecemeal adaptation of traditional patterns.'[101] There were many key issues requiring further study, and so a number of working parties were formed to prepare for another conference in 1965.

The need to broaden the educational background of professional specialists involved in the administration of rural areas was also agreed at the conference. Already, land-use studies had been added to the training of forest officers at Oxford and Edinburgh Universities. In the latter case, graduates have since been given encouragement to take a diploma course in landscape architecture. At Aberdeen, forestry education has been widened to include natural resources, and the training of planning officers at Newcastle and elsewhere was broadened some years ago to include land-use and landscape subjects.

Administratively, a more liberal approach to problems is perhaps becoming apparent. Following a change of Government in 1964, an entirely new Ministry of Land and Natural Resources was established.[102] The Forestry Commission and, to a large extent, the National Parks Commission, were placed under the control of the new Minister. He was also made responsible for certain other planning matters, notably Tree Preservation Orders, and for a re-appraisal of common land, currently in progress. The Forestry Commission, after forty-five years, has now employed a landscape consultant, and work upon the better layout of new plantations and improvements to the appearance of some older areas, has begun. All felling licence applications have been made subject to 'scrutiny in the public interest', and planning authorities are therefore involved whether or not the woods or trees have a previously declared amenity value. A review of the arrangements for Tree Preservation Orders was put in hand to seek ways and means of integrating the interests of amenity and commercial forestry more effectively.[103] And in May 1965, the new Minister declared that legislation to amend the National Parks Act of 1949 was imperative and urgent. Proposals for this, and for 'a more comprehensive and ambitious countryside policy', were soon to be made known.[104]

A few months later, however, the Government's proposals for the reorganization of agriculture and forestry under Rural Development Boards, were published.[105] These came as a shock to National Park authorities who had not been properly consulted. A Bill, since prepared, indicated that the Boards would be expected to take the needs of tourism and recreation into account — which means amenity — but, by implication, these would be subsidiary to the main task of ensuring that the best economic use was made of land for farming and forestry. This pattern is a familiar one. The re-creation of attractive scenery does not follow automatically upon the intensification of economic land-use in rural areas, unless at the same time careful attention is given to design. And over-emphasis upon one set of economics in the countryside could easily destroy much of the raw material upon which the new and important tourist economy now depends.

Some reassurance was to be had when, towards the end of 1965 at the second conference upon *The Countryside in* 1970, the Minister of Land and Natural Resources gave an indication of the lines on which a fresh amenity policy might be prepared. He proposed a stronger National Parks Commission, reconstituted as the Country-side Commission with much wider powers and better financial support.[106] At both this conference and another held by the Institute of Landscape Architects, the Minister stressed the need for more research into techniques of conservation and of management. New yardsticks were required to help rationalize landscape values in relation to other claims upon land, and landscape criteria needed definition. A Natural Resources Advisory Committee had been set up and the Government's proposals for the countryside might be expected in 1966. (See Postscript, page 245.)

Whether all this reorganization affecting the economics and amenity of landscape will be finally dovetailed together through legislation, or whether conflicts will continue under new banners, remains to be seen. At present the situation is fluid. There is no doubt, however, that with determination the stage could be reset in preparation for the overall and balanced management of the resources of the countryside in a way which could reunify all rural interests, including amenity. The problems involved are far more complex than those which faced the landowners two centuries ago, and there are great difficulties to be surmounted. Some of these are already being tackled. For instance, in spite of nearly twenty years of national planning, there is an extraordinary dearth of basic information about rural land-use. This is being overcome, largely through private initiative, by a Second Land Use Survey of Britain.[107] And it seems to be acknowledged that whatever patterns of multi-use planning finally emerge, attention to the principles of landscape design should be included in their preparation.

In fact, there have been many general statements about the need for landscape planning in recent years. But few attempts have been made to define fundamental criteria or to apply them in the production of long-term plans on a regional basis. The discovery, with some precision, has yet to be made of the extent to which it may be desirable to modify economic projects for the sake of amenity in areas of fine landscape. The National Parks are obvious regions for research in these fields. To provide information, the next two parts of this book contain accounts of studies undertaken in the Exmoor National Park upon the integration of forestry projects with amenity and multiple use. At the same time, an attempt is made to define a grammar of design principles and a method of working based upon landscape analysis. These may be of value, with appropriate local modifications, in similar studies elsewhere.

PART II

Trees, Amenity and Multiple Use
in the Afforestation of Open Land

1 THE EXMOOR NATIONAL PARK AND PLANNING ADMINISTRATION

The Exmoor National Park (Plan D, page 148), is ideal for detailed studies of forestry in relation to landscape, whether for the afforestation of open land or the restocking of existing woods. The Park contains large areas of upland moor and heath suitable for planting and also many broadleaved woods which could be restocked with more immediately profitable trees. Moreover, the beauty of the landscape was one of the principal reasons for the designation of Exmoor as a National Park.

Other than heavy industry, practically all interests with which forestry operations may compete or combine are represented in the area. Agriculturally, much of the hill land is capable of being reclaimed or improved; there are water undertakings; there are many features of scientific interest, some of sufficient importance to be scheduled by the Nature Conservancy. The tourist trade is growing apace; more people want to enjoy more of the moor every year; field sports are well supported. The National Trust owns large estates in the Park and there is a thriving preservation society allied to the Council for the Preservation of Rural England. Finally, the landowners, through the Country Landowners Association, the Timber Growers Organization and the National Farmers' Union, as well as the Forestry Commission and the large forestry organizations, are actively concerned about future land-use in Exmoor.

Exmoor was first listed as a potential National Park in 1945 by John Dower. This was repeated in the Hobhouse Report of 1947 and, under the National Parks Act of 1949, Exmoor was finally

135

designated in 1954. The administration of Exmoor as a National Park is complex. About two-thirds of the area is situated in West Somerset and about one-third in North-East Devon. In the early days of the National Parks Commission it was expected that Parks which involved more than one local authority would be administered by a Joint Board, with proportional representation upon it by each authority concerned. In the case of Exmoor, and some others, it was decided finally to appoint a separate Committee for the administration of each local authority's portion of the Park, together with a Joint Advisory Committee responsible primarily for advising the individual committees on matters of policy. Accordingly, Exmoor is governed by two County Committees and a Joint Advisory Committee.

Before the designation of Exmoor, it was the practice in Somerset for forestry matters to be dealt with by the Planning Committees as and when proposals arose.[1]

Good relations were built up with the Forestry Commission, landowners, agents and timber merchants. Apart from felling proposals affecting declared amenity woods, it was agreed that any felling amounting to more than 25,000 cu. ft. of timber would also be subject to joint consultation. In the last decade about 60% by volume of all clear felling licences and 80% by volume of all selective felling licences in the county have been considered between the Forestry Commission, the Planning Authority and the owners concerned. This system of negotiation has depended a great deal upon tact and understanding on all sides and personalities can make or mar such an arrangement. By and large, it has succeeded well; well enough in fact for the use of Tree Preservation Orders by the Somerset County Council to have been minimal. There are only two Orders of long standing in the county and two more of recent date cover seven woodland areas in the Somerset part of the National Park. Altogether about 850 acres are affected in Somerset, 700 acres of which are in Exmoor. The County Council believes that an Order does little to secure the proper management of an amenity woodland, which is essential if the feature is to survive; consultations under an Order are no less complicated than those undertaken without it, and an Order may, indeed, antagonize the owner and others with whom it is necessary to negotiate. Orders, therefore, have been kept in reserve.

In the early nineteen-fifties, in Exmoor at least, proposals affecting amenity woods were not extensive or complicated and were usually easy to agree. Beech was much used for replanting and this undoubtedly helped negotiations. As in the rest of Somerset, private planting included rather more hardwoods during the 'fifties than was usual outside the county.[2]

The areas of open land which the Forestry Commission were then acquiring for afforestation in Exmoor, were mostly small and not controversial; plans for dedication were few, the slow pace of change envisaged and the liberal use of mixed species in replanting helping to secure settlement. The large forestry organizations had not yet developed. It was not surprising, therefore, that when the new Park Committees were set up in 1954, forestry matters continued to be considered on the same *ad hoc* and informal basis as in the rest of the county. The only important change made was that the Forestry Commission agreed to notify the Committees about felling proposals affecting all woods in the Park area, instead of confining consultation to those affecting declared amenity woods or involving more than 25,000 cu. ft. of timber.

For a few years little happened to upset these arrangements. Then, in the second half of the nineteen-fifties, the Forestry Commission put forward in quick succession several proposals to acquire substantial areas of woods and open land. The most important project affected some 1,200 acres on The Chains, one of the most remote and high-lying watersheds in the National Park, a few miles north-west of Simonsbath. The Chains, in 1952, had been the storm centre of a great deluge which drove 50,000 tons of debris out of a 38 square-mile catchment area, causing the tragic Lynmouth flooding and great damage elsewhere. In 1957, it became a storm centre of controversy about amenity and forestry.

The National Park Committees, supported by the National Parks Commission, opposed the Forestry Commission's proposals on The Chains. Local opinion against afforestation in the region was also organized rapidly and the Exmoor Society was born. After wide-spread consultation and much publicity the Forestry Commission withdrew, but the affair has not been forgotten. The area now is incorporated in a farming enterprise and cattle are ranched upon it, but the case of The Chains marked a turning point in the policy of the National Park Committees towards forestry matters and landscape.

Afforestation being then the subject most hotly debated in Exmoor, the Joint Advisory Committee decided in 1958 that, to give fair thought to land requirements for forestry, a survey should be made to discover where and how planting could take place in the Park without impairing its essential beauty.[3] At the time this was the first venture of its kind. Succeeding chapters are based upon work occasioned by the survey, but later developments and further studies are also included.

2 THE AFFORESTATION SURVEY

a — The Main Objectives

The objectives of a survey such as that carried out in Exmoor, and since requested of all National Park Authorities under the Voluntary Scheme over Afforestation, are not as obvious as they may seem. They are, in brief, to find land which is not only suitable for afforestation with coniferous trees, but can be so planted without detriment to landscape and other land-uses. These positive aims and their implications should be understood clearly at the outset and always kept in mind during a survey; it is remarkably easy for anyone undertaking the work to be distracted from them by personal bias or misinterpretation.

First, there is the need to accept conifer plantations as new elements in landscape. To study the countryside only with a view to finding hiding places for them would be entirely the wrong approach. The right attitude is to seek positively for places where plantations may be established as attractive and interesting additions to the landscape and where — perhaps surprisingly often — they would actually improve the appearance of the countryside. The areas where conifers should not be planted can be left to emerge as the survey proceeds.

It follows that it is desirable to describe how the new plantations should be designed. To state where they should be placed is not enough and this is one of the weaknesses of phraseology in the Voluntary Scheme over Afforestation. (Appendix 1.) There are obvious differences, for example, between a rectangle of spruce and a belt of pine and larch. Therefore, a clear record of the design and composition of the plantation envisaged for each chosen site adds tremendously to the value of the survey.

It should also be understood that such a survey is first and

139

foremost a review of landscape and land-usage. In planning terms it is comparable to the survey which precedes a development plan; just as that, when analysed, leads to conclusions upon the proper siting and design of new industry, housing and other needs, so the landscape and land-use survey and analysis will indicate, among other things, where and how afforestation can best be sited. To that extent it provides information for a landscape development plan.

For the field work on Exmoor it was found convenient to carry a complete set of Ordnance Survey maps at a scale of 6 inches to 1 mile covering the Park area. These were re-numbered and a small key plan made so that individual sheets could be found quickly. All field notes were made directly on to the maps. In all 69 sheets were required. As information was gathered and plotted on the maps, the rough shapes of potential planting sites gradually developed. This sieve-map method of pin-pointing the most suitable land for afforestation was found to be particularly appropriate to the work in Exmoor.

b — Geographical Factors and Silviculture (Plan D, page 148 refers)

The Exmoor National Park covers about 265 square miles of which 188 are in West Somerset and 77 in North-East Devon. East of the main highland plateau of Exmoor itself, most of the Brendon Hills are included in the Park. To the north, the land borders the Bristol Channel with tall, steep, and often thickly wooded cliffs, running almost continuously from Minehead to Combe Martin. Southwards, the gentler foothills overlook the vales between Barnstaple and Dulverton and thence towards Taunton Deane. The Park is shaped roughly like an inverted triangle; the base along the coast measures about 25 miles with a further 10 miles curving inland and the depth from base to apex at Dulverton is about 14 miles.

In general, Exmoor is a highland area, most of the land being above 700 feet, much of it above 1,000 feet and the highest point, Dunkery Beacon, rising to 1,706 feet above sea level. Steep gradients of $1:7\frac{1}{2}$ or more are frequent and the area is intersected by deep valleys and combes which are often well-wooded or emphasized by streams or rivers. These contrast dramatically both with the bare sweeps of upland heath and grass moor, and with the agricultural character of the more sheltered areas and the lower highlands.

Although many of the highest and steepest slopes face north and the deeply seamed terrain lends itself to the seasonal formation of frost pockets, much potential coldness is offset by the moderating influence upon climate of the nearby seaboard. This effect is most noticeable along the coast itself; there are north-facing places, such as Porlock Weir and Glenthorne, where a wide range of exotic and tender trees and shrubs can be grown due to the relative rarity of serious spring frosts.

Overall, rainfall is high and reaches 60 inches a year in places : sometimes more has been recorded, particularly around Simonsbath. The occurrence of mist, fog and snow is higher than average but, like the mild summer weather, is typical of a south-western upland region. Much of the land is widely exposed to south-westerly winds, especially on the plateau, while northern sections are also affected by salt-laden winds from the direction of the Bristol Channel.

The underlying geology is mostly Devonian and the soils from these rocks are generally poor. Over much of the highest moorland a thin clay-and-iron pan has developed, impervious to water, and upon this thick layers of peat have been deposited. Better soils, mostly derived from the Trias Sandstones, occur on the fringes of the Devonian uplands, especially in the fertile Porlock Vale where alluvial deposits are also present.

Of all these factors, exposure to south-westerly winds is the most serious limitation to the planting of conifers in Exmoor, although sometimes northerly salt-laden winds provide an extra hazard. Frosty hollows and impeded upland soils of low fertility can be largely overcome, if at some extra cost in the latter case, by appropriate choice of species, deep ploughing and fertilizer applications. Steepness of gradient does not present the problems in forestry which it does in agriculture, although it may sometimes prove difficult and expensive to provide access in such terrain. Where shelter and good soils occur together, the predominantly moist, warm, climatic conditions are strongly favourable for the growth of species such as Douglas fir, the spruces and a wide range of other conifers, but the pines are less suitable.

Broadly, therefore, there is plenty of geographical and geological evidence to suggest that while much of the plateau and hill tops in Exmoor are hostile enough to make afforestation with conifers difficult, both practically and economically, such work is not impossible or doomed to failure. On lower slopes, and more sheltered areas, and on better soils, the indications are that softwood afforestation with a variety of conifers is both practical and likely to prove economically attractive.

These indications are borne out by the growth of existing woods and plantations. Most of the plateau and hill tops of Exmoor are devoid of broadleaved woods but there are occasional small privately owned plantations, usually containing beech, larch, pine and spruce. The stultifying effects of exposure and poor soil on small plantations are amply demonstrated; generally spruce and beech survive best under those conditions. At Simonsbath, Birch Cleave, a beech wood planted about 1840 with Scots pine nurses, at an elevation of 1,100 feet, is believed to be one of the highest-lying examples of its kind in the country. Beech as a hedge plant along the tops of the banks dividing the fields, or in shelter belts near farms, is characteristic throughout Exmoor. The timber is seldom of good quality unless grown in sheltered positions on better soils. Birch, rowan and hawthorn appear sporadically on the uplands and sycamore is infrequent. Most of the major hardwood timber trees such as oak, ash and sweet chestnut, as well as sycamore and beech, are confined to or grow best upon the lower lands.

On the other hand there are several sizeable and successful conifer areas at high elevation. For example, much of the Forestry Commission's Brendon Forest is situated above 1,000 feet and parts of the area rise to 1,100 and 1,200 feet above sea level. Started in the nineteen-twenties, this forest now provides its own sheltered climate in the sense that second generation crops planted within its bounds can be more protected from exposure than were the pioneer crops. Nevertheless, fringes and shoulders of older trees have to be maintained continuously or this advantage, which the large forest has over the small isolated plantation, could be lost. Sitka spruce grows well in Brendon Forest at high elevation and, in the sheltered areas and deeper combes, Douglas fir and most other conifers make excellent growth.

Indeed, on the lower and richer sites in Exmoor, many varieties of conifers grow exceptionally well. Douglas fir and Sitka spruce near Dunster have long been admired in forestry circles. Results obtained with larches, cypresses, hemlock and, to a lesser extent, with pines, indicate that softwoods in many instances grow much better at the lower elevations than some of the indigenous hardwoods, especially oak which is not normally of very good quality. At higher elevations conifer species are often the only species to make any satisfactory growth at all.

c — Plantable Land and National Parks' Policies

The recording of basic conditions of terrain and climate, and any limitations which they impose upon softwood afforestation, forms the first step in the survey. The next step is to discover the position and amount of land which could be used for planting. The ownership of the land is immaterial at this stage and its value for other uses has to be weighed in detail later. For the present, it is enough broadly to exclude areas under relatively intense agricultural, industrial or urban use and to concentrate upon the marginal lands and sparsely stocked uplands.

Much valuable information should be available already from the field work done during earlier surveys of public rights-of-way and access to open country. Under Sections 27 and 61 of the 1949 National Parks Act, all local planning authorities have been required to make these surveys, with any necessary consultations, to ensure that there is sufficient freedom of access to open country for public enjoyment, and to produce definitive maps of public rights-of-way which previously had caused much confusion.

Decisions to make access agreements or orders over land, and to close old paths or establish new ones, rest upon the results of these early surveys. If there is ample open land over which the public can walk or ride at will without objections from the owners, the chances are that access formalities are not required.

The term 'open country' is defined in Section 59 of the 1949 Act as any area consisting wholly or predominantly of mountain, moor, heath, down, cliff or foreshore. While access agreements or orders may be made over land in any of these categories, they cannot be made over agricultural land, other than that which is agricultural only in the sense that it provides rough grazing.

Both the Dower and Hobhouse Reports place strong emphasis upon the presence of substantial areas of 'relatively wild country' being a fundamental factor determining the suitability of an area for designation as a National Park. Indeed, John Dower deliberately excluded from his list of potential National Parks some districts which, though beautiful, contain too little wild country to justify national action. It is not surprising, therefore, to find that many of the larger tracts of open country that remain to us are now contained within the boundaries of the Parks, and many of the smaller ones within the Areas of Outstanding Natural Beauty. These tracts are also the principal reservoirs in England of the type of land which could accommodate new, large-scale afforestation with softwood plantations.

The Act of 1949 stresses the need to preserve and enhance open country for the enjoyment of the public, provided that 'due regard' is paid to the needs of agriculture and forestry. What constitutes 'due regard' in this context is a matter for conjecture, but it may be reasonable to assume that the phrase suggests some degree of subordination rather than dominance in relation to primary objectives in a National Park. John Dower acknowledged that the appearance of many of our finest landscapes owes more to past farming and forest practices than to any other activities, and saw nothing inconsistent between further land improvement and National Park objectives. He made the important provisos, however, that care for landscape effect in matters of detail, and willingness on the part of landowners and farmers to consult Park Authorities, were necessary to ensure harmonious development in the future.

A survey of open country in the Exmoor National Park was undertaken in 1954–55 and reviewed in 1962–63. There are no mountains or downs in the area and, owing to the nature of the coastline, new forestry or farming ventures are unlikely except near resorts such as Combe Martin, Lynmouth, Porlock Weir and Minehead where conditions are less hostile. The precipitous cliffs, rocky shore, lack of sand, dangerous currents and difficulty of access maintain the isolation of much of the coastline, which is mainly explored by a venturesome minority. Most people enjoy the grandeur of the coast visually from inland viewpoints and moorland promontories. Heather and grass moors and rough

33. Luxborough Valley, near Roadwater: The Forestry Commission's conifer plantations are often separated from the valley road by small fields, hedge trees and a stream.

34. Exe Valley: At Miltons, there are good examples of mixed cropping and of contrasting types of tree on the convex and concave valley curves.

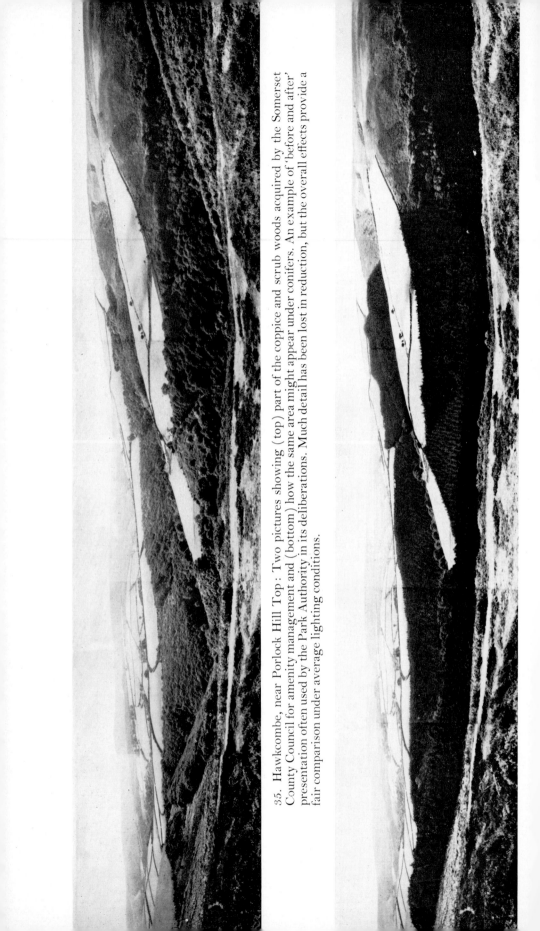

35. Hawkcombe, near Porlock Hill Top: Two pictures showing (top) part of the coppice and scrub woods acquired by the Somerset County Council for amenity management and (bottom) how the same area might appear under conifers. An example of 'before and after' presentation often used by the Park Authority in its deliberations. Much detail has been lost in reduction, but the overall effects provide a fair comparison under average lighting conditions.

grazings therefore constitute the principal categories of open land in Exmoor; these are also the most vulnerable to change and the open country surveys made a particular study of them.

In 1962–63 there were about 48,000 acres of land in Exmoor classified in the moorland categories.[1] This area represents some 28% of the total Park area of 169,600 acres. It is noticeable at once that more intensive use, in this case mostly agricultural and woodland, is already made of nearly three-quarters of the National Park. Although much of the woodland is classifiable on silvicultural grounds as derelict or semi-derelict and scrub, and offers opportunities for public enjoyment akin to those of open land, woods cannot be included in the definition of open country laid down in the 1949 Act. This matter has received further attention in a woodlands survey of Exmoor (Part III).

The most important fact revealed, therefore, by the open country surveys is the relatively small proportion of open land which is contained in the Park. This sets, as it were, a limit to the scale upon which further afforestation, and agricultural reclamation for that matter, could take place without altering drastically the character of the National Park. Even at this stage of the afforestation survey, the indications are, therefore, that new plantations of trees would have to be severely limited if the open nature of some of the landscapes were to remain unimpaired. An alternative course would be to redesign certain areas of Exmoor and give them an entirely new character but this is outside present terms of reference.[2]

The distribution of the open land in Exmoor, both in type and on the ground, is also revealed in the open country surveys and is of factual value in the afforestation survey. Of the 48,000 acres of open land, the *truly unenclosed* moorland occupies only about 23,600 acres: that is, scarcely 14% of the whole Park and a remarkably small proportion. This type of moor is characterized by complete freedom of access and a vegetation of heathers, bilberry, bracken and gorse interspersed with grassy swards which together provide a rich variation of colour throughout the seasons.[3]

Moorland of this kind coincides broadly with old commons on the edges of the former Royal Deer Forest. The commons of Brendon, Yenworthy, Porlock and Anstey are all good examples. There is scarcely any open heather moor left now in the Brendon Hills, and a small proportion only along the western side of the

Park. This is due mainly to agricultural improvement but some moorland has been taken for forestry purposes, chiefly in the Dunster–Minehead area. The largest single area of remaining unenclosed heather moor of about 6,000 acres is in the Dunkery Beacon vicinity and is owned by the National Trust which also controls another portion, on Winsford Hill, of about 1,200 acres, between Exford and Dulverton. In 1962, the Somerset County Council purchased North Hill, near Minehead, to protect its existing character and keep complete freedom of access for the public. About 400 acres of open moor are included in the area. In 1965, a further 300 acres of heather land on Mill Hill near the Oare Valley were acquired for public enjoyment in Somerset, through the generosity of the previous owner.

Rather more than half (about 24,400 acres) of the Exmoor open land is grass moor and rough grazing and is enclosed, either partially or securely, with earth banks, sometimes topped with beech hedges, or post and wire fences.[4] Some of these moors, like The Chains, mentioned previously, are overlaid with peat. Grass moor is especially characteristic of the former Royal Forest area where many of the enclosures date from the time of the Great Reclamation undertaken by the Knight family of Simonsbath in the mid-nineteenth century. Nevertheless, because many of the individual enclosures are so large as to provide the appearance of open moor, and much of this type of land is situated on the high plateau of Exmoor, there is a quality of uninterrupted spaciousness about this type of scenery. Strangely perhaps, this is rather more noticeable than on the unenclosed heather areas, probably because the latter occur sporadically whereas the grass moors are concentrated mostly in one large block. Smaller moors and rough grazing appear in other parts of the Park but sometimes, notably in the Brendon Hills, they may be reduced to narrow strips along the sides of combes or valleys too steep for the plough.

It is also worth noting that between the two Open Country Surveys in Exmoor, in 1954 and 1962, an estimated area of about 3,000 acres of land passed out of the open categories into more intensive use, mostly for agriculture.[5]

It is clear, therefore, that the bulk of land suitable for afforestation is to be found either on the main plateau in the old Royal Forest, where conditions are somewhat hostile, or else scattered on the shoulders, slopes and old commons which fringe the Exmoor massif, where conditions are also most favourable for agricultural improvement. The Brendon Hills do not contribute much in open land other than strips left over from reclamation.

At this point in the afforestation survey it becomes apparent that Exmoor is not of one homogeneous type of landscape. Reference has been made already to differences between the coast, the commons, the old Royal Forest and the Brendon Hills. Before examining the various claims which may be made upon the open land, it is desirable to understand the special qualities of the various types of scenery involved. It is important in this exercise to note the appearances of any existing softwood plantations in relation to the particular landscapes which they affect, and to decide whether or not they are visually attractive. So far, the survey work has been factual but at this stage, in addition to a thorough knowledge of the area concerned, artistic perception is an accomplishment which the surveyor should be able to contribute to the work.

d — Landscape Descriptions (Plan D, page 148 refers)

The Exmoor National Park may be subdivided for convenience of reference into five broad geographical zones. Each of these possesses a pronounced type of landscape although in some areas the types merge gradually into one another. The subdivision is as follows:

The Brendon Hills

Usually regarded as an outlier to the main Exmoor plateau, and separated from it by the Dunster–Dulverton valley roads, the Hills occupy approximately the eastern quarter of the Park. The northern slopes rise steeply to a ridge road, running between 1,200 and 1,350 feet above sea level from Elworthy to Wheddon Cross. The southerly gradients are more gentle until they rise sharply again, in the extreme southern part of the Park, to the Haddon Hill ridge.

One of the most noticeable features in this landscape is the dominance of agriculture. Stock rearing, in the form of sheep and bullocks, is the principal farming enterprise but some dairying is also practised. Almost the entire area of the Hills is divided into

147

neat fields, and the boundary banks topped with beech hedges are characteristic of the scene. Beech is much used as a shelter tree around farmsteads, but hedgerow trees are not a general feature.

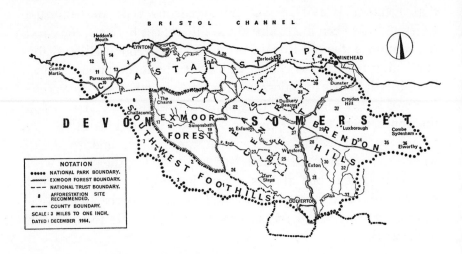

PLAN D: EXMOOR NATIONAL PARK — AFFORESTATION SURVEY 1958–64

There is also a noticeable lack of open moorland in this section of the National Park. Reclamation and enclosure on the Brendons, dating back over several centuries, are practically complete. Except for Haddon Hill, no sizeable area of easily accessible open country is left.

The presence of large woodlands on the northern slopes of the Hills is a special feature. The Forestry Commission's Brendon Forest is mostly under conifers. This forest includes the Luxborough valley where conifers on the valley sides are separated informally from the road by small meadows and a meandering stream. The effect is pleasant: the traveller is interested by the vistas of meadow, stream and woodland which unfold in variety along the route and the feeling of being unduly overshadowed by trees is relieved.

Brendon Forest also includes Croydon Hill where the blanket effect of a large hill-top mass of conifers may be seen. In this landscape, where agriculture predominates, the sheltering of the lower cultivated land by the tree-clad highland creates a scene which has

148

some merit. The arrangement of the species upon the ground sometimes contradicts the natural contours, but no subtle hill modelling has been obscured, and the area is in a portion of the Park where trim orderliness and maximum husbandry are the dominant notes.

The Crown Commissioners' Dunster Estate, also in the north Brendons, contains some interesting and well established woods of mixed species. A rich variety is provided by the various arrangements of conifers, hardwoods and open land.

The East Central Belt

This part is bounded approximately by the Dunster–Dulverton valley roads on the east, and by the Porlock Weir–Exford–Withypool route, and the Barle Valley to Dulverton, on the west and south. It possesses a transitional landscape between the agricultural pattern of the Brendons to the east and the moorland wildness of Exmoor Forest to the west. Both types of scenery either mingle or contrast sharply here with great variety of effect.

The northern coastal portion of the belt contains a moorland ridge with high cliffs overlooking the sea. This ridge extends from Minehead to Bossington, ending abruptly at Hurlstone Point, which dominates the alluvial levels fringing Porlock Bay.

The southern slopes of the same ridge are well wooded with mixed species, mostly hardwoods, and shelter a lowland of lush fields, small coverts and picturesque hamlets in Porlock Vale. South again, the scene changes quickly, the land rising steeply through National Trust woods, where conifers are plentiful but not obtrusive. Then comes the heather moorland of Dunkery Hill and the Beacon itself, which is the highest point in the entire Park. From here vast views can be seen — northwards across the Channel to the Brecon Beacons in Wales, eastwards along the Somerset coast to the Quantock and Mendip Hills, and southwards to Dartmoor.

Away to the west and north-west, the moors stretch continuously from Dunkery into the old Exmoor Forest, intersected by steep valleys of which, in this belt, the most important group is Horner Water and its ancillary combes. Fold upon fold of valley slope, clothed with coppiced oak trees, tone perfectly with the moorland above through all the seasonal variations of colour and texture. Economically useless today, the old system of cropping oak for tan bark now helps to provide a landscape feature of great beauty.

South of Dunkery, the lower land towards Wheddon Cross and Exford, Withypool and Dulverton, is dominated by farming similar to the Brendons. Good roads, scattered hill farms, beech hedges, but generally fewer woods and trees, form a pleasant if sober pattern. In this quiet scene unexpected contrasts are to be found. The little known bracken-clothed combe between Room Hill and Staddon, which the River Exe follows, can be easily overlooked. The windswept moor on Winsford Hill is a foretaste of the wide spaces of Exmoor Forest which can be seen from there. Then there is the old hardwood valley of the River Barle which must be considered with those of the Exe and Haddeo. All of them meet just south of Dulverton, where the great size of the river system and its influence on the landscape in this area can be better judged. The presence of much understocked or derelict woodland in these valleys is noticeable.

Exmoor Forest

This section of the National Park is, in fact, the parish of Exmoor which is virtually contiguous with the old Royal Deer Forest and has an area of approximately 20,000 acres.

This has been the shape of Exmoor Forest since 1400 and thus, historically, it forms a clear sub-division of the Park to which it now gives its name. Scenically, too, it is distinctive from the moors and commons which surround it. Fundamental differences occur in vegetation, and the general dominance of grasses gives the mile upon mile of rolling highland a gentle subtlety of colouring and texture. The absence of trees is also noticeable. Before the sale of the Forest in 1818, the surveyor's report of 1814 counted only 37 trees, excluding the Hoar Oak, and these were all growing round Simonsbath House. Earlier evidence indicates that, throughout recorded time at least, the Forest had been a 'Baren, and Morisch Ground' as Leland called it. After the sale of the Forest by the Crown to John Knight, who was virtually the architect of modern Exmoor, very little tree planting was done for a time. The 26 acres of Birch Cleave at Simonsbath was the only woodland planted before 1840. Later, under Frederic Knight's direction, other woodlands were laid out around Simonsbath and a nursery was established there, probably for the raising of beech plants for hedging and shelter belts on what were then the newly-created

Forest farms. During the 1914–18 war most of the timber, which included conifers, in Cornham Brake, Halscombe and Flexbarrow was felled. Some of the woods have since been replanted with conifers, others remain derelict, but the beech in Birch Cleave still stands, forming the oldest woodland in the area and contributing greatly to the amenities of the small village.

The story of the reclamation of Exmoor Forest in the nineteenth century by the Knight family, has been told by Dr. C. S. Orwin.[6] The effect of that activity upon the landscape is mainly demonstrated today by the presence of enclosed farmlands, usually on the southern slopes of the moorland hills. The upper lands, used mostly for sheep walks, have much the same appearance as they have had for centuries. Large stretches of these highlands can be overlooked from good modern roads and it is, principally, the clean sweeping lines of the grassy hills and the uncluttered spaciousness of the land which convey a special distinction upon the Forest scene. After the restlessness of modern urban life, the visitor can find here the elements of true refreshment and re-creation. Away from the roads, feelings of remoteness and quietude are added to the visual qualities. The rolling plateau is intersected by deep combes, many of which are concealed from general view, and their discovery is a further delight for the connoisseur who is prepared to walk the Forest. Numerous streams and rivers thread the combes and add the sparkling movement of water to the simplicity of this landscape pattern. Here and there in some combes the remains of small softwood plantations may be found, planted for shelter and farm use but felled during war-time and seldom replaced. The careful contouring of these old plantations and their small scale must have made them unobtrusive but interesting additions to the landscape.

Within the Forest, variation of this basic pattern — grassy highland, watered combe and four-square farm — is obtained mainly by the infinite rearrangement of the components and the play of cloud shadows upon them. Attempts to grade the landscape importance of different areas must necessarily be a matter of personal bias. All that may be said factually is that by reason of more difficulty of access, fewer farming activities or greater altitude, the higher parts possess the qualities of remoteness, peace and simplicity in the most marked degree. Of such places, The Chains is the highest point in the Forest and the richest in these qualities. In varying degrees, these same values are apparent in those parts of the northern sector which are furthest away from main roads. South of Simonsbath and Exford, however, they are less effective, although the southern ridge with its wealth of ancient burial mounds and fine views over Devon, is important in this classification.

The Coastal Strip

Mention has been made of the contrast in coastal scenery near Porlock Weir. The high moorland ridge from Minehead drops, at Hurlstone Point, to an area of neat, level fields. Westwards from Porlock Weir, high cliffs, covered nearly to the beaches with woods of oak coppice, stretch almost uninterruptedly to Heddon's Mouth. This is one of the finest lengths of wooded coastline in the country, and the resulting scenery possesses immense grandeur. Special features of interest are the emergence at the coast of deep wooded combes at Lynmouth and Heddon's Mouth, and the dramatic bareness of the Valley of Rocks at Lynton. Attempts have been made at Ashley Combe, near Porlock, to introduce better timber trees, including Douglas fir which shows promise, on the cliff sites and some fellings have taken place here and at Glenthorne. In the main, these activities have caused little visible difference to the overall appearance of the coast.

Inland from the cliff edges, a little agricultural land and a few farms occur but heather moor predominates — except where reclaimed in recent years. A mile or so from the coast, the main Porlock–Lynmouth road is reached. This road crosses Culbone Hill where examples may still be seen of unfortunate landscape effects caused by the planting of high moorland with silviculturally unsuitable conifer species, principally larch. There are, however, nearby in the valleys around Pitt, examples of correct choice of species, principally spruce, pine and fir, and better siting of plantations. The improved effects upon landscape may be judged.

The high road to Lynmouth provides endless points from which long views southwards may be obtained across the fringing moors and commons and into the Forest itself. Almost all the principal highland ridges in the northern part of the Forest can be seen and, from near County Gate, there is a view along almost the entire length of Badgeworthy Water into the heart of the fictional Doone country.

A valley road, south of the high road, should also be mentioned. It leaves the high road at Oare Post and follows the combe beside Oare Water westwards to Malmsmead and Brendon. The scenery is composed of woodland and farmland, streamside and combe, and is warm and intimate after the cooler spaciousness of the uplands. The road leads finally through combes of coppiced oak owned by the National Trust from Watersmeet to Lynmouth.

West from Lynton, through the Valley of Rocks, a narrow coast road provides views of another section of the wooded coastline and leads to more combes of coppiced oak meeting at Hunters Inn near Heddon's Mouth. From here, the road winds round Trentishoe Down, one of the last western outposts of typical Exmoor moorland. After turning inland a little through agricultural scenery, the road skirts Great Hangman, said to be one of the highest cliffs in England, and thence leaves the Park at Combe Martin Bay.

The South-West Foothills

Bounded on the north by a portion of the coastal strip already described, this Devon section of Exmoor lies between the Park and County boundaries.

Inland from the coastal area, the landscape is conventionally agricultural in the vicinity of the main Lynton–Barnstaple road. South-eastwards from this road, past Challacombe, the ridges and combes fringing the Exmoor plateau provide a transitional scene, where agriculture alternates with moorland, the deep valley woodlands tail out, and remoteness begins. From the tracks and roads along or near the County boundary, a continuous pattern of moorland buttress and scrub-scattered combe can be seen, sloping southwards and becoming increasingly agricultural or wooded until an expanse of rural Devon stretches away beyond the boundary of the Park. Northwards, the bare hills of Exmoor contrast sharply with the timbered lowlands to the south and, within the foothills, there are occasional isolated farms and hamlets. Some contoured conifer plantations in the combes look well in the landscape, helping to emphasize its transitional nature.

Near Twitchen, the grain of the country changes and the heather-clad commons of Molland and the Ansteys carry a long ridge road eastwards to the Somerset boundary near Dulverton.

Seen from the Devon lowlands along the Barnstaple–Bampton road, the foothills slope up to the higher land of the Forest's southern ridge which dominates the skyline. The foothills, although attractive in themselves, play an introductory role to the more dramatic scenes in the highlands to the north.

These notes on major and specific aspects of the several Exmoor landscape patterns have been kept to a minimum in order to avoid confusion in conveying a picture of each of the different sections of the National Park. In practice, many more notes were made upon the set of six-inch plans and tentative sites for afforestation were plotted, pending the investigation of other interests. In order to accomplish this part of the survey and to appreciate fully the lie of the land and its scenic value, almost every road, lane and track in Exmoor were traversed by car or on foot and no corner was left unseen.

It is most essential to obtain as intimate a knowledge as possible of an area under this type of survey. The outdoor work in Exmoor occupied, almost uninterruptedly, a period of three months: previous knowledge, gained from official journeys, farming and living in the area, shortened the need to spend more time in the field. For an afforestation survey in an almost unknown region, it would be necessary to allow very much more time.

The main broad conclusions reached from a study of the different landscapes, and without considering design detail at this stage, are:

1. The Brendon Hills offer limited opportunities for afforestation, but the neatness of the landscape, and the strong influence of modern forestry in several parts of the Hills, should enable some new plantations to be established without much conflict.
2. The East Central Belt offers scope for afforestation, by reason of the mixture of landscape patterns within it and the great variety of the terrain.
3. Exmoor Forest, on the other hand, is homogeneous as a section, and spaciousness is a special feature. Opportunities for forestry projects exist, but great care will be needed in design because the style of landscape could easily be disrupted.
4. The Coastal Strip contains few potential afforestation sites, because of the panoramic and constantly changing views which it affords. These would be considerably curtailed by plantations.

5. The South-West Foothills offer even more scope for forestry than the East Central Belt, because extensions to existing woodlands could be carried out in the combes, emphasizing the transitional nature of the landscape between the Devon lowlands and the Exmoor plateau.

e — Existing and Foreseen Land Uses (Table 6, page 169 refers)

The next matter to be weighed is the extent to which new forestry projects can be introduced, without hindrance, and if possible with benefit, to other established or foreseeable land-uses as well as to the economy and appearance of the region. The subject may be sub-divided as follows :

Agriculture

The oldest, most widespread and important form of enterprise in the National Park. An appreciation of the various farming patterns is necessary if afforestation sites are to be suggested which will not conflict with agricultural efficiency.

The patterns vary within the Park in accordance with the qualities of soil, exposure and elevation. In association with the sheltered, fertile and well-drained sandy loams in the Porlock Vale, partly or wholly self-sufficient dairy farming may be practised. A proportion of each holding may be devoted to rotational cropping and leys, thus providing winter feed. The use of land for agriculture in this area is intensive.

Arable farming is associated generally with good quality land where deep, well-drained, fertile soils are developed on gently undulating sites with moderate elevation and good aspect. The lower slopes of the Brendon Hills form part of one of the traditional arable areas in Somerset.

Grassland dairying, associated with rich river meadows, is of importance in the Dulverton district and this type of dairy farming occurs widely, if not always economically, on higher land in the Brendons and Exmoor in conjunction with other forms of enterprise.

A large amount of land within the Park is devoted to stock rearing. The upland slopes of the Brendons and Exmoor, where soils are shallow and of medium or low fertility, are traditional areas for the raising of beef cattle and sheep. The enclosed land on the Brendons is suited to the rearing of both sheep and bullocks but, on Exmoor, sheep form the mainstay and the largest sheep runs occur on the virtually unenclosed hills and commons. This is the further extreme in the farming pattern within the Park, where land-use is at its most extensive. In recent years there has been a marked tendency towards further enclosure and land improvement, enabling larger numbers of stock, especially sheep, to be carried. Most of this activity has occurred in the mid-west and south-west sections of the Park, chiefly in Devon.

Generally, the complete and successful agricultural reclamation of peaty upland requires very sophisticated techniques, and there is not much evidence yet of these being employed in Exmoor. Such highland coincides broadly with the areas which can also be regarded as relatively hostile for tree planting. Reclamation and improvement for farming, like afforestation, are easier and more satisfactory on the lower slopes and fringes of the moor. Thus, at present, many of the heather areas would appear to be more vulnerable to change than the central grass moors.

No set rules may be laid down, however, regarding the relative importance to an Exmoor sheep farmer of the differing types of land which may be included in his farm. Generally the land may be divided into three kinds : the upper highland, the middle slopes and combe sides, and the lower sheltered lands. The uplands provide extensive summer grazings and the lower lands are used for hay, cropping and sheltered grazing. The middle ground, including the combes, may provide some keep and be very valuable for sheltering. Alternatively, the middle land may be useless owing to exposure. The economy of each farm is closely related to the lie of the land where it is situated. Thus, while it may be thought that the best place for afforestation would be upon middle ground, this is not always the case. By siting plantations indiscriminately in this way the risks are run of cutting off access from the lower to the upper lands, or of immobilizing combes which may be vital for sheltering or feeding stock at certain times of the year.

On some farms, land reclamation may have an important bearing upon the question of afforestation. The agricultural improvements may result in better returns from a smaller amount of land, thus leaving a surplus of ground which might be planted. The sheltering effect of trees might, in the future, confer additional benefits upon the farmlands and improve productivity still further, but this is a possibility which does not appear to have received very much attention yet in Exmoor. Shelter belts, except round farmsteads, are uncommon.

At the present time, it can be said only generally that middle lands which are bracken covered may be regarded as potential forest sites. Land where cultivations are impossible owing to gradient may be similarly regarded, but with caution, as such areas may provide valuable shelter or a picking of keep at certain times.

In weighing any afforestation proposal within the National Park it is, in fact, very necessary to understand fully the economy of each farm which may be affected, in order to integrate forestry and agriculture to the best advantage of both interests. Consultation with the Land Commissioner is always advisable and the question of common rights must be considered in some cases.

The Zuckerman Report of 1957, upon the integration of forestry and agriculture, contains factual information and well-considered opinion upon the question of combining the two activities in upland areas and under conditions such as those found in Exmoor.[7] Although the amenity aspects involved, particularly in National Parks, are only lightly touched upon, there is much material which has a bearing upon the problem of finding the correct places for forestry in the economy and landscape of Exmoor.[8] In particular, Paragraphs 129–136 are worth noting and some remarks from Paragraph 130 may be quoted :

'. . . efforts should be made to obtain those parcels of land which can best be spared from individual farms within the marginal hill areas. In aggregate there is a large area of land which is too steep, broken, or thin for mechanical improvement. There are, indeed, many places where continuous if narrow bands of steep "side lands" lie between valley fields and hilltop pastures. These are of little use to the farmer, and are frequently infested by bracken or gorse. Even allowing for adequate access to the upper pastures, they could provide a large and not unduly costly planting area, often without taking more than a small and unprofitable section of land out of adjacent farms . . .'

The main conclusions to be drawn from a study of Exmoor's

agriculture are four in number. Firstly, there is little room for afforestation in the relatively intensively farmed lowlands. An occasional corner where a farmer could grow a small copse for domestic use, a few shelter belts and some new hedgerow trees are examples of the very small scale upon which fresh planting could be carried out.

Secondly, on the fringes of the main plateau, modern techniques of reclamation and improvement are enabling a greater head of stock to be carried. More stock require more shelter in winter. There is little English information yet available about the improvement known to be obtained in the survival rate of animals as a result of well-designed shelter belts or woodlands, and the use of trees for shelter has been almost wholly ignored on Exmoor. Therefore, there may be a case one day for planting for this purpose on the moor but, if carried out widely, a new type of landscape would result.

Thirdly, in terms of area, the middle lands of the Brendons, the East Central Belt and the South-West Foothills appear to offer the best opportunities for afforestation on a substantial scale. In the Brendons, there are a number of narrow but continuous bands of steep 'side lands', as described in the Zuckerman Report. There are also so many sheltered combes and steep but reasonably hospitable slopes in the lower highlands generally, that consultations with the Land Commissioner and the National Farmers' Union should lead to the agreement of areas for afforestation without detriment to agriculture.

Fourthly, it is clear that the land bank of 'open country' previously noted as the absolute maximum which might be available for forest expansion in Exmoor, has to be substantially reduced. Certain limitations are imposed by physical conditions, but a much larger allowance has to be made for present farming use and the trends in agricultural improvement. On these counts, it is estimated that probably not much more than 20,000 acres can be regarded realistically as the maximum area available for planting. And the claims of recreation and amenity, high priorities in a National Park, have yet to be assessed.

Forestry

The appearance of woodlands in the various geographical sections of the Park needs more detailed attention in view of the fundamental objects of the afforestation survey.

The positioning of the older woods in relation to other elements in the landscapes of Exmoor is of special interest, because the siting of new woods is the first objective of this survey. In the past, woodlands of hardwoods, principally oak and oak coppice, were concentrated along the coastline, in the long deep combes running north towards the coast, in the combes of the South-West Foothills, in the valleys of the Barle, Exe, Haddeo and Avill Rivers and on the northern slopes of the Brendon Hills. On estates such as Dunster, Pixton Park, Nettlecombe, Miltons and Combe Syden-ham, deliberate landscaping with woodlands of economic value was undertaken.

The general arrangement of woodland in the National Park, therefore, has been distinctive. It has occurred almost entirely on steeply sloping land, and woodland on flat ground, even around landscaped estates, has been and still is relatively unusual. There are two principal features to be noted in this general arrangement. Firstly, the woods, being sloped, are widely visible and the planting designs within them are important if their appearances, as well as their positions, are to be satisfactory in the landscape. This subject is treated in detail later. Secondly, woodland in Exmoor has for centuries occupied an intermediate position between lowland and highland. This has been emphasized not only by the intensification of agriculture, which normally spreads upwards from lowlands, leaving steeper or less amenable land under woodland, but also by the centuries-old use of the principal highland plateau as a treeless Royal Forest devoted to the chase and the extensive pasturing of livestock.

Thus, by long established and largely unchanging usage of the upper and lower lands, the bulk of the Exmoor woods have been confined to the middle slopes. Long twisting ribbons of woodland defining river valleys, combes and hillsides, underlining and repeating like shadows the gently curving skylines of the high-lands above them, are characteristic of the area and an integral part of the landscape. It seems, therefore, that for new planting an arrangement in the landscape similar to the old woodland pattern would be the one most likely to have an unobtrusive and natural appearance. Such a pattern, related to existing landscapes, would assist in the design of new plantations of conifers which have colour and textural effects strikingly different from those of the

159

older woods. Clearly, large softwood plantations on the open plateau would seem unrelated to established landscape forms; on the lower land, while small woods could be absorbed without much difficulty, particularly on level sites, the intensity of farming is likely to exclude large-scale afforestation.

These observations can be supported by the manner in which a number of forestry projects have developed in Exmoor during the last half century or more. First, on those estates where a high standard of woodland management was maintained, despite periods of national indifference, war and economic uncertainty, the restocking of old valley woods and the extension of plantations on the lower hills was carried out in keeping with the basic woodland arrangements. Dunster, Miltons and Pixton Park are notable examples and their woods are now greatly admired for their beauty.

Later, in the nineteen-twenties, when the Forestry Commission acquired land and planted Croydon Hill and the slopes south of Dunster, this development, while exhibiting some of the crudities in design and scale associated with some of the Commission's early work, was nevertheless sited in the well-wooded northern Brendons. Because of its consequent relationship to an area of long-established forest activity, the new plantations were more readily acceptable in the overall landscape pattern.

More recently, proposals by the State and private organizations to afforest open land in situations similar to older woodland positions have been agreed by the National Park Committees without much difficulty, and received by amenity organizations with a minimum of controversy.

Public opposition to afforestation in Exmoor, when it occurs, is always most vociferous when a proposal affects a large area of high-lying land. Many opponents to the establishment of large plantations on The Chains, Trout Hill, Kittuck or above Flexbarrow might not be able to describe objectively why they found such projects distasteful. Nevertheless, their instinctive feelings that the plantations would, somehow, look wrong, were correct in terms of landscape design. Both in scale, and in relation to what might be described as the grain of the countryside, the afforestation of those sites would have introduced seriously disruptive elements to the landscape. The existing composition is of a quality which should be altered only in detail, or otherwise completely re-

36. Holnicote Estate: Now a National Trust property—from an eighteenth-century painting. No woods appear on the coastal ridge between Bossington (left) and Selworthy (right).

37. Holnicote Estate: The same hills today. Woods planted by the Acland family included much evergreen oak (left). Wartime fellings (centre) made good by the National Trust which manages these woods with a strong amenity bias.

38. Selworthy: Trees in the setting of the old village and a view southwards across Porlock Vale.

39. North Hill, Minehead: Most of the woods and high moorland in the picture have been acquired for amenity management by the Somerset County Council.

designed as it was in the time of the Great Reclamation. This is not to say that planting on some parts of the areas would also have been unacceptable, but rather that the proposals as they were made were unsuitable.

In the event, the proposals, which were made by the Forestry Commission, were all withdrawn following consultations with the Park Committees and the weighing of other relevant interests. It is worth digressing to suggest that these projects, and the controversy they raised, illustrate the haphazard circumstances, unlikely to favour good landscape design except by chance, which have dogged the Forestry Commission in forest planning until quite recent years. Proposals of this kind have occurred throughout the country, not always as a result of deliberate intent by the Commission, but rather because the land happened to be on offer.

Landowners, trying to maintain the best of their estates in face of taxation and other problems, have been able to sell or lease unprofitable sections to a Commission constantly under pressure to grow timber in bulk on poor land. The land has passed from the protection of the traditional trustee of landscape into the hands of a Government Department which, until lately, has had no real brief to consider amenity.

Fortunately, circumstances were already changing at the time of these proposals. Now, it seems to be accepted that, while such land is capable of being planted, the work cannot be as well justified economically as afforestation on better and more sheltered sites. If amenity considerations also weigh heavily, the Forestry Commission is often not unwilling to withdraw.

Aesthetically, the middle slopes in Exmoor provide the best positions for new woods, and this seems to suit agricultural and silvicultural requirements as well. The integration of the two main rural industries can be well served by this arrangement, provided any special agricultural needs are safeguarded. Soil fertility and shelter are usually of a sufficiently high standard for good quality timber to be grown. Access may prove difficult and contoured roading expensive, but these problems are now regarded with much less disfavour in forestry circles than was once the case. They would seem to be counterbalanced to a substantial extent by a better production potential than could be expected from the near level but otherwise hostile land on much of the central plateau.

L

Moreover, extensions of existing woodland systems are likely to prove more attractive for overall management than haphazard arrangements of disconnected blocks.

Some information upon the existing use of land for forestry in the National Park (Table 6, page 169) also deserves attention. At present — February, 1966 — the total woodland area is in the region of 17,000 acres or 10% of the whole Park. More than half of the woods are either under direct Forestry Commission control or are being managed privately in accordance with plans of operations agreed with the Forestry Commission under dedication or the approved woods scheme. Most of these are situated in the northern Brendons, on slopes in the Coastal Strip and in the river valleys and combes of the East Central Belt and the Devon Foothills. The balance of rather less than 8,000 acres of woods are at present largely uncommitted so far as Forestry Commission influence upon their management is concerned.

Many of the uncommitted woods and a number of dedicated areas possess high amenity value in the landscapes of the Park. These, together with others already under special amenity management, or which form parts of several Sites of Special Scientific Interest scheduled by the Nature Conservancy, are reviewed in a separate woodlands survey (Part III).

The relevance of the total existing woodland acreage to this afforestation survey stems from the duty laid upon National Park administrators to have due regard for forestry requirements. Reference has been made to the problem of correctly interpreting this duty. Knowing that 10% of the Park is woodland and that this includes 5·3% under efficient productive management, are useful starting points in assessing what would be a reasonable additional apportionment of land for afforestation. As a rough guide, every $1\frac{3}{4}$ thousand acres earmarked for new planting would raise the total woodland proportion by 1%.

The existing total proportion must be well above the current national average, even allowing for the increase in woodland area which has occurred throughout the country since the 1949 Census, when it was recorded as 5·8% for England and 6·1% for Great Britain. Moreover, the present proportion in Exmoor is only 1% below the target of a national average of 11% which, although abandoned now as official policy, will be approached slowly if the current rates of progress in private and State afforestation continue.

It may even be reached by the end of the century as originally intended.

It has to be borne in mind, however, that the old national target envisaged 11% of *efficiently managed* woods in the country. Much of the uncommitted Exmoor woodland is unproductive or in the scrub category and does not contribute effectively in terms of timber. To what extent such areas might do so, without loss of amenity aspects, is examined in the woodlands survey. Until the production potential of existing woods has been realized, it is reasonable to suggest that, in the first phase of planned expansion, the urgency to provide new sites for planting is lessened. Nevertheless, it may be contended that to raise the national average area of land under good quality woods, National Parks, containing large amounts of open country, should contribute a very much higher acreage for planting to offset agricultural and urban land where there is little, if any, room for woodland expansion.

Recreation

Long before its designation as a National Park, Exmoor, as a result of its landscape beauty, was attractive to visitors. Now the tourist trade plays an increasingly important part in the economy of both the counties concerned with the Park.

For instance, in the Somerset Development Plan Report of Survey, 1964, it has been estimated that between £12 million and £15 million may be spent annually by holiday-makers in the county, in addition to whatever is spent by day-trippers. The county contains roughly a million acres and, if every acre were equally attractive, the annual return from amenity would be at least £12 per acre. Even at this flat average rate, the Somerset part of Exmoor — about one-eighth of the county area — can be assumed to draw £1½ million or thereabouts in tourist trade each year. Because the landscapes remain to repeat the attraction again and again, they form one of those valuable assets now commonly called an invisible export.

In American terms, Exmoor is a scenic resource. As such, it has an economic value which can be overlooked sometimes by operators seeking to establish new enterprises within its boundaries. It is probable, although difficult to substantiate until cost-benefit analyses have been made, that afforestation or agricultural reclamation in certain areas may be no longer as economically attractive in a national sense as the maintenance or enhancement of the existing scenery. Nevertheless at local level, although the tourist trade helps to supplement farm incomes in this largely marginal area, it is not yet generally attractive enough to prevent a slow drift of land workers from Exmoor. Forestry has already proved to be a useful diversifier of employment helping to counter this drift.

It is therefore necessary to plan the siting of new forest areas in Exmoor so that they may help to provide local employment and strengthen the overall economy, but without injuring the beauty of the countryside which attracts the tourist trade. Both the majority of visitors who simply enjoy scenery from roads or lay-bys, and the selective minority who prefer less accessible places or have special interests, should receive consideration if the full purpose of a National Park is to be respected. Some analysis of all recreational activities within the area is therefore helpful. The pleasures of residents and the increasing popularity of the Park for retirement should also be borne in mind.

Recreation in Exmoor may be divided as follows :

Motoring and Picnics Traffic congestion is greatest in the summer months and in the northern section of the Park. That part contains the largest proportion of hotel or other accommodation, as well as being readily accessible and possessing both coastal and inland attractions. The least frequented sections are in the east and south-west of the Park. Congestion may be aggravated at weekends by the arrival of local visitors. The motor-car enables Exmoor to be an objective for a day trip for people living within at least 60 miles of the area : this radius includes Bristol and several medium-sized towns. Coach trips to the Park are increasing.

Although most traffic is to be found in the north, the small size of Exmoor — it is one of the smallest National Parks — and a road system which is remarkably good for a highland region, make the area very vulnerable to the motor-car. The dispersal of vehicles in annually increasing numbers causes the two County Committees to prepare each year a programme of new parking places. Individually these are kept as small and unobtrusive as possible, but many have to be sited at proven points of special interest or at viewpoints. They can now be counted in dozens within the Park.

Afforestation can play a useful secondary role in masking glittering concentrations of parked vehicles. An example of this benefit can be seen at Webber's Post on the northern slopes of Dunkery where self-sown pine trees, outliers to neighbouring plantations, conceal or soften the appearance of large numbers of cars on almost any sunny day. At the same time trees can provide shelter and shade for the parking area, and may be used to enhance the views obtained from such places by obscuring the superfluous and framing special features.

Those sections of the Park fringing the central grassy plateau contain most of the favourite tourist routes and parking or viewing points. The principal heather moors, particularly popular for picnics and the gathering of heather or bilberries in season, are in these fringe areas. It has been noted that the flanks of the main plateau contain some of the most promising afforestation sites, but it is clear that a very careful selection must be made to avoid masking important views or reducing accessibility, particularly on the most popular of the heather moors. The matter of colour in the landscape, provided in these areas especially by the heathers, also requires thought and is examined later in relation to the design of individual plantations. Finally, the fire risk can be high in some densely frequented places and this may influence both the siting and layout of new woods.

Although the central plateau is not well served with roads, there are several very popular routes on the north, east and west which command extensive views over much of its relatively unconcealed surface. Afforestation on the plateau, if desirable at all, needs to be designed with great care if the appearance of it from one direction or another is not to be ugly. There is much to be said for projects being either of such small scale as to provide only points of interest in distant views, or so large as to be strong features in keeping with the size and form of the surrounding landscape. Indeterminate designs, sporadically arranged, would certainly provide indifferent visual effects.

It might be contended that there is more than enough room for picnic parties on the open moorland in Exmoor. Experience has shown that sheltered and wooded picnic areas are in demand. The Somerset County Council has provided one such place at Pittcombe Head above Porlock and the Forestry Commission another in the pine woods on Croydon Hill. More may be established.

Generally they need to be sited to command good views and provision has to be made for parked vehicles.

Camping   The Park Committees generally try to deflect motor-
drawn caravans to well-designed and sited parks on the perimeter
of Exmoor. The steep gradients in the Park form a natural
deterrent to many caravaners, but some penetrate into the area
and are accommodated for short periods on farms.

Tented camping by organized groups such as Boy Scouts is
encouraged officially, and educational camps for natural history,
adventure training and initiative receive similar support. Private
camping in tents is catered for almost entirely by local residents
and farmers. It seems clear that the demand for camping facilities
will increase, bringing the major associated problems of hygiene
and fire.

The Forestry Commission has gained experience already in
providing camping grounds in their forests together with water
points, conveniences, barbecue hearths and other amenities. In
Exmoor, the Commission would develop such sites in their forests
if required and if suitable land could be found. The Somerset
County Council may soon establish a similar area on North Hill,
near Minehead.

Basically, camps require dry, level ground which is sheltered
but not overshadowed. Water should be available and reasonably
good access for the transport of equipment. Attractive surroundings are essential. These conditions, to be found in Exmoor chiefly
in those parts which flank the plateau, should be remembered
when selecting land for afforestation. Encouraging public camping
in forest areas may lead to some risk of damage to plantations,
especially by fire, at various stages and seasons, but making the
facility available may help towards redeveloping forest conscious-
ness and respect among the public.

Rambling and Riding   Walking, rambling and pony trekking are
popular pastimes in Exmoor. The distribution of footpaths and
bridleways is widespread over the whole Park. Some of the
routes are way-marked by the Park Committees with the consent
of the landowners concerned. This both helps people to find and
enjoy the paths, and aids the dispersal of visitors. The coastal
path around the south-western peninsula of England, designed by

the National Parks Commission, traverses the full length of the Exmoor coastline.

Sections of some of these routes might be absorbed within afforestation schemes provided public rights-of-way are respected, and special viewpoints along them are taken into account in plantation design. Indeed, the added variety resulting from a path passing through trees, and the shelter which may be given, can enhance the attractions for ramblers and riders. Monotony, caused by lack of variety in the planting pattern beside public routes, or insufficient breaks in tree cover, should be avoided.

Sport   The hunting of deer, fox and otter are traditional sports in the district. The hunts are strongly supported locally and are also followed by large numbers of visitors on foot or in cars. As well as the staghounds and otter hounds, there are eleven packs of foxhounds. Their combined hunting territories cover virtually the whole of the National Park.

Exmoor is one of the few places in England where the red deer is found in the wild state, and the area is therefore an important one scientifically as well as to the hunt. Deer may do considerable damage to young trees, and in many parts of Exmoor have to be excluded from newly formed plantations. Later the fences may be removed, because as long as the numbers of deer do not become excessive the damage they do in maturing woods is generally light. As deer are true woodland dwellers, forestry can assist in conserving these animals.

There is some shooting of ground game in the Park and rabbits appear to be increasing. Game birds, however, are few and rearing is not practised much at present. There is nothing incompatible between shooting and forestry, and additional afforestation could help to foster certain birds if required.

Fishing the rivers of Exmoor is popular, particularly with residents, and all rights are privately owned. It is not uncommon for clauses to be included in leases of woodland in Exmoor to the effect that no conifers shall be planted within one chain of river banks and along tributaries. Light hardwood timbering or open stretches alongside rivers and streams serve fishing interests best, and are also preferable on aesthetic grounds because the beauty of water is not obscured.

Sailing and boating are based upon a few places along the coast,

167

and steamers cruise in the Bristol Channel carrying many visitors who enjoy the pleasure of seeing the coast from the sea. These interests are concerned mainly with the appearance of the existing coastal woods and cliffs and are unlikely to influence afforestation for which there is little suitable land in coastline situations.

Scientific Pursuits The general natural history of Exmoor is of interest to many people; certain sections of the Park possess a local or national scientific importance.

Five areas at Heddon's Mouth, Watersmeet, Knaplock, Burridge Wood and the Dunkery Beacon locality have been notified by the Nature Conservancy under Section 23 of the National Parks Act, 1949, as Sites of Special Scientific Interest. They are described in Appendix 2. Forestry activity within these areas, some of which include open moorland, would alter the ecological or other natural patterns. Consultations with the Nature Conservancy would be necessary before contemplating any afforestation, however limited.

Elsewhere, as a general rule, it is always desirable to consult recognized botanical, zoological or other scientific authorities before embarking on a planting scheme. For example, on the screes in that part of Cornham Brake, near Simonsbath, running westwards above the River Barle to Cornham Ford, the Parsley Fern, *Cryptogramma crispa*, was found ten or twelve years ago after having been unrecorded since 1870. This rarity will survive only under rather precise conditions of light intensity and, if these are altered by afforestation, the plant would disappear. Similarly, the Oak Fern, *Thelypteris dryopteris*, grows on the side of the Exe Valley south of Warren Farm, and the whole section of that valley from Prayway to Exford is of botanical interest.

In the same way, archaeological sites require attention and tree planting should not interfere haphazardly with the many ancient barrows, stones, camps and hut circles to be found throughout the Park.

One of the purposes of a National Park is that matters such as these should receive proper attention. Exploring the physiographical peculiarities of The Punchbowl on Winsford Hill is as much a form of recreation to one section of the public as a picnic on Brendon Common may be to another.

Miscellaneous Interests

In Exmoor, water catchment makes claims upon land and a number of water undertakers are involved. At present reservoirs within the Park are few and small but, as the demand for water by outside urban populations increases, the importance of the highland area as a source of supply may rise. For example, the large new reservoir at Clatworthy on the southern Brendon Hills, outside the Park in Somerset, already utilizes supplies from part of the Park for Taunton and other towns.

TABLE 6

AN ESTIMATE OF LAND USE: EXMOOR NATIONAL
PARK, FEBRUARY 1966
(Acreages and percentages are approximate only and the beaches
and foreshore are excluded)

Primary Use	Acres	% area	Remarks
Agriculture			Total: 149,500 acs. or 88% + of Park
Intensive	101,500	59·8	
Extensive[9]	48,000	28·4	Includes heather moor (23,600 acs. or 14% −) and grass moor (24,400 acs. or 14% +)
Forestry			Total: 17,000 acs. or 10% of Park
F. Commission	3,350	2·0	F.C. owns additional 200 acs. under agriculture
Dedicated & Approved	5,700	3·3	
Other woods	7,950	4·7	
Settlements	1,100	0·6	
Miscellaneous			
Roads, rivers, etc.	2,000	1·2	No railways inside Park boundaries
TOTAL:	169,600 (265 sq. miles)	100·0	Divided between Devon (49,280 acs. or 77 sq. miles) and Somerset (120,320 acs. or 188 sq. miles)

ADDITIONAL INFORMATION (Acreages included in appropriate primary use above)
1. National Trust: Total 15,000 acs. (3,100 acs. of woods, 3,150 acs. agric. land, 8,750 acs. of moor)
2. Somerset C.C.: Total 1,100 acs. (400 acs. of woods, 700 acs. of moor)
3. Sites of Special Scientific Interest: Total 7,500 acs. (2,000 acs. of woods, 5,500 acs. of moor)
NOTE: Some of these interests overlap, e.g., some N.T. lands, both moors and woods, are included in S.S.S.I.'s scheduled by the Nature Conservancy.

The effect of tree cover on run-off and stream behaviour is still a vexed subject among scientists but recent studies indicate that at least under conditions of high rainfall on soils that may be eroded easily, the presence of forest cover is valuable. After the Lynmouth catastrophe in 1952, the question of afforestation in relation to water conservation should not remain an academic one in Exmoor. It seems therefore that some planting in the Park might be linked advantageously with water undertakings, and such arrangements would be in accordance with the Ministry of Health's Report on Gathering Grounds, 1948.

River Boards in both counties also have an interest in Exmoor and in recent years have undertaken flood control works on a number of streams and rivers. Such operations can be integrated with forestry projects without difficulty.

Electricity Boards consult with the Park Committees upon the best routes for new overhead power lines. Amenity and economic values have to be carefully weighed because the alternative of undergrounding the lines is enormously, often prohibitively, expensive. Sometimes the presence of woodland, near which a line may be erected unobtrusively, has helped in the selection of a route. To this extent forested land, preferably irregular in pattern, can facilitate the problem of taking electricity to an isolated farm or hamlet with the minimum of detriment to the landscape.

There are no major industrial undertakings in Exmoor similar to those which have been accommodated in other National Parks, such as oil refineries, power stations or cement works. If such developments were to occur, then landscaping on a scale which could be described as afforestation might be necessary.

3 PRINCIPLES OF LANDSCAPE DESIGN

So far, the majority of the material collected in the report of survey has been factual. Mention has been made, however, of less obvious, but equally relevant matters, such as the existing arrangement of woods in relation to the grain of the countryside, and the likelihood of some sections of the Park lending themselves more easily than others on aesthetic grounds to the accommodation of forestry projects.

Such remarks are not fanciful. They stem directly from basic principles of design. The application of these principles in landscape work, as in any form of art, has varied from century to century, but they are the constant factors discernible in all good design of whatever period. Therefore, they should be evident in both site selection and the layout of subsequent plantations — if an afforestation survey in a National Park is to fulfil its special purposes of indicating land for a rural industry which, when developed, will enhance the attractions of the countryside.

The same principles were employed in the creation of famous eighteenth-century landscapes. Later they were neglected, becoming almost, and sometimes entirely, subservient to economic expediency. Much of the ugliness in the country today has been caused by this disregard. Forestry has been neither the worst offender nor the only activity wherein unsatisfactory visual effects have resulted at times. Fortunately, the practice of landscape architecture is now revived and recognized, but it is still only on the threshold of participation in many modern enterprises which can have widespread effects upon the appearance of the countryside.

Afforestation surveys in National Parks offer fine opportunities to re-introduce principles of good design to a rural industry which

171

already deals in all the fundamental materials of landscape, and now seeks room for expansion in some of the most beautiful scenery left in the country.

Although the plant materials of modern forestry, namely softwood trees, have different characteristics from the hardwoods upon which most classic English landscaping has been based, these have to be accepted as part of our changed economy and national life. The achievement of satisfactory patterns with the new materials may be more of a challenge than with traditional or indigenous plants, but it is one which the old landscapers would not have hesitated to take up with enthusiasm.

The relevance of design principles to afforestation in Exmoor may be reviewed thus :[1]

Unity

Sylvia Crowe has described this quality as one which is found in all great landscapes, based on the rhythm of natural land-form, the domination of one type of vegetation, and the fact that human use and buildings have been kept in sympathy with their surroundings. When it is said that a landscape has been spoilt, what is meant is that it has lost this unity.

In Exmoor, the quality is most easily discernible in the simple landscape of the central plateau. There it can be seen at once that unity based upon such simplicity is extremely vulnerable to disruption if a new element is introduced without thought for the fundamental design. To appear satisfactory, therefore, the development of extensive afforestation in that section of the Park would have to be planned for the area as a whole, and a new re-unified design agreed. Alternatively, and more practically under present terms of reference, physical conditions and land usage, afforestation might be introduced on a small scale more for the benefit of farmers than for large forestry interests. Plantations in some of the combes could be arranged to appear in the overall pattern rather as shading to underline land-form; shelter belts, carefully contoured and sited, could look like the cloud shadows which continually play over the land and echo the shape of the hills. Forestry designed in these ways would not destroy unity; so long as the new interest is planned in sympathy with the surroundings, a simple re-unified pattern, still dominated by the old, would result.

172

Elsewhere in the National Park, unity becomes less obvious as complexity of use increases. In the Brendon Hills, the consistent theme of neat husbandry and the characteristic network of beech hedges are features contributing to the quality. The slightly unkempt appearance of shallow but steep-sided combes could be improved by tidy afforestation, which would be on a larger scale than in the central plateau but in keeping with the well-ordered Brendon landscape. On the northern slopes there is even more scope where valleys are larger, and woodland occupies a traditional position in the design. Similar comments apply in the South-West Foothills where the scope is greater still and a new landscape, much enhancing the old in variety, could be designed, with woodland continued up the main combes to underline the massive buttresses of the highland plateau.

In areas of considerable complexity, like the East Central Belt, unity may be conveyed by colour and texture or homogeneity of vegetation as well as by land-form. The qualities of variety and surprise, which also characterize this section, can help in the siting of new afforestation, provided individual plantations are arranged and shaped in harmony with the underlying landscape pattern. Variety should not be confused with a jumble of arrangements which only destroys unity. In this part of the Park, therefore, while it is advisable to plan most new woodland on middle slopes or in valleys, the addition of features, such as a wooded hill-top or a strong landmark of trees, may appear as interesting diversions rather than intrusions.

Scale, Proportion and Space

The unity of a landscape composition is broken if the classic artistic values of scale and proportion are ignored. The undulations of land-form, atmospheric conditions, angle of view and perspective complicate landscape design in the countryside compared with design on the drawing board. Nevertheless, the fundamental rules have to be observed both within the relatively narrow limits of individual plantation design, and in the larger composition of a section of countryside in which the plantation may be seen as a component related to other features.

In the last context, a plantation represents a solid mass and it is the peculiar arrangement and proportion of solid masses and open spaces which give to each landscape its own special character. Five such distinctive patterns have been described in Exmoor and, while the component solids and voids are basically the same in all cases, namely woods, hedges or hills and open fields, moors or water, the manner and proportion of their several mixtures make each pattern characteristically different from the rest. To preserve or enhance but not to change drastically these landscape types, the introduction of new afforestation must conform with the style of arrangement already established. The size of a plantation, its shape and the layout of its internal access roads, fire breaks and crops should echo existing patterns if congruity of appearance is to be maintained.

Much prejudice against modern forestry has been caused by the combination in some plantations of unnatural shape and great size. At once the local landscape pattern may be contradicted and the small and intimate scale of the surroundings overwhelmed. This type of poor design is generally most noticeable on hillsides or on land which can be overlooked from high viewpoints. In such terrain any harshnesses of internal design are also immediately apparent.

Similarly, the proportion of afforestation in a district can appear to be too great, and this is aggravated if monotony of layout and species are present. It is not always the total physical area under trees which can be oppressive; the manner in which the plantations are presented to the eye can have this effect. Herein lies one reason why some modern conifer forests of solid blocks are compared unfavourably with old hardwood regions of scattered woods. Colour and texture enter here again, because conifers do not provide the splendid seasonal variety of hardwoods. Hardwoods have the advantage of colour ranges and shapes which are in sympathy with the soft hues and gentle formation of much of the English countryside. Even so, a continuous forest of these species can seem to overwhelm the rest of the landscape, whereas a series of large woods interrupted by fields or commons, glimpses of streams or farmsteads, glades or distant views of hills, is usually more in keeping with moderate English values. Conifers, therefore, which mostly lack an English concept of natural congruity in form and colour, have even more need to be arranged in apparently irregular formations of relatively small individual scale, if they are to add to the variety and interest of scenery rather than obliterate these values. The arrangements must, of course, relate to the basic landscape pattern.

One adjunct to the fundamental division of space between solid and void is the scattered planting of outlying trees near a plantation. Both the view inwards, of a massed effect behind outliers, and the view outwards, from between the trees, may be greatly enhanced in this way. Moreover, the actual perimeter of a plantation may be softened, and a natural effect of woodland petering out into open country can be gained.

In all sections of Exmoor, except for large portions of the South-West Foothills and the old Royal Forest, good indications of the most suitable scale for new plantations are provided by the scale of existing woods and fields. Furthermore, owing to the broken nature of the terrain, many of the best sites for planting are in the valleys and combes. In such positions space is defined by shoulders and hill slopes, and the amount of new planting which could be undertaken — without overwhelming the relatively confined scenes — may be assessed without undue difficulty. This suggests that for plantations to marry satisfactorily with existing patterns, they should be usually not larger than 100 acres in individual extent. This is not to say that every hillside should be planted in this manner, or that no plantation should be larger or smaller than average, but the figure is given as a general guide. Similarly, the shaping of new woods should generally conform with established patterns.

In the South-West Foothills, where opportunities to enhance the landscape with afforestation are substantial, the scale of planting areas can be greater. The distant views across Devon and a huge expanse of sky provide an enormous frame to the composition. To be in keeping with these spacious surroundings the woodland element actually needs to be strengthened, and the allocation of land for planting can be agreed more generously than in other sections.

On the central plateau the spaciousness of the scene might argue similar treatment, but this is the heart of the National Park, and while it has been stated previously that extensive afforestation could be planned there, other factors already reviewed must outweigh forestry at this time.

Colour, Texture and Light

The principal problems involved in the siting and design of new conifer plantations within traditional English landscapes arise from the special shapes, colours and textures of the trees and the effects of light and shade upon them, most of which are different from those provided by hardwood trees.

The majority of hardwoods adopt a generally rounded outline of crown from a relatively early age, are deciduous and undergo a cycle of change in colour and texture every year. The seasonal changes are matched in the hedges and vegetation of the surrounding countryside. There are exceptions to these characteristics : the evergreen holly and oak, one glossy and pointed, the other matt and rounded, being examples.

Most conifers, on the other hand, have a sharp silhouette and are evergreen, and such seasonal variations as occur are not immediately apparent in the landscape. The larches with their autumn colour change, deciduous habit and distinctive twig colouration, are well-known exceptions. Plantations of evergreen conifers, which are required in large numbers in a modern forest economy, may appear therefore as relatively static and sombre features against a varying background. Only snowfall can transform their winter appearance, and in summer their prominence may seem to be lessened only because other trees are in full leaf.

In Exmoor, too strong a prominence or domination may be lessened, unless required for special effect, by siting and shaping new plantations in combes and on middle slopes as already described. The much disliked serrated appearance of conifers against skylines may be considered at this point. This is a matter of proportion, the silhouette of the species involved, the relationship of the plantation to other features, including traditional woods, and the relative importance of the skyline in question. Sometimes the deliberate planting of skyline conifers as a form of prominence may be justified for variety, surprise, contrast, or to improve an otherwise dull hill-crest. Occasionally, a skyline beech hedge may be used to soften immature planting pending the development of the silhouette required. Serration, by contradicting the land-form, has a jarring effect and should be employed with restraint. In this matter, therefore, as in the positioning of main plantations, design principles indicate relatively unobtrusive and background sites for most projects and the exceptions help to prove the rule.

This preference is supported by the colour range of the trees concerned. The dark greens and dense texture of softwood trees in the mass make them excellent material for background positions

176

(i) An impression of the spacious central plateau in Exmoor Forest.

(ii) The same, irregularly afforested to form an attractive but uncharacteristic scene, the sense of spaciousness being greatly reduced.

(iii) In the Foothills or East Central belt. Plantations in combes and background emphasize land form, and could be extended further to enrich variety of woodlands between open moor and farmland.

(iv) The same, Too much afforestation and replacement of hardwood overwhelms original character. Moorland component lost.

(v) Similar area to (iii). Piecemeal afforestation showing disregard for contours in shaping plantations.

(vi) The same, showing new planting merging with old woods and the basic landscape pattern.

(vii) A moorland river valley. Planting on one side only, leaving a wide waterside verge adds shelter and interest without loss of dominant open character.

(viii) The same. Planting on both sides close to the water shuts out moorland but adds variety if confined to selected stretches.

(ix) A popular viewpoint near a tourist route. Planting arranged to flank view, leaving generous open space.

(x). The same, with view obscured and open space severely reduced and wrongly sited. Fire and damage risks probably increased.

(xi) Typical valley woods adjoining tourist route showing effect of sunlight and shade. Note rounded forms and soft textures of hardwoods in keeping with scenery.

(xii) The same, replanted with evergreen conifers showing dulling effect upon sunlight and emphasis of shade. Note sharp silhouette and harsher texture of conifers conflicting with the gently rounded land form.

(xiii) Conifers planted on shaded slopes provide good contrast to sunlit hardwoods.

(xiv) Conifers planted on sunlit slopes contrast less effectively with shaded hardwoods. This may not be so if larch is used.

(xv) Artificial effects produced by geometrical planting methods. Regular group mixture on left and line mixture on right.

(xvi) Roughly 50% conifers and 50% hardwoods in irregular mixture; the best scenic effects of both types of tree are lost.

(xvii) A suggested compromise scene: Evergreen conifers merging with roadside hardwoods; dominant hardwood slope selected for amenity management which includes enrichment with conifers.

(xviii) Conygar near Dunster. A well-known landmark and amenity woodland. The proportion and arrangement of conifers do not overwhelm the traditional character but add interest and emphasize the shape of the hill.

(xix) One method of riverside treatment; hardwoods kept to furnish pathways and to merge with extensive conifer crops on higher slopes.

(xx) The riverside treatment in (xix) viewed from above, showing conifers carried up to meet agricultural land but without hardwoods to soften skyline effect.

and as a foil to lighter foliage. Their colours merge into the blue, grey or violet of distant hills seen under the usually soft light and often misty conditions of English highland areas. Sitka spruce has a faintly blue sheen which in some lights may have a frosty appearance. Norway spruce is a medium green, Douglas fir and hemlock are dark green subjects with a rather soft texture resulting from their lax foliage. In connection with perspective, these colours seem to add distance and depth; bolder and warmer colours have reverse effects. Evergreen and densely textured conifers are less susceptible than deciduous trees to the play of light and shade. Their presence deepens shadow and their reflection of sunlight is muted.

Therefore, in general views, the majority of the darker conifer crops should appear to be tucked into folds in the topography where they will add firmness to the background or emphasize the shadows of combes or hillsides. Owing to the wide accessibility of Exmoor, however, not all views are distant ones and a dark plantation may have to play a part in several compositions including one in which some portions of it may occupy foreground. This is why the internal design of a plantation must be considered from all reasonable angles of view, and the principles upon which wider compositions are based have here to be applied again in microcosm.

In the foreground positions, the darker conifers should be used more sparingly to emphasize topography or to set off trees with lighter effects. Outliers from a main plantation will provide an open texture and hence more lightness, but a change of species within the woodlands, arranged to suit the land form, may also be required. Larch, soft green in spring and summer and pale yellow in autumn, merges well with moorland colours and hard-wood trees. It is a useful species for frontal areas, hill shoulders and in linking new planting with neighbouring traditional patterns and woods. The russet twigs of Japanese larch in winter, similar in colour to bracken, have an obvious value. Scots pine, blue-green in youth, dark green, flat-topped and red-stemmed in maturity, also lends itself to foreground use. Where dark conifers, such as spruce, have to be used in the foreground by reason of site conditions, glades penetrating into the wood lighten appearance. Reverse effects, using lighter foliage on the flanks, will help to lessen prominence if the darker element provides too much contrast.

Existing hardwoods can sometimes be kept to help soften the transition between a plantation and neighbouring countryside. On moorland, thorn, birch or rowan are suitable, their scale being intermediate between plantation and moor. If necessary, such species may be planted between outlying groups of plantation trees, their effect far outweighing the slight extra expense involved. In agricultural scenery, use may be made of old hedgerows and boundary trees of beech, sycamore or other species on the borders of a plantation, and naturalistic groups or single specimens of suitable hardwood forest trees may be planted as part of the crop. Under no circumstances should the trees be showy exotics such as laburnum or Japanese cherry, which only introduce a suburban note into the countryside of no value to rural amenity or forestry.

Time

This is a value peculiar to landscape design. Time has to be allowed for the growth of plant materials, especially trees, before the full effect of landscaping can be seen. What is not generally appreciated, however, is that while immaturity of appearance may be inevitable for a period, this is no excuse for ugliness in design. Young trees, particularly young plantations, possess more potential than actual beauty, but if the fundamental planting design is sound, they can provide both pleasure and interest as the intended pattern unfolds with their growth. If the design is ugly from the start, maturity will do little more than soften some of the harshnesses. That is one reason why the initial siting, shaping and internal layout of plantations are so important.

A second reason, also connected with the time factor, is that, by careful choice of site and design, the immature period of growth can be offset to some extent. If young trees are so arranged that they seem to be related naturally to older features — mature trees, hedges, rock outcrops, water, etc. — an appearance of continuity can be achieved. At first, the old components in the scene will dominate, then recede; later some may disappear but, all the time, the gradualness of a natural rhythm of change should be conveyed. Finally, a pleasing balance should be reached between the newly maturing trees and those older features which have been chosen from the start to figure in the completed composition.

The old landscapers had the imagination and far-seeing ability

178

to employ these techniques. Through sound designs related to matured elements, they enjoyed the sight of their work in their own time, long before the new trees reached maturity. A forester, by profession, has to be equally far-seeing, but in this century his eye has been focussed principally upon timber production, with not enough regard for the appearance in the landscape of some of the production methods. With imagination, however, arrangements of new trees need not be ugly. The unjust reputation which conifers have gained of being unsightly is due to the often unfortunate manner in which they have been set in the countryside.

Style

This may be defined as the manner in which design is executed. The individual flair of a designer may add something special to a composition and even stamp it with a distinctive personal style. The artistic abilities of those concerned with all stages of afforestation projects, however, are bound to vary. Therefore, an important part of this study must be to translate fundamental design principles into simple practicalities which, if put into effect, will help to improve the appearance of conifer plantations in traditional surroundings.

Style can be left to take care of itself so long as design is soundly based on both aesthetic and functional grounds. Although respect may be paid to earlier influences and other materials in landscape, a simplicity of style — springing from an honest interpretation of the artistic potentialities and physical needs of softwood trees — is more likely to be effective than that produced by uninspired imitation, fanciful patterns or blurred compromises.

The Voluntary Scheme over Afforestation in National Parks calls only for agreement upon the allocation of open land for planting. It apparently overlooks the fact that however well chosen a site may be, the manner in which it is planted is equally important. If planning control stopped at land allocation for various forms of development, and thought was not given to the design of individual projects, the chances of improving the appearance of towns or industrial areas would be slight. Similarly, a good site for afforestation could become an eyesore if planted without regard to design principles.

In summary, therefore, the principles outlined suggest that, in

179

Exmoor, the following practical steps should be taken in afforestation projects if good visual effects are to be achieved:

1. *Siting of Plantations*
(a) Background positions in relation to principal access routes, viewpoints, settlements and existing traditional woodlands of special scenic value are preferable for most extensive projects.

(b) Middle slopes and combes, especially the shaded north-facing sides, offer the best opportunities to site plantations so that they will merge satisfactorily with existing landscape patterns.

(c) Prominent positions may be selected occasionally and deliberately for special effects, but such plantations must be designed with the utmost care as an integral part of a larger composition.

(d) Skyline positions should be chosen with restraint and a scrupulous examination of likely effects.

(e) Existing landscape patterns indicate that the choice of suitable sites is limited severely in the Coastal Belt and Exmoor Forest, is wider in the Brendon Hills, and most promising in the East Central Belt and the South-West Foothills.

2. *Shaping of Plantations*
(a) The outline of the plantation should not contradict the grain of the countryside but should flow with the contours and topography.

(b) The use of outliers to a main plantation may help to improve shape at small extra expense.

(c) In size, individual plantations should only occasionally be more than 100 acres; many should be half this size or less. It is preferable to plan a number of smaller plantations separated by access routes and agricultural land than to compress the planted area into one large block. The scale of the locality should determine the scale of plantations within it.

(d) By relating a plantation to existing mature features, such as old woodland, streams, rock outcrops or tree clumps, an impression of natural continuity may be gained and such features should not be obliterated by clumsy shaping.

(e) The perimeter fencing of a plantation should be concealed or contoured as much as possible, using outliers, topography and existing features such as hedges, even if a rather larger area than the shaped plantation is enclosed.

3. *Layout of Plantations*

(a) Avoid severely geometrical methods of planting and mixing species or scatter mixtures which provide indeterminate effects.
(b) Utilize the colours and textures of species to echo land form, the darker colours to give depth, distance or contrast, and employ lighter colours or special qualities in more prominent situations. Reverse effects may have to be accepted on occasions if site conditions dictate.
(c) In conjunction with (b) use the effect of light and shade upon the species to enliven the composition. The qualities of surprise and variety should be introduced with caution, mostly on a small scale at viewpoints, along pathways or in foreground.
(d) Boundaries between crops should merge and curve harmoniously in relation to the outline of the plantation and the local topography.
(e) Ancillary works such as access routes and fire breaks within the plantation should also be contoured to provide gentle gradients.

In this chapter attention has been focussed on softwood trees and their values as material in landscape, with the minimum use of hardwoods as softening elements. In practice, it is usually possible to introduce a small proportion of hardwoods, even on the most difficult sites which have to be pioneered almost exclusively with conifers. Nevertheless, the primary purpose of modern afforestation is to grow softwoods, and it would be unrealistic, economically or silviculturally, to suggest high proportions of hardwoods in pioneer crops. The place of conifers in the restocking of fertile old hardwood sites, many of which in Exmoor occupy lower land and slopes prominent in the foreground of views, is a different subject considered in Part III.

Sketches

In all landscape work, the use of sketches to demonstrate various effects is invaluable. Humphrey Repton was the best known exponent of this technique among the classic landscapers, and his idea of 'before and after' illustrations is well worth adopting in the weighing of forestry proposals. The method is used frequently in consultations between the Exmoor National Park Committees, forestry operators and others concerned with the design of projects in the Park. It has been welcomed by all parties as an effective and time-saving way of presentation.

Sometimes illustrations in colour are desirable and the effects of planting schemes at various seasons of the year need to be shown. Usually photographs with the new effects superimposed are sufficient. Soft sepia and grey tones are better than harsh black and white for conveying a realistic impression of woodland.

Sketches i–x after page 176 are provided to illustrate some of the points made in this report when describing Exmoor landscapes and the effects of various forest patterns within them.

4 OVERALL PRINCIPLES, RECOMMENDATIONS AND PRACTICE

In presenting a survey report in an official manner, it is usual to divide the text into three parts — data, analysis and recommendations. To relieve some of the tedium of repetition which that method can entail, information in this account of the Exmoor survey has been assessed as it has been recorded.

The position now reached may therefore be summarized briefly in the form of six fundamental principles, upon which it was found that the selection and layout of land for afforestation could be based. To satisfy major interests within the National Park, each site and its planting pattern should be :

1. Acceptable on technical and silvicultural grounds for economic forest management.
2. Planned with regard for agricultural interests — especially those of shelter and improvement.
3. Related in size and shape to the special characteristics of the type of landscape in which it is situated — particularly land form, established woodland patterns, the interest of water and the quality of spaciousness.
4. Arranged to enhance the recreational values of the National Park — notably motoring, views, picnics, rambling, riding, camping, sport and scientific pursuits.
5. Integrated with the needs of water catchment and other special interests as and when they may arise.
6. Positioned and planted in accordance with principles of good design which should also apply to the arrangement of ancillary works.

Site Number (1″ plan) (1)	Name and Owner (2)	Area (acres) (3)	Description (4)	Land-scape Type (5)
15	Slamborough Common. Mr. G. Giles, Slamborough Great Farm, Fairwater, Watchet.	80	Steep, north-facing, bracken covered, lower slopes of hillside. Some rocky outcrops and unusual crags. F.C. plantations meet eastern boundary. 750′–1050′ a.s.l.	Brendor Hills
16	Chillworthy Old Pits. Hannington Estate Trustees. c/o. Benson, Harcourt & Chuff; 125 Corkscrew Lane, Taunton.	110	A rough worked-out area near the foot of the extreme western tip of heather moor on Sherford Hill. Reverted to heath with some wet patches. Unsightly intrusion between moorland and farmland. Gentle gradients, westerly facing, 450′–550′ a.s.l.	East-Central Belt
17	Catchpenny Water. Sir Jason Bligh-Miller, Huxtables, Exford.	55	The north and south sides of the upper part of a narrow combe about $\frac{1}{4}$ mile from the head at Hagsend Moor. Wet, waste or steep, old agricultural land, adjoining Pinny Wood lower down the combe. Would make a useful extension to estate woods. 750′–900′ a.s.l.	East-Central Belt

AFFORESTATION SUR

ABBREVIATIONS:
D.L.C. — Divisional Land Commissione
F.C. — Forestry Commission
N.C. — Nature Conservancy
S.S.S.I. — Site of Sp

Land Uses or Interests Affected				Outline Notes on Suitable Planting Plan
griculture (6)	Tourism (7)	Scientific (8)	Other (9)	(10)
ommon ;hts ex- ;guished. gher ntle »pes and l-top ·eady :laimed. ·nfirm ·th L.C. that further ·ricultural ·pansion .sible.	No rights of way. Blind farm lanes near site. Hill- side seen mostly as part of background from lower land to the north.	Some bo- tanical interest believed to be associ- ated with certain small screes. Check with N.C. or C.N.T.	None known.	Continue spruce and Douglas fir from F.C. boundary into eastern end of site where conditions suit these species best, tailing out in first of the three shallow combes. Shoulders appear ideal for larch, merging into spruce, hemlock, Douglas etc., in shaded combes. Keep crags bare, also their tops and screes. Some pine irregularly grouped above larch, and dominant feature of pine climbing up westernmost bluff. Access route to follow old farm track at base of hillside; diagonal spurs to combes.
nsult L.C., but ·ears to useless agri- ·ture.	No rights of way. Widely seen in middle ground from numerous routes and view points. Needs planting to enhance land- scape value.	Although inside boundary of Sherford S.S.S.I., the N.C. confirms that interest is minimal.	Just within Chill- worthy water catchment area. Consult W.B.	Site roughly triangular, the apex being the highest point and the base curving round the foot of the hill. This shape will help planting to appear to peter out naturally into moorland at higher contours. A few irregular groups of pine outliers on the sides would strengthen this effect. Lower down, pine should merge into spruce, the main species, but a few poplar near the stream along the western boundary would soften the transition to farmland.
·pears to ·e little ·ny agri- ·tural ·ue but ·sult ·.C.	Right of way along footpath by stream in combe bottom. Little used because of wetness but could be- come pleasant woodland route from Hagsend Gibbet to Huxtables Meet.	None known. Consult C.N.T.	None known.	Woods lower down combe are semi- derelict but fine timber has been grown; conditions suitable for wide range of species. With this extension an area of about 200 acres could be brought back into production under mixed species. In the extension there are places where Douglas fir, spruce, poplar, larch, pine, beech and sycamore could be grown and a design of contoured sections under some of these species pure or mixed would enhance scenic values. Merge uppermost species with existing birch and thorn on moor. Access by improved streamside rides.

:.N.T. — County Naturalist Trust
V.B.   — Water Board
.s.l.   — above sea level
·ntific Interest

In the original Exmoor report of 1958, final recommendations were contained in a register, which included tabulated information and very brief notes on planting design for each site. The register was illustrated by a map of the National Park at 1″ scale showing the numbered sites in colour.

Much of the information gathered remains confidential and therefore Table 7, pages 184–5, is a dummy form of register, the statements made under each heading being only for demonstration. Similarly, Plan D, page 148, is not a copy of the survey map, but shows the distribution of numbered sites at one stage only, during later consultations.

Altogether, about 4,000 acres of land divided between 58 sites were recommended for planting after the original survey. In size, most of the individual sites were under 100 acres in extent, nine were over 100 acres each and three were over 200 acres each. The larger areas were recommended for separation into smaller units by open land which would provide firebreaks as well as access routes for farming and recreation.

Except where economic afforestation could also provide special effects in the way of landmarks, improvement of skylines, views etc., the chosen areas were mostly positioned and shaped on middle ground, in accordance with the findings of the survey. In line with the same findings, most of the sites, including the larger ones, were proposed in the South-West Foothills and the East Central Belt; some useful substantial areas were suggested in the Brendon Hills and lighter treatment was recommended in the Coastal Strip and Exmoor Forest.

The total of 4,000 acres put forward for planting represents about 2·5% of the land in the National Park. Added to existing woods, this would increase the amount of forest land from 17,000 acres to 21,000 acres or roughly 12·5% of the Park area. At first sight this may seem a small extension, but it would raise the total percentage well above existing or proposed national averages. The new areas, when planted, would come within the productive category, and the proportion of this type of woodland in Exmoor would be increased from just over 5% to nearly 8% — again a significant figure. And there is still the productivity of the woods which are lying idle to be investigated.

Moreover, it should be recalled that after physical conditions and farming needs have been taken into account, there are probably

186

not much more than 20,000 acres of land likely to be available for afforestation in the Park. The allocation of one-fifth, or 20%, of this land-bank to forestry, in the first phase of a land-use plan which can be reviewed periodically, is not over-cautious. The reasonableness of the contribution is emphasized by the fact that, as a National Park, Exmoor has special amenity values in the form of large open spaces which are traditionally treeless and should generally remain so if their peculiar qualities are not to become submerged.

An Example of Plantation Design

Some comments on the later history of the Exmoor Survey as a basis for a Voluntary Scheme in the National Park are given in Appendix 3.

Meanwhile, the survey has been the backbone of the Park Authorities' policy on afforestation and no major outcry has been heard about planting on open land for the past eight years. Several of the numbered sites are now planted and problems of design have been solved through discussions with owners and agents, without much difficulty. If necessary, and with the agreement of owners, full-scale plans and sketches may be prepared before work begins on the ground.

For example, at Grabbist Hill near Dunster, about 117 acres of the steep south-facing hillside became the subject of a planting proposal in 1961. Some parts had grown conifers, felled during the last war, but an area of open land was included, and the whole hillside had come to be regarded by many people as open country.

There were numerous amenity values to take into account. The land formed a break between an old oak woodland to the east, called Grabbist Coppice, and large softwood plantations to the west, belonging to the Forestry Commission. On the opposite side of the valley, to the south, mixed estate woods of great beauty have been managed for some years by the Crown. Planting on the Hill therefore needed to be very carefully planned to have a transitional effect between three separate examples of forest practice — old hardwood coppice, typically mixed estate woods and modern plantations of conifers.

The hill-face overlooks a popular valley road from Dunster and, on or near the hill, there are several pathways and tracks, much used by walkers and riders. The views from the crest are pano-

187

ramic and include stretches of the Somerset and Welsh coastlines. The crest line itself, seen from below, flows into unusually craggy and distinctive formations above Grabbist Coppice. The surface of the hillside undulates in a series of broad hollows and shoulders terminating at the western end with a pronounced flat-topped bluff called Avill Ball.

The forestry operators realized that planting might be a contentious matter. They were prepared to use mixed species, including hardwoods, and had chosen these to suit silvicultural and economic requirements. But they wanted to arrange the trees so that amenity interests would also be satisfied. So they agreed that a sketch and planting plan should be prepared on their behalf, provided that the same species were used in the same overall proportions.

The layout of species in the new design is shown on Plan E, page 189. A water colour sketch was also made to give an idea of the appearance of the woods after about twenty-five years' growth; an impression of this is inset above Plan E. From these it can be seen how trees with darker foliage are placed to emphasize hollows and to underline land-form, the lighter shades being on the shoulders and bluffs. Beech hedges, where they existed, are thickened along the southern boundary, and ride sides are given variety and interest with groups of the ornamental forest species originally suggested by the operators. A small group of Scots pine is placed in a frontal position against a background of paler deciduous species. The upper planting limit is allowed to breast the skyline at the western end but drops gently eastwards, except for a twist of beech and pine as a feature near Blindman's Well. Views from the crest path are therefore kept, the open land also serving as a firebreak between the plantation and nearby moorland over the hill. A viewpoint, combined with a collection centre for woodland produce, is designed on the top of the westernmost bluff. From there a new diagonal ride is opened for public use and provides a fresh alternative route for walkers.

The scheme was acceptable to the forestry operators and the Forestry Commission, with whom the owner agreed a Dedication Covenant. It is also worth noting that the outline of the design was screefed on to the hillside, the various sections then being filled in with the appropriate species. Final planting costs were reported to have been no higher than estimates for planting the land in a conventional manner.

Impression of the appearance of the plantations after approximately 25 years' growth

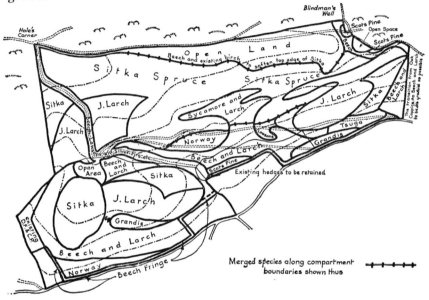

Merged species along compartment boundaries shown thus

Scale 0   ¼   ½   ¾   1 mile

DETAILS OF SCHEME

Evergreens	Acres	Deciduous	Acres
Sitka spruce	34	Japanese larch	22
Norway spruce	6	Beech and larch	19½
Silver fir (grandis)	2	Sycamore and larch	3
Scots pine	1	Beech	1
Hemlock (tsuga)	1	Beech for fringes, etc.	3
Lawsons cypress	½		48½
Various decorative species including Lawsons, grandis, nobilis, tsuga, etc.	4½		
	49		

	Acres
Open land	14½
Fields	3¾
Existing Douglas fir and Corsican pine retained	1¼
	19½

Total area of scheme 117 *acres*

PLAN E: **WOODLAND PLANTING SCHEME — GRABBIST HILL, DUNSTER**

189

PART III

Trees, Amenity and Planning in
the Restocking of Woodlands

1 EXMOOR AS A SAMPLE AREA: ADMINISTRATIVE PROBLEMS

A woodlands survey in Exmoor would have been a logical sequel to the afforestation study under any circumstances. It was accelerated by events which took place in the early nineteen-sixties.

Private organizations, acting as agents for clients wishing to invest in forestry, became more interested in the restocking of existing woodlands than the planting of open land. This interest continues and woods are, of course, excluded from the scope of the Voluntary Scheme over Afforestation.

The old deciduous woods of Exmoor, many of which are technically under-stocked, scrub and coppice or semi-derelict, usually offer more sheltered conditions and fertile soils than the open moors. Their restocking with valuable conifers is therefore often a more attractive financial and silvicultural proposition than the pioneering of fresh ground with relatively inferior species. If, however, the composition of the woods were to be changed from deciduous trees to evergreen conifers, on a wide scale and without thought for landscape, a vital part of the character of the region could be completely altered. This would not be in line with the fundamental objectives of National Parks.

In the early 'sixties, the ease with which anyone considering the acquisition and dedication of woods could avoid consulting National Park Authorities on amenity interests, has already been described.[1] In the Somerset part of Exmoor some projects seemed likely to go ahead without consultation or to be announced at too late a stage, after acquisition had been completed and replanting put in hand, for consultation to be effective. It appeared that the time had come to make Tree Preservation Orders upon woodlands of high amenity value to forestall these situations and ensure proper notification of forestry proposals.

Seven critically important amenity woodland areas totalling 700 acres were chosen in a first list. The Orders were confirmed in 1961 after a public inquiry. Later, the Conservator for the Forestry Commission in the South-West greatly helped the Park Authority by sending very early notification of impending proposals for dedication so that amenity discussions had a better chance. This special arrangement continues and is thought to be administratively more streamlined than the setting-up of a Forestry Consultative Panel, which has been done in some National Parks for broadly the same purpose.[2]

The making of Orders on a few woods of obvious amenity value helped to steady a situation which might otherwise have got out of hand, but supplied no solution to long-term problems. The Exmoor Joint Advisory Committee decided that it was equally important for woodland restocking plans, as well as planting proposals on open land, to be weighed against the background of an overall landscape policy. To consider either in a piecemeal way could ultimately damage the character and beauty of the Park.

So a woodlands survey was authorized in 1961, and the Somerset part of Exmoor was to form the first phase. Following some preliminary discussions, the survey was limited to the principal areas where woodland plays a dominant part in the landscape — altogether two hundred woods covering about 6,000 acres were included.

The objectives were to examine the woods in detail to determine how, and to what extent, they might be altered by economic management, without overwhelming the traditional appearance of landscape or lessening other recreational values. After the survey, any need to make further Orders, or to take action to secure varying degrees of amenity management in individual woods — through consultation, subsidy, lease or acquisition — could be decided more objectively.

2 THE WOODLANDS SURVEY

a — Objectives and Method

The objectives laid down by the Exmoor Joint Advisory Committee largely decided the method of working, and suggested a form in which the survey could be presented.

Unlike the survey of land for afforestation, the limits of the second study were clearly defined from the start by the area of woods on the Committee's list. A reference plan could be prepared immediately and, to match the afforestation survey, a map of the National Park at 1″ scale was used. This was not large enough for woodland names to be shown, but the areas were coloured and each one given a reference number. As most of the woods were in well-defined groups, each group was named on the plan.

Plan F, on page 212 is at too small a scale to number the woods, but the group names are given. This map also shows the Devon groups which were surveyed as a separate operation after Somerset, and are not included in this account.

A record of ownership would be required when the time came to discuss future treatment. Also the type of treatment desirable for each wood had to be recorded, and this would depend upon a careful assessment of silvicultural, recreational and landscape values. To set out this information clearly and concisely for each of two hundred woods, it was decided to build up a register, similar to that used for the afforestation sites. Each named woodland could then be listed under its group and number shown on the reference plan.

Implicit in the terms of reference was the need to work out a system of grading the woods in amenity merit. Although they all possessed amenity values, some would be more important than others. The relative importance of each would decide the course of action taken later by the Park Authority. Therefore, as in the afforestation survey, the study had to be as objective as possible. A discipline that only overriding amenity values would justify labelling a wood as one requiring the virtual exclusion of economic management would have to be maintained throughout the survey.

Even at this stage, it seemed likely that three categories of amenity woodland might emerge. One would include areas where economic management under conifers could contribute as much, and perhaps more, to the landscape than the existing hardwoods; the second, where a combination of traditional and modern forestry might be planned; and another, where the amenity management of areas predominantly under hardwoods appeared to be necessary. To illustrate some of the landscape aspects, it was decided to use sketches (after page 176) and they are referred to from time to time in later chapters.

For the field work the Ordnance Survey sheets at 6″ scale, used for the afforestation study, were brought out. There was already much valuable information recorded on these sheets because an afforestation survey cannot overlook existing woods. It has already been shown that they provide sources of silvicultural and aesthetic evidence which have to be taken constantly into account when planning new woods.

There is, in fact, much to be said for a woodlands survey preceding an afforestation survey in a National Park, because the first is more straightforward, and provides much of the basic information which has to be collected before the second can be completed. Circumstances and the Voluntary Scheme over Afforestation dictated the order of the surveys in Exmoor. Nevertheless, both are chapters in the same review of forestry development, and neither is complete without the other. The close connection between the future management of existing woods and the allocation of additional land for planting has to be remembered throughout both studies.

b — Natural Factors and Financial Considerations

Information about geography, geology, climate, soils, fire risks, and similar matters in relation to tree growth in Exmoor, had already been collected in the afforestation study.[1] It was equally fundamental to the woodlands survey but need not be repeated.

However, an even closer examination of existing woods enabled some of the earlier information to be amplified or confirmed. Site conditions, for instance, reflected in the growth of trees, were sometimes easier to assess in woods than on open land.

For example, the degree of exposure to wind, whether a prevailing south-westerly or a local but repetitive turbulence caused by deflection, is often demonstrated strikingly by the shape and appearance of trees. Sometimes, the exact contour above which wind-shaping takes place can be defined. Such precision is of value in deciding alternative species which will resist exposure. Generally, most distortion in Exmoor is apparent on slopes open to the south-west, especially if the soils are poor or thin. And some of the best tree growth in the region, provided other site conditions are satisfactory, occurs on northerly and easterly aspects.

Most of the Exmoor woods, being on sloping and often very steep ground, possess well-defined aspects. It was noted that, as a broad generalization, Douglas fir, the larches and spruces show a certain preference for situations facing northerly or easterly directions, and some of the pines make good growth on south or west facing slopes. Most of the hardwoods prefer the milder situations; but beech and sycamore are vigorous under hard conditions and oak will grow moderately well, provided the soil is suitable, on the colder slopes.

Many of the woods have benefited from the downwash of soil from higher ground throughout the centuries and, with the accumulation of humus from continuous tree cover, deep and fertile soils have developed. If such woods also enjoy shelter, the ground is usually capable of growing a wide range of good quality timbers including both hardwoods and softwoods. At the other end of the fertility scale there are woods on poor, thin, rocky soils where tree growth has been too weak even to arrest erosion. Most of these areas occur, significantly, on very exposed westerly aspects, and generally support only inferior quality hardwoods. Where sites of this kind have been replanted with suitable softwoods, improvements in growth and timber potential are usually evident.

The survey has as a principal objective the integration of productive forestry with characteristic woodland in the National

197

Park. So, an appreciation of site conditions and, hence, the production potential of each wood, is a first requirement. The surveyor can thus assess alternative forms of restocking and management and weigh them against their probable visual effects. Furthermore, an idea of the value of each site in terms of timber production helps to maintain an economic discipline in a matter which is liable to be regarded too subjectively or emotionally.

An economic discipline may, in fact, be of more importance throughout a woodlands survey than during an afforestation study. If land is excluded from being afforested, it may still remain available for another use which is, most often, agricultural. On the other hand, if a wood, especially one containing poor trees, is excluded from restocking with commercially attractive species, this usually means that no other profitable use can be made of it. Loss of expectation of profit cannot be bridged, therefore, by means of an alternative use of the land.

Planning legislation allows payment of compensation only for the value of trees which an owner is prevented from felling under the terms of a Tree Preservation Order. If a wood contains few timber trees and is mostly coppice or scrub, a condition often found in Exmoor, the amount of compensation is likely to be small. Moreover, existing arrangements under planning, to secure the planting of amenity trees on private land, are not adequate, or intended, to assist owners in the management of large areas of woodland.

Where woods are better stocked initially, and of a site quality which enables a range of species, including hardwoods, to be well-grown, there may be less difficulty in marrying amenity requirements to profitable management. Woods of a good enough site quality for first class hardwoods and softwoods to be grown, may usually be expected to present the least difficulty in terms of visual amenity. This is especially so if they are worked selectively rather than by clear felling and block planting methods.

In Exmoor, it is the indifferently stocked woods with low site values which present the most serious problems. Restrictions upon their economic management may prove to be intolerable to an owner and involve the Park Authority in a claim for financial redress. At present it seems that such a claim can be met adequately only by the outright lease or purchase of the wood by the Park Authority, at proper valuation and with the owner's agreement.

Arrangements of this kind are supported by a Treasury grant to local authorities of 75% of the cost; subsequent amenity management by the authority is also partially grant-aided. Reluctance to conclude these transactions may arise in two ways. Some authorities feel that, as the acquisition and management is undertaken in the national interest, the full costs should be borne by the Exchequer, and local ratepayers should not be partially involved. Some owners, on the other hand, do not wish to convey parts of their property to public ownership or management, and have a real fear that the resulting public use will depreciate the value of adjoining land and bring additional problems of trespass, damage or fire.

In recent years, there has been some thought about making grants to owners for amenity management in woods — either directly or linked with a covenant for the dedication of land to National Park purposes. Owners could then be offered these alternatives to the leasing or purchasing of their property, and National Park objectives might be more readily secured. Government opinion about suggestions of this kind, including the raising of Exchequer grants for the benefit of Park Authorities purchasing or managing land, has not yet been made known.[2]

The financial complexities which can arise, as a result of trying to obtain amenity management in poor woods, may suggest that in a regional survey such areas should be accepted unequivocally as potential softwood sites. In more hospitable woods, a wider variety of effect could be designed with a larger range of species, while the maintenance of traditional hardwoods could be confined to the places where the species will produce good quality timber. This functional approach to the subject, if combined with attention to the principles of landscape design, could lead to the creation of satisfactory visual effects and should certainly form the basis of a realistic woodlands survey.

Exceptions to this general basis can be foreseen. Woods scheduled by the Nature Conservancy, where there is a scientific interest which might be disturbed by restocking, and other woods related to established beauty spots, may require forms of management in which economic timber production occupies a subsidiary place. In Exmoor, if the special purposes of a National Park are to be fulfilled, particularly in the conservation of characteristic scenery, additional areas of woodland may have to be recommended for amenity management, so that a blend of modern and traditional patterns is achieved in which the latter are not submerged.

Thus, the amenity reasons for excluding certain woods from re-development will be similar to those for excluding land from planting. Indeed, if the development of afforestation and existing woodlands is to be planned jointly and in harmony with the landscape of a region, the aesthetic criteria employed have to be consistent throughout both preliminary surveys. The financial difficulties which may result do not weaken the value of either survey. These difficulties may help, in fact, to determine whether, and to what extent, there is a need for amending legislation to reconcile National Park purposes more realistically with private landowning interests.

The management of woodland primarily for visual and recreational values has already been secured in a variety of ways, both inside and outside National Parks, throughout the country. The National Trust is prominent in this field, and many of the Exmoor woodlands owned by the Trust are maintained principally for amenity purposes. Sometimes, in other parts of the country, woods have been purchased by local subscription and tended by voluntary labour in the interests of amenity, especially in the neighbourhood of towns or villages. The same kind of treatment has been undertaken by local authorities and other public bodies : the management of Epping Forest by the Corporation of London, and of the 'ancient and ornamental' parts of the New Forest by the Forestry Commission, are two examples on a large scale. Recommendations about amenity management which may stem from a woodlands survey will not therefore create a precedent, but may help to measure the size of this particular problem. And creative amenity management can offer as good employment opportunities as conventional forestry, once any initial financial difficulties have been overcome. It should not be mistaken for the dead hand of preservation in this account of the Exmoor survey.

c — Woodland Descriptions (Plan F, page 212 refers)

An important characteristic of the scenery in the National Park is the arrangement of most of the older woodlands in continuous patterns along the sides of river valleys, slopes of hills and coastal cliffs. Nearly all the woods contain deciduous hardwood trees, oak being widespread and often in the form of coppice, used in the past for the production of tan bark, fencing materials, firewood, and pitprops for the iron ore mines in the district. Pitprops were also shipped to South Wales until comparatively recent times. Now, most of the coppices are useless except for occasional farm purposes and firewood. Infrequently, small quantities of tan bark may still be in demand for high quality leather work.

Lately, however, the better stems have become marketable for pulping, but the nearest mill is in Monmouth. For several years there has been the possibility that a chipboard mill might be built in the South-West — of a kind capable of using the poorest quality hardwood material as well as softwood thinnings. If that happens, many of the coppice and scrub woods of Somerset and Devon might become economically attractive again.[3] Of course, oak might be replaced by faster growing hardwoods, such as chestnut or birch, in certain areas. Also, there would be rotational changes in appearance, as cutting took place, to which the public has been unaccustomed while the woods have lain idle.

Even so, an alternative, but less profitable, form of treatment to restocking with conifers could be considered in some woods, and their broadleaved character sustained. A mill would also benefit amenity management in areas of special recreational value, where even coppice rotations might be considered too disruptive. To be able to market material from unobtrusive improvement fellings would help to reduce costs.

In some places in Exmoor where coppicing has ceased for a long time, the best poles have suppressed the weaker ones and grown into sizeable trees, so that the appearance of conventional oak woods has been created. Elsewhere, the coppice has degenerated into scrub, providing little more than attractive foliage effects. Birch has invaded many of the woods and beech has spread gradually by natural means. Holly, rowan and other species, including alder, and occasionally sycamore, ash, elm, and some conifers, are helping to change the composition from pure oak into mixed woodland, but the process is a slow and natural one.

Some of the coppice or scrub areas have been cleared and replanted with conifers such as larch, spruce and Douglas fir. In places this has been done without much regard for landscape values, which is evident from the geometrical shape of restocked sections, arrangement of species or other disharmony with the surroundings. At other places, usually near old estates such as Dunster, Pixton, Holnicote and Miltons, the owners have been less drastic in their operations. By irregular mixtures in groups and areas of hardwoods and conifers of varying ages and species, they have introduced a wide variety of interest and range of seasonal effects into the landscape. As might be expected, the sites where this progress towards mixed selection cropping has been most successful are those where conditions of soil and shelter are favourable. In appearance the woodland landscapes have been greatly enriched; the traditional hardwood element is carried on by fewer but better trees, including beech, sycamore, ash and oak, and their effect is heightened rather than dominated by contrast with the evergreen softwood species.

Generally, small isolated woods are of secondary concern in Exmoor scenery, although some form local features or landmarks, or are important in the settings of country houses or villages. Groups of woods in these categories, near Nettlecombe and Simonsbath for example, have been included in the survey.

The Luxborough Valley, in the Brendon Hills at the eastern end of the National Park, was not put in the amenity list for reasons which are worth some comment. It cuts through agricultural land and the main access is a valley-bottom road. Immediately to the north-west is the pine and spruce forest of Croydon Hill, and the valley connects southwards at Chargot with large spruce plantations which ascend the northern slopes of the Brendons. These woods collectively form the principal areas of the Forestry Commission's Brendon Forest.

The valley sides are now almost entirely under softwood trees, interrupted occasionally by a few hardwood crops or separated from the road by small meadows and a meandering stream. The aesthetic values of this area were referred to during the afforestation survey and they will probably increase if the appearance of the plantations becomes more varied, following thinning, underplanting and more irregularity of cropping. Nevertheless, the valley is no longer typical of Exmoor because the traditional character has been almost completely altered. It is a good example of how other Exmoor valleys could appear, if changed by economic cropping to an extent beyond that envisaged in the

202

provisions of the National Parks Act of 1949 regarding the conservation of traditional scenery.

The valleys and groups of woods in Exmoor listed for investigation by the Somerset Park Committee may be sub-divided as follows:

The Quarme/Exe Valley

From Pixton Park at Dulverton, near the southern boundary of Exmoor, northwards to Wheddon Cross, this valley divides the southern Brendon Hills from the main Exmoor massif. The woods line an important tourist route, the main road from Minehead to Exeter passing along the full length of the valley bottom. As a result, it is probably one of the most frequented valleys in the Park, but the woods are not entered by many people and there are only a few points from which parts of the area may be overlooked from higher surrounding agricultural land. Therefore, to the majority of visitors, the most important visual effects of the woods are those obtained from driving a car along the roadway. There is a need to remember the interests of local residents and fishermen, and to anticipate a probable increase in numbers of ramblers; consequently some additional footpaths may be required in the future. Otherwise, the appearance of the woods from the main road is likely to remain the first amenity consideration.

In this connection, it is worth noting that because of the winding nature of the valley, the side slopes on which the woods are situated are rarely straight, and usually form a series of strong convex and concave opposing curves. From the roadway, a traveller cannot see more than a proportion of a convex area at one time, but a concave site is exposed wholly to view like the inside of a bowl. This circumstance gave rise to the thought that, other factors permitting, in this and some other Exmoor valleys, evergreen conifers could be used plentifully on certain convex curves, if a balance in favour of traditional crops or mixtures could be secured in appropriate concave curves. By this means, the new element in the landscape might be made to appear subordinate to the old although, in terms of area, the reverse might be true.

Also, because of the twisting valley, almost every aspect is represented among the woodlands and this is a broad characteristic of other wooded valleys in Exmoor. Thus there are better opportunities to diversify forest crops and to provide varied land-scape effects than might be the case on more uniform land. Additionally, the Exe Valley provides good examples of the effects of sunlight and shade on different species of trees — a subject needing careful thought in landscape planning in the region. Reference was made to this matter in the afforestation survey and it is illustrated by sketches xi–xiv after page 176.

Woodlands in almost every condition, from well stocked to derelict and felled areas, line the valley sides. Most of the sites are fertile and sheltered but there are some where soils are thin and rocky, usually on westerly aspects and often indicated by the inferior quality of the trees growing upon them.

In the northern or Quarme section, the slopes are lower and less steep, and the woods are smaller, less continuous and do not dominate the landscape as in the Exe section. The Quarme woods are introductory to the almost cliff-like appearance of those over-looking the Exe river. Changes in the composition of parts of the Quarme woods would be less noticeable than alterations in some of the more prominent features in the south.

Throughout the valley broadleaved species predominate, chiefly oak, in standard, coppice and scrub forms, but many areas also contain good quality beech, sycamore and ash. There are some pure conifer crops, chiefly larch and spruce, and groups of other softwoods, such as Douglas fir, mixed in otherwise mainly hard-wood areas. The Miltons Estate, where group and selective cropping is practised, and Pixton Park, which contains old land-scaped woods in the mansion's setting, are both situated in the Exe Valley area.

The Avill Valley

This lies between Wheddon Cross and Dunster and, being a northern extension of the Quarme/Exe Valley, it is equally well used by visitors travelling along the Minehead to Exeter route.

The scenery is varied but generally less dramatic than that adjoining the river Exe, and the course of the valley is tortuous only in its southern section. In that part lie the seven woods on the amenity list. More than half of them, by area, belong to the Forestry Commission and include those which are most prominent in the landscape. The sites are reasonably fertile and moderately sheltered from the south-west, as the valley runs down a northerly slope. Most of the woods have been creamed of the best timber.

By an agreement with the Forestry Commission, dating back over ten years, consultations with the Park Committee take place before the restocking of each State woodland. The aim is to settle plans for mixed planting in such a way as to satisfy site conditions as well as landscape values — including colour, texture, local topography, shaping of crop boundaries and other matters of design.

Silviculturally and aesthetically, mixtures of hardwoods and softwoods are well suited to these areas. Eventually, transitional patterns are expected to develop and will be appropriate between the northern part of the Avill Valley, where many of the slopes have been planted with pure conifer crops, and the Quarme/Exe Valley, where hardwoods may predominate for many years to come on the more fertile slopes.

The Haddeo Valley

This meets the Exe Valley close to the southern boundary of the National Park at Pixton, near Dulverton. From there, it takes an easterly course to Rainsbury, skirting round the north side of Haddon Hill, which forms the southernmost ridge of the Brendons.

A private drive, available to the public, runs almost the full length of the valley-floor beside the river. It is not easily negotiable by motor vehicles and is enjoyed mainly by ramblers, riders and local residents. The eastern part, where the woods are smaller than elsewhere, can be overlooked from open moorland on Haddon Hill, a favourite picnic place.

This valley, therefore, is the first so far examined which is virtually free of motors and where the attractions of the scenery are most often enjoyed in a leisurely fashion by people on foot. Walkers and riders have time and opportunities to see much more detail in landscape than motorists. Account of this may be taken in the design of woodlands, and an intimate scale introduced in relation to footpaths and bridleways which is subordinate to, but integrated with, the overall composition. Where views of woods unfold before a passing motorist like a cinematograph film, the patterns may generally be bold in character because finer detail will usually remain unnoticed. Consequently, compared with the Exe Valley, the Haddeo calls for more attention to design for contemplation.

In the Haddeo valley at present the woods at the western end are large, mostly sheltered and fertile, and predominantly composed of oak and oak coppice. There is room for much restocking, and the introduction of economic species need not be seriously curtailed by amenity considerations. At the eastern end, several smaller woods have already been replanted with pine, larch and spruce, which compose satisfactorily with the surrounding landscape. Most of the valley woods are subject to a Dedication Covenant of long standing, and to plans of operations which appear to be geared to a slow pace and small scale of change. Generally this seems to be an area where, at most, consultation with the owner upon minor points of detail might be needed.

The Barle Valley

This is the third of the main river valleys which meet near Dulverton; the wooded section extends from there north-westerly to Withypool.

For most of its winding length the valley is not easily accessible. A short stretch near Dulverton is followed by the road to Exford, and the ancient bridge at Tarr Steps may be approached along narrow roads from north and south. The bridge is a focal point for large numbers of visitors, and the woodland footpaths on either side of it are well used. Beyond this area, towards Withypool on one side and Dulverton on the other, there is a path along the entire length of the river bank which is way-marked and therefore likely to be used increasingly in the future. Because the valley cuts mostly through agricultural land and there are few roads bordering it, the area is not much overlooked, but there are short sections which contribute to panoramic views seen from higher moorland.

Like the Exe, the Barle River is well known for its fishing and — beside the fishermen — riders, local residents and the more enthusiastic ramblers can still enjoy solitude and peace in large isolated stretches of the valley. There is some archaeological interest in the area provided by several Iron Age encampments, and three of the woodlands have been scheduled as Sites of Special Scientific Interest by the Nature Conservancy (Appendix 2).

For the most part, the woodlands are of oak with large areas of coppice. Birch is widespread and there are sections containing standards of oak, beech and other hardwoods. Some conifers, mainly spruce, have been planted, but not widely except in the vicinity of Dulverton, near the Pixton and Northmoor estates. Pine, hemlock, Douglas fir, spruce and larch are growing well in that neighbourhood in small areas or in mixture with hardwoods, including poplar. The resulting enrichment of the scenery is reminiscent of that achieved in similar ways at Miltons in the Exe Valley.

Some of the woods near Dulverton are subject to plans of operations under recent Dedication Covenants. However, most of them remain uncommitted to systematic management and offer opportunities for re-development. Rocky outcrops in the valley cause some variations in soil quality, but generally the sites are fertile. There is a wide variety of aspects and some are very exposed to south-westerly winds or local deflections. On the whole, the northerly aspects seem the most favourable in terms of soil and shelter for tree growth, but there are a number of exceptions.

This is a valley, therefore, where conditions appear to be favourable for advance planning to integrate forestry and amenity requirements. The riverside pathways and the fishing interests suggest a need for attention to detail in the valley bottom; at the southern end of the valley, landscape planning on a rather bold scale in relation to the roadway appears desirable; at focal points such as Tarr Steps, and in archaeological or other scientifically interesting areas, the conservation of traditional scenery clearly deserves priority; where the valley can be overlooked, a mixed effect would enrich the landscape; and in places where access is limited, or where the woods do not play an important part in views from higher land, simple designs with high proportions of economic species could be introduced.

The Horner Valley and Hawkcombe

Both these valleys lie to the south and west of Porlock, between the northern slopes of Dunkery Beacon and Porlock Hill. Horner is not easily accessible for most of its length except on foot or by horse. The western half of Hawkcombe is similar, but a narrow road serves a number of houses and cottages in the eastern half nearest to Porlock.

The valleys and the side combes which branch from them are frequently visited, especially Horner, by campers, walkers and riders. Large numbers of motorists collect at several moorland picnic places, such as Webber's Post on Dunkery and Whitstones on Porlock Hill, which offer panoramic views over the woods. Nearly all the woods in both valleys, as well as large stretches of adjacent moorland, are included in the largest Site of Special Scientific Interest scheduled by the Nature Conservancy in Exmoor (Appendix 2).

The amenities of these areas are highly prized by the public. This has been recognized by the National Trust, which owns the Horner valley and looks after most of the woods for amenity rather than timber production. In 1965, the Somerset County Council purchased the western half of Hawkcombe, by agreement with the owner, and this area will be managed for amenity purposes by the National Park Committee.

In western Hawkcombe, as in most of Horner, it is chiefly the combination of easy access by ramblers and riders, and the great extent to which the woods can be overlooked, which cause their high amenity rating. Even so, there are parts of both valleys where the addition of evergreen conifers would enhance the visual pleasure to be gained from the woods. At present they are almost entirely of oak and oak coppice with the better trees, including some beech, on the lower north-facing slopes. The darker colours and contrasting forms and textures of conifers could well be introduced in shadow-like arrangements to underline topography occasionally in the bottoms, and to offset the rounded shapes and paler colours of broadleaved trees. In places, a bolder use could be made of conifers to provide background to prominent shoulders of hardwoods. By such means and with attention to design, scientific interest and recreation, the woodland scenery could be enriched without submerging the traditional character. There would also be some return from the economic management of the softwoods which, linked with renewed work in the better hardwood sites, would help to offset the expense of upkeep in the purely amenity areas.

The Somerset County Council, in managing western Hawk-combe for public use, will be partly supported by funds from the Exchequer and will not be expected to practise economic forestry. Nevertheless, if it is thought that the introduction of some ever-green conifers would enhance the scenery, this would appear to be permissible under the National Parks Act of 1949 — but possibly embarrassing later if a profit was made from the trees. The National Trust, on the other hand, in managing Horner, is not supported by public funds. Although the National Trust Act of 1907 is clear about the preservation rather than the enhancement of scenery, a time may come when the amenity woods have to be re-examined with a view to introducing some economic cropping to help meet mounting expenses. The woods in both Horner and Hawkcombe were therefore assessed during the survey with these possibilities in mind.

The Oare Valley

This lies in the northern section of Exmoor and runs from Oare Post on the main Porlock–Lynmouth road to the village of Oare, and thence to Brendon in the Devon part of the Park. The narrow, twisting lane through the valley is a popular route for every type of visitor as it leads to the famous 'Doone Country'.

There is more agricultural land than woodland along the valley sides. Aesthetic problems arise in seeking to conserve the effects of small individual woods rather than of large continuous patterns of woodland. The whole valley and its components are on a miniature scale compared with others in Exmoor, and almost every wood has to be considered on its merits as a local feature. Ideally, the scale and pace of operations in the woods should be small and slow. They need careful overall planning, with the owners' agreement, to try to avoid several individual operations coinciding in time, and thereby possibly disrupting the character of the area.

Weir Wood, at the eastern end of the valley, is an oak coppice site so ancient as to be considered of near-natural origin. Other woods contain mostly broadleaved trees such as oak and beech but there are also patches of pine, spruce and larch.

The Coastal Woods

These cover the coastal hill slopes and cliffs from Porlock westwards to Glenthorne on the County boundary. A toll road from Porlock winds through part of the eastern section. From Ashley Combe to Culbone, said to possess the smallest church in England, there is a popular footpath through the woodlands. Further west, the cliffs become less accessible, but the South-Western Peninsula Coastal Path passes through or near some parts and provides views over others. The whole stretch of coast is seen best from the sea and is an attraction for passengers on local pleasure steamers.

o

Most of the trees on the cliff faces and exposed sections of the coast are coppiced oaks, some small areas of which have been successfully, if somewhat expensively, replanted with beech, sweet chestnut, Douglas fir and other conifers. In the several short and sheltered combes which cut inland from the coast the soils are better: hardwood standards grow moderately well and conifers, including larch, spruce and Douglas fir, appear even more promising. Near the mansions of Ashley Combe and Glenthorne first quality specimen trees and groups of several broadleaved and softwood species have been raised.

The wooded coast is a unique feature in the National Park and compares favourably in extent with other examples elsewhere. It was given a high value on amenity grounds in the Hobhouse Report on National Parks in 1947. Tree Preservation Orders have been confirmed in recent years upon some areas of the woods.

Generally the physical difficulties of management on the steep cliffs, and doubts whether they could be sufficiently productive to justify the expense of building new access routes, make it unlikely that great changes will take place in these woods. In the past, men worked with safety ropes to extract tan bark and small pit props from the oak coppice, but the production of large timber, even if the land is good enough to support it, could not be managed economically in this way. In the combes and sheltered areas where access is reasonably good, some economic forestry with mixed species could be undertaken. Suitable places are small in individual size, positioned slightly inland and dominated by a preponderance of inhospitable seaward areas. Aesthetically, the growing of evergreen conifers in the combes on a limited scale would have the effect of emphasizing the hardwoods on the cliffs and exposed shoulders, without seriously altering the overall character of the coast.

The Woodland Groups at Selworthy, Minehead, Dunster, Nettlecombe and Simonsbath

For convenience these groups can be considered collectively. With the exception of Selworthy, where the woods merge into one another along a south-facing hillside, the groups are made up of separate woods. They are mostly either landmarks or prominent features in the landscape (Sketch xviii, after page 176) or, together, form a setting to a town, village or country house.

In the case of the Selworthy woods, for instance, several of them provide a background to the old village of thatched cottages and a church clustered round a green which draws very many visitors. Numerous paths through the woods are used by ramblers and riders, and connect with the moorland ridge between Bossington and Minehead. The whole area can be seen from roads in the Porlock Vale and the high moorland of Dunkery to the south. The National Trust owns all the woods, some of which are subject to a Dedication Covenant, while others are managed for amenity like the Horner Valley. Heavy fellings during the last war have been replaced with mixed species, particularly beech, larch and pine, arranged informally, and special care has been given to the integration of economic and amenity requirements in overall management.

In the Minehead group, some of the woods are on North Hill, purchased by the Somerset County Council with the principal object of keeping unrestricted public access to moorland. The woods are used for recreation by the public and are being managed for amenity purposes.

In other groups, access to the woods is limited, and the main reason for including them on the list is their individual visual merit. Most of them, being on lower land, on deeper and richer soils and in fairly sheltered positions, are capable of growing fine timber of several species. At present, hardwoods dominate in almost all the woods, but they have been depleted by war-time felling, or are over-mature and deteriorating. Some woods, at Nettlecombe and Dunster, were probably established long ago as amenity features near landscaped parks; others, such as the high-lying beech wood at Simonsbath, the clump at Nettlecombe which formed a navigational aid to shipping in the Channel, and the woods of evergreen oak near Selworthy, have interests which are additional to their visual effects.

As in the case of the Oare valley, many of the woods in the groups have to be considered on their individual merits, as well as in relation to the larger compositions or settings in which they play a part. Changes in the appearance of isolated woods are often more noticeable than those in areas which form part of a continuous arrangement. This is because each separated woodland may be

211

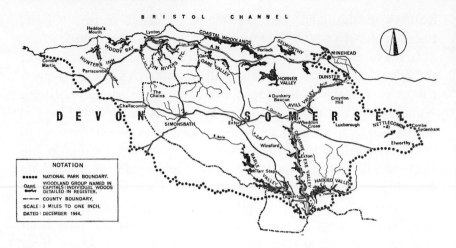

PLAN F: EXMOOR NATIONAL PARK — WOODLANDS SURVEY
1961–64

seen as an entity; there are generally no other timbered features
close enough to distract the eye from the effects of fellings and
other operations. Consequently changes should be made gradually
and unobtrusively. A selection form of management is preferable
in these cases, and there are a number of woods in the Exmoor
list which lend themselves to such treatment. There are others
which have deteriorated badly for one reason or another, and clear
felling and replanting would be the most economic course of
action. If the loss of a feature for some years can be accepted and
replanting in a pattern suited to the landscape agreed, this may
be the best course. Otherwise, the extra cost involved in con-
verting an area slowly to selective management may prove to
be more than an owner should be expected to bear; and financial
problems similar to those described earlier may arise.

d — Economic Management and Recreational Design

The study of Exmoor woodlands is concerned with the integration of fewer and less widely spread interests than the afforestation
study, but is possibly more complicated financially.

Agriculture, for example, which figured largely in deciding
new planting areas, is much less affected by activities within

212

established woods. The shelter or minor produce which some of the woods provide for neighbouring farms may have to be thought of in management, and occasionally small woodlands may prove to be reclaimable for farming. The major problem of deciding which land may be spared from agricultural use for the creation of new woods does not arise.

Access

Many recreational interests, especially the question of public access, are much more clearly definable in woodland than on open land. In open country the freedom of the public to wander at will is an important consideration which afforestation restricts. In existing woods specific access rides and tracks are usually already established.

For a variety of reasons including, perhaps, fear of becoming lost among trees, short cuts being less obvious than on open land, visitors do not seem to stray very far from clear-cut routes in the depths of woodland. People wander inside small isolated woods in open country or, which is more usual in Exmoor, in the edges of large woods where they adjoin moorland, picnic or beauty spots and viewpoints. The area affected is generally a narrow belt of only a few yards in depth which, if excluded from a management plan, would be no great loss. Indeed, old hardwood fringes can help to shelter new crops, reduce fire risks, keep an irregular out-line and conceal fencing.

When an old woodland comes under renewed management it is usual for the surfaces and widths of existing access routes to be improved and, sometimes, for new tracks to be constructed. If this work is carried out with thought for local scale and topography, opportunities for rambling, riding and many other interests may be enhanced rather than restricted. The dual use of forest tracks for management and public enjoyment has proved satisfactory in State forests where recreation is now being encouraged as a matter of policy. There does not appear to be any serious obstacle, other than prejudice, to the development of a similar pattern in private woods, especially in National Parks. There may be a need for routes to be modified slightly to connect with viewpoints, picnic areas, camping grounds, sites of scientific interest and other special features, but the economic management of woodland is not incompatible with public access.

Encouraging more people to enter woods is likely to increase the risk of fire and damage and may also present problems of hygiene. The same hazards underlie the whole concept of National Parks and are not confined to woodlands. In State forests, the Forestry Commission is accepting these risks in the belief that through a combination of instruction, better facilities and a growing appreciation of forestry, the public will eventually come to respect growing trees and misuse will decline. Certainly, keeping people out of woodlands does little to help them to understand trees, and it may be that the present lack of a national forest sense is due in part to the rigid prohibition upon access widely practised in the past.

The perpetuation of hardwood trees is usually necessary in woodland areas of scientific interest where disturbance could upset ecology or damage archaeological and other values. Broadly, however, most physical forms of recreation involving access to woods do not of themselves call for large proportions of hardwoods in management plans. The small amount generally included in economic cropping, for shelter, firebreaks, soil improvement and the like, can be claimed as sufficient — but only if physical exercise is to be the main criterion of recreation.

To stop at this point is to play down the value of mental refreshment from visual amenity. This, in National Parks at least, is by far the most important and complex part of recreation with which the economic management of woods may conflict.

Felling

The first phase of most management plans likely to alter woods is usually the felling of marketable and unwanted trees to make room for the planting of new crops. The condition of the trees largely decides the pattern of felling. In Exmoor, complete clearance is most likely where there is either a quantity of mature and more or less even-aged timber, or a dense distorted mass of scrub. Group felling may be practicable where there are patches of mature trees interspersed with areas of young pole crops or good coppice. Selective felling is usually only appropriate in mixed woods of uneven-aged trees where management has been consistent for many years : such areas are rare in Exmoor. The dappled shade method of felling may be used in good coppice and pole crops, where there are sufficient stems with narrow crowns. The method usually entails an initial drastic thinning of existing cover, so that a dappled overhead shade is left in readiness for new planting beneath. As the new crops grow under this light sheltering cover, more of the older trees are felled from time to time until, within a variable period of up to ten years, all have been removed. The skill of the method lies in the manipulation of the overhead cover to assist the growth of the new crop in the best possible way.

Clear felling has the disadvantage of exposing woodland soils to erosion, especially on steep slopes under high rainfall, and to other forms of physical and biological deterioration. From the amenity point of view, it can cause the complete loss of a woodland or a feature for some years. In Exmoor, however, there are many woods which do not lend themselves easily to any other method of preparation for economic management. If such woods are also highly prized for landscape reasons, the utmost thought must be given before deciding that amenity values are so great that economic management should be excluded. To keep the character of woods by such means as enrichment with hardwoods, and other arboricultural rather than forestry techniques, can be expensive.

Sometimes the phasing of clear felling over a period of years may be feasible within a plan of operations covering a large area of woods. If the siting and shaping of the felled parts can be arranged to fit local topography, and this is as important aesthetically as in the design of new plantations, a phased programme may help to reconcile forestry and amenity. It has the effect of reducing the apparent scale and pace of operations by distributing them in the landscape. There are also places where phased clear felling can be arranged to reveal a succession of views previously closed — the operations thus providing some recompense for the disappearance of other amenities. Clearings often add variety to woodland paths, while the interest of practical work and the scent of felled timber can be most attractive.

In many of the sloping and widely visible woods, phasing seems to be the best way of moderating the shock of clear felling. Attempts to compromise with selective felling in areas unsuited to this treatment can result in a derelict appearance, because the trees left standing may not be vigorous enough to continue growth and therefore become ragged and liable to wind-blow. Neither amenity nor silviculture is well served by this process, sometimes misguidedly recommended.

During the Exmoor survey, the degree of prominence of clear felling in various situations was studied. Generally, from high viewpoints, clearances in valley bottoms were the least noticeable, and were foreshortened in views along the valley. From roads and tracks in the valley bottoms, fellings on the middle slopes were least obtrusive. From both high and low viewing positions, cuttings in the upper edges of woods were most noticeable, either by causing an unnatural outline or by affecting long sections of skyline. Keeping the upper edges of woods may therefore be worth thinking about for the sake of overall visual amenity as well as for the reasons previously mentioned.

Group and selective felling, particularly the latter, are easier to agree in relation to landscape. By definition, they affect smaller areas than clear felling, are more scattered and, therefore, less obtrusive. Dappled shade methods provide an alternative to clear felling in many coppice and scrub areas, and help the appearance of woodlands to be changed gradually instead of suddenly. Even so, the hardwood cover left behind is usually sparse. And if the initial heavy thinning is made by clearing strips on steep slopes, a striped effect across the contours can result, often more disruptive than clear felling. Thus, irregularity in using this technique seems desirable if as natural an effect as possible is to be gained.

Replanting

In replanting old woodland, there are generally better opportunities to satisfy landscaping than in afforesting open land. The shaping of felled areas, unlike many new plantations, can almost always be helped by surrounding trees, with which replanting can be merged and within which fencing, if needed, may be concealed. If a site is capable of growing some larch, the transition between traditional woods and areas under a high proportion of evergreen conifers can be made to appear even more gradual. On sites where there are patches of young hardwoods worth keeping, and on soils where a proportion of new hardwoods may be introduced, there are good opportunities to diversify the appearance of the woods at an early stage of their redevelopment.

In re-designing woodlands in Exmoor, as has been said, attention should be paid to the treatment of opposing convex and concave curves along valley sides, especially if there is a major road route through the valley. In valleys such as the Barle and Haddeo, where there is only a footpath or bridleway beside the river, and the existing woods close in, it is important to keep much of the character of the riverside and pathside fringes. In some sections where, beyond these fringes, the woods are less attractive, substantial areas of conifers may be placed. In all cases, however, the possibility of a valley, or parts of it, being overlooked from popular viewpoints on high ground has to be remembered and taken into account in the designs.

Otherwise, in relation to scale and proportion, topography, colour, texture and light, special needs such as skylines, and the peculiar time factor in landscaping, the restocking of woodlands, like afforestation, needs to satisfy basic design principles if the results are to harmonize with the surrounding countryside. These principles have already been described.[4]

Replanting can be with one species alone (sketch xii, after page 176) or with several species in mixture, including hardwoods. Mixture patterns may vary widely, from simple line and regularly spaced group mixes (sketch xv,) to irregular arrangements of groups and areas planned to suit site conditions and landscape requirements (sketches xvii and xviii). Generally all, of necessity, appear artificial in the early stages of growth, but the more irregular gain an apparent naturalness more quickly than the strongly formal patterns.

As a rule the geometric, striped or regular group mixtures, because of their formality, clash with the topography in Exmoor, and appear out of character with neighbouring established woods. The irregular scattering of evergreen conifers in hardwoods, or vice versa, has sometimes been advocated on the grounds of compromise, and in the belief that this might avoid the exclusion of some areas from economic management. In practice, to make such arrangements economically or silviculturally attractive on the poorer sites, the proportion of hardwood would need to be so small (15%–20% at most) that the traditional character of the woods would be submerged. Even if as much as 50% hardwood could be employed on some of the better ground, the area would for many years appear to be dominated by conifers and the best scenic effects of both types of tree would be lost (sketch xvi, after page 176).

Pure crops of evergreen conifers, often in substantial areas, can

217

look particularly effective in background positions where they may be linked with afforestation sites. Advantage can be taken of their dark colours and dense textures to emphasize shade and depth, and so enrich the seasonal effects of deciduous trees in foreground positions. Group mixtures of irregular pattern, co-ordinated with topography and site conditions, lend themselves to many intermediate positions, where fertility and shelter are suitable for a strong hardwood theme to be maintained under economic management. This is the type of arrangement noted at Miltons in the Exe Valley and in a few other places in Exmoor and is preparatory for group selection management. The enrich-ment of aesthetic effect and the apparent emphasis of hardwood forms and colourings are pleasing attributes of these patterns. They also increase variety alongside access rides, and are of great interest seen from valley roads and high viewpoints on moorland.

A New Design

From descriptions of Exmoor woods, it is clear that the best features are those with unity in their design. The Horner Valley has this quality and it is achieved with traditional trees. The Luxborough Valley also possesses unity but with softwood trees.

Somewhere between these two examples a new design, more complex than either but re-unified in appearance, has to be evolved in order to offer a solution to the problem of combining traditional and contemporary woodland patterns so that the first appears to dominate without unduly restricting the second. Such a design is required particularly for the woods which are halfway, in amenity and forestry terms, between those suitable for substantial soft-wood crops and others best suited to hardwoods. Woods like those at Miltons, where amenity and economic management are pleasantly combined, provide examples of the type of design which meets these transitional requirements.

What is more, woods of this pattern possess a unity of appear-ance which is gained, whether deliberately or fortuitously, by the satisfaction of design principles. The blending of hardwoods and softwoods links the woods in time-scale with both the traditional and contemporary patterns seen in their simplest forms at Horner and Luxborough. The arrangements of species in areas and groups are related to ground-form, and the scale and proportion of the component parts of the designs are in harmony with each other and with the surrounding landscape. The effects of colour, texture, light and shade contribute variety without confusion, and the pace of felling and replanting has a natural rhythm echoing the seasonal changes in the woods.

It seems, therefore, that an overall plan for integrating wood-land management and amenity in Exmoor might be based upon three distinct types of woodland. The monuments of traditional character, and other woods or parts of woods possessing critical aesthetic or recreational values, could be conserved to form a main amenity framework. From these conifers would not be entirely excluded, but they would play a subsidiary role. Then, in woods of intermediate amenity values, some hardwoods, including coppice, could be sustained as part of the economic cropping programme — but they would be combined with softwoods in substantial areas and groups. To complete the range of the new regional design, there would be woods where large-scale restocking with conifers could be carried out: these would normally be in less dominant positions and would sometimes be linked with afforestation sites.

3 A SYSTEM OF WOODLAND GRADING

As in the account of the afforestation survey, information gathered during the study of Exmoor woodlands has been assessed as it has been recorded, instead of making a separate analysis. The findings of the woodlands survey may therefore be stated shortly in the form of five fundamental principles. It was decided that, upon these, the final grading of woods and putting together of a coherent landscape plan could be based :

1. A landscape plan for the integration of economic forestry and National Park interests should stem from an equally objective regard for both these interests.
2. In addition to those sites which are capable of producing good quality hardwoods under economic management, certain less productive hardwood areas of overwhelming recreational or aesthetic value may have to be maintained as such under amenity management — so that a main framework of traditional forestry is sustained as a dominant feature of the overall plan.
3. Woods which are at present of secondary value for National Park purposes may be managed so that their aesthetic effects and productivity are both enhanced in the future. These objectives may be achieved by :
   (a) The development of uneven aged mixed crops managed under group selection methods.
   (b) The conservation of sufficient hardwoods on suitable sites for their effects to appear prominent, but not necessarily dominant, in the landscape.
   (c) The employment of conifers to extend deciduous effects, to emphasize hardwoods by evergreen contrast and to enrich woodland scenery by providing variety, interest and surprise.

(d) The arrangement of conversion processes and group plantings with regard for design principles, as well as for site conditions and with special attention to viewpoints, access routes, skylines and topography.

4. Woods which seem most likely to remain of subsidiary importance in relation to National Park values, may be substantially converted to economic management under softwoods, provided that the principles of design, already outlined in relation to afforestation sites, are satisfied.

5. Where it appears desirable on aesthetic grounds seriously to restrict the economic management of a woodland area, such grounds should take precedence in a National Park, even if financial compensation of some kind is involved.

Other than areas capable of growing first-class hardwoods, either as timber or coppice, woods likely to qualify for the top amenity category are usually either :

    I. Sites of special scientific interest and others of archaeological value, where minimum disturbance is necessary,

    II. Prominent in the general landscape,

    III. Special local features,

    IV. Popular for public recreation,

    V. Very suitable for recreational use in the near future, or

    VI. A vital part of a larger scheme, e.g. a section which, even if only temporarily, should remain under hardwoods for some overwhelming aesthetic reason — such as there being no other way of keeping a satisfactory balance between traditional and contemporary patterns while new crops are growing.

In choosing woods for the second category, it is essential to bear in mind that they may appear much more attractive than many of the traditional woods to another generation. At present, they are usually :

    I. Intermediate in position between foreground and background in general views.

    II. Suitable for mixed cropping.

    III. Of lesser value for recreation dependent upon access.

Woods most likely to come within the third category usually either :

    I. Occupy background positions in the general landscape,

   II. Connect with afforestation sites in side-combes or near valley-heads, or

 III. Offer opportunities to create strong contrasting effects in the main valley or hillside woodland groups.

A methodical system of grading woods in three such categories establishes some standards upon which a Park Authority can base its policy about amenity and woodland management. The recorded details of the overall scheme provide a guide in readiness for negotiations and decisions on dedication plans or other management proposals, as and when they have to be considered in individual woods. The Exmoor system is not put forward dogmatically — it is one possible basis for the ordering of National Park woodlands in a way which could satisfy present terms of reference, and enable a changeover to more productive use to be made without upsetting other values. The need to keep a dominantly traditional appearance sets certain limits which might not apply outside a National Park. Moreover, the principles of design can be interpreted in many styles — in landscape as in other forms of art. In each woodland category there will be exceptions, dictated by circumstance or discovered as other changes take place. While there is room for flexibility in this scheme, alterations or revisions should not be made without further study of the design principles which may be affected.

4 RECOMMENDATIONS: COMBINED AFFORESTATION AND WOODLAND FORECAST IN EXMOOR

As in the afforestation study, recommendations stemming from the woodlands survey were presented in a register, which also contained tabulated information about each wood. Table 8, pages 224–5, is a dummy form of part of this register, the names of owners and woodlands being fictional. Plan F, page 212, is a reduction of the survey plan; the numbering of individual woods has been left out.

Although, for confidential reasons, much of the information in the register cannot be disclosed, it can be described in round terms and the recommendations summarized in statistical form. This gives a clear picture of the probable allocation of woodland acreage between economic and amenity management which might result if the overall plan was put fully into practice.

The two hundred woods studied in Somerset total 6,054 acres. Individual woods range in area from just over an acre to more than 300 acres, the majority being less than 50 acres each and only ten being more than 100 acres in size.

The notes made in the register upon amenity values included an assessment of the overall grading of each wood. This was indicated by three stars for an area of exceptional amenity merit, two stars for an intermediate site and one star for a subsidiary woodland. Sometimes, but not often, part of a wood was rated in one grade and part in another.

Furthermore, the outline notes upon recommended treatment in each wood contained an estimate of the overall proportions, by

TABLE 8 : Dummy form of register for woods based

Wood Number (1" plan) (1)	Name and Owner (subdivided into Groups) (2)	Area (acres) (3)	Description (4)	Recent Management or Known Proposals (5)
104	Sherford Ball. Hannington Estate Trustees, c/o Benson, Harcourt & Chuff, 125 Corkscrew Lane, Taunton.	268	A dome-shaped moorland hill in the angle of the last curve of Sherford River before it enters the Blackmore Vale. The steep hillsides carry pure oak coppice on aspects from west, through south to south-east. 550′–1250′ a.s.l. Coppice probably all 50–60 years, but best is on lowest slopes or to the south-east. Soils best in same positions. Elsewhere thin, rocky and acid.	Regular coppicing ceased about 1910. Estate now regards this as an amenity area. No positive work except some thinning on lower slopes for fence posts or firewood stacks for campers. This has improved growth and appearance of stems left standing.
	Sherford River Group Total Area :	1091		
	Catchpenny Valley Group			
105	Pinny Wood. Sir Jason Bligh-Miller, Huxtables, Exford.	34	Semi-derelict, creamed of best timber, mostly beech, larch and oak, in 1942. Some useful patches of beech and sycamore poles, rest scrub coppice or blank areas. Northerly aspect, slight convex curve, deep fertile soil, well sheltered combeside. About 650′–800′ a.s.l.	No management since 1942 felling. Owner interested in dedication if woods Nos. 106 to 109 and afforestation site No. 17 can be included.
106	Pikes. Sir Jason Bligh-Miller, Huxtables, Exford.	16	Similar to No. 105 except for 3 acres of beech and larch at eastern end near Sybil's Bridge; planted 1945 in a partial attempt to restore the setting appropriate to its romantic associations.	Beech and larch (P. 45) has been well tended. See No. 105 for proposals.

ABBREVIATIONS:
- D.L.C. — Divisional Land Commissioner
- F.C. — Forestry Commission
- N.C. — Nature Conservancy
- S.S.S.I. — Site of Speci

Special Interests (6)	Amenity Assessment (7)	Outline Notes on Suitable Management Plan (8)
Riverain habitats are among the most important in the Sherford S.S.I. of which this is the dominant woodland feature. Freely accessible and widely seen.	***A critical wood from all amenity points of view — scientific, visual, accessibility etc.	Predominantly arboricultural type of management is desirable, at least for next 30–50 years. But the low, close-cropped coppice on upper, exposed areas of poor soil is degenerating fast. Where this is already dying out and invaded by birch on the west side, some pine could be planted to connect with upper part of No. 103. On middle slopes, coppice selection and hardwood enrichment advised. Small areas suitable for planting with Douglas and Silver firs, also beech/larch, at lower levels near main bridle way — up to 15% of total area.
Amenity interests very localized at present. Has more potential than present value.	*Of lesser importance generally. But this is one of a group of estate woods which offer fine opportunities to improve future economic and amenity values.	Keep and thin beech and sycamore poles. Merge new planting into these pole areas : mostly spruce on middle slopes running upwards into pine groups to join with afforestation site No. 17. On lower parts Douglas fir, larch and some poplar/Norway spruce groups. Overall 80% conifer acceptable.
As for No. 105 generally, but eastern half of wood prominent in relation to Bridge Lane.	**for eastern half. *for rest. The higher rating for the eastern half is given, like that for No. 108, because of the focal point around Sybil's Bridge.	Expand area at eastern end under beech and larch. Chestnut and ash in small suitable pockets. One group of Silver fir on flat area south end of Bridge as contrast. Western background part suitable for Douglas fir, spruce, etc. to merge with No. 105. Overall about 60% conifer acceptable.

C.N.T. — County Naturalist Trust
W.B. — Water Board
a.s.l. — above sea level
entific Interest

area, of hardwood and softwood effects which were thought to be desirable in each grade in the future. Of course, during the earlier stages of management, higher proportions of softwoods would be needed — to nurse hardwoods, and provide early returns — than would appear in the final crop. Also, in some areas, the deciduous larches might be used to extend economic working : usually in places where foliage effect, rather than texture or tree form, was of importance in the landscape.

Bearing in mind the need for some flexibility in management plans, each of the three woodland grades therefore also indicated the proportions, by area, of deciduous (mostly hardwood) and evergreen (softwood) effects envisaged in the re-designed landscape of the future. In broad terms, a three-star grading meant that at least 75% deciduous, and not more than 25% evergreen, was recommended. Most areas so graded would have to be managed entirely or predominantly for amenity, unless hardwood cropping was reasonably economic. In a two-star woodland, it was thought that production and amenity could be blended, without much difficulty, under overall economic plans of management designed to secure, on average, a fifty-fifty deciduous-evergreen balance in the later stages. In a one-star wood, it was pictured that 75% evergreen and up to 25% deciduous crops could be established.

On an area basis, the total of 6,054 acres was subdivided between grades as follows :

One star   :   802 acres or 18% of the woodlands.
Two stars   : 2,293 acres or 34% of the woodlands.
Three stars : 2,959 acres or 48% of the woodlands.

If the same total area is divided between the deciduous and evergreen trees, which would appear when the later stages of the plan have been reached, then 3,664 acres, or 60%, would be deciduous and 2,390 acres, or 40%, would be evergreen. Taking into account areas of deciduous conifers and the softwood nurse crops required to establish hardwoods, a conservative estimate of the division between amenity and economic management would be 50% in each category. When further account is taken of those areas where hardwoods could be managed profitably there is a strong probability that the final division might be 60% under economic and 40% under purely amenity programmes. In other words, not more than about 2,500 acres of the woods need be considered for the strictly arboricultural type of amenity treatment which has been referred to — and might entail initial financial difficulties. In at least 3,500 acres of woods, amenity requirements could be satisfied within economic plans.

Of this last total, some 1,500 acres of woods were either already being managed under plans accepted by the Forestry Commission before the Exmoor survey, or have come under such management since then. About half of this acreage is in the latter category — and care for amenity, following the usual consultations, has been safeguarded in final plans. The findings of the survey, although not yet fully considered by all interested parties, have been used during consultations with promising results. It is still too early to judge the soundness of the general plan, but there has been much less controversy. In only one case, affecting 200 acres of woods of outstanding amenity merit, agreement was not reached upon a plan of management. In that instance, the Somerset County Council purchased the woods with the owner's consent.

At present, therefore, it seems that there is a balance of about 2,000 acres of woodland in the Somerset Park Committee's list which could be managed economically without upsetting National Park purposes. There are also about 2,000 acres of woods, some of which are very small but could serve local farming needs, which are neither listed as amenity features nor committed to productive use. Thus, it is calculated that some 4,000 woodland acres in the Somerset section of Exmoor could become productive without spoiling amenity.

In the Devon section of the Park a similar survey has been carried out too recently to have been fully studied. There are fewer woods in that region and most of them, being concentrated along the popular coastal area between Lynmouth and Combe Martin, are highly prized for their beauty. Nevertheless, a preliminary assessment suggests that in at least 500 acres of woodland in the Devon section, economic management and amenity interests could be satisfactorily combined.

For the whole National Park, therefore, it is possible to make an overall forecast of forestry development, based upon the results of the two surveys, which might reasonably satisfy economic, aesthetic and recreational interests in the region. Of the 17,000 acres of woods of all kinds in Exmoor, 9,050 acres, or 5·3% of the land area, are controlled by the Forestry Commission, or managed under agreed plans for dedication and approved schemes (Table 6, page 169). The balance of 7,950 acres, or 4·7% of the Park area, are uncommitted to economic management. Of these, it is estimated — but not yet accepted officially — that more than half, or about 4,500 acres, could become productive without damaging landscape or other National Park interests. The balance of about 3,450 acres need mainly, but not exclusively, various kinds of amenity management under traditional hardwood species.

So approximately 13,500 acres of existing woods are, or could be, managed for timber production combined with amenity. A further 4,000 acres of afforestation, carried out in the ways put put forward in Part II, would raise the total productive forest area to some 17,500 acres, or more than 10% of the National Park acreage. It may be noticed that the amount of land suggested for afforestation slightly outweighs the area of woods recommended for exclusion from general economic management. It must be emphasized, however, that the amenity woods also require management, and need not be discounted as places of employment in the overall economy of the Park. In fact, because of the intricacy of management required in many areas, they may offer more employment than an equivalent area of economic woodlands.

Altogether, these figures amount to an eventual gross total woodland area of 21,000 acres, or 12½% of the land in Exmoor. It so happens that this is in line with the area regarded as desirable to provide adequate employment opportunity in forestry within the National Park, according to the Economic Survey of the South-West made in 1965 on behalf of the Government.[1] In so far as this larger survey applies to Exmoor, it does not appear to take amenity, especially landscape, sufficiently into account. It seems, however, from the combined findings of the woodland and afforestation surveys in Exmoor, that a comparable target might be reached in a way which would also safeguard National Park interests.

Finally, particular attention should be drawn to the delineation in the woodlands survey of those areas, some 3,450 acres in all, which are recommended mainly for amenity management under traditional hardwood species. Of this total, the National Trust already owns about 1,550 acres; and the Somerset County Council now looks after a further 400 acres. A balance of about 1,500 acres is thus left unsecured.

To show up these woods is as important in planning the development of landscape in Exmoor as to pick out, during the afforestation survey, the areas of open land which should remain unplanted. Both are measurements of the hard core of traditional landscape which should be conserved if the character of the National Park is not to be submerged. Both are revealed only after positive studies have been undertaken to list those places where well-designed and economic forestry could benefit the industry and the landscape of the Park. Already in Exmoor, a policy based on the findings of the afforestation survey has proved workable. It has helped to dispel much of the uncertainty about amenity, especially in visual terms, which has been experienced by members of Park Committees and landowners alike. Early results suggest that the woodlands survey may have an equally satisfactory outcome.

PART IV

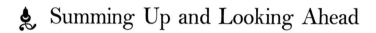 Summing Up and Looking Ahead

SUMMING UP & LOOKING
AHEAD

History

History reveals how the replanning of the English countryside
in the eighteenth and early nineteenth centuries was carried
through by the landowners with great care for aesthetic as well as
material effects. The standards and services of practitioners in
landscape design were recognized as widely, and drawn upon as
readily, as those of the forester or the land agent in rural projects.
The type of countryside which resulted was dominated by hardwood trees in woods and small coverts, hedgerows and parkland,
and was tailored to the needs and tastes of the period. It may
justifiably be regarded as one of the best examples of co-ordination
between economic redevelopment and landscape planning ever
achieved.

Much of this type of landscape survived, virtually intact, until
the early years of the present century, and some of it lingers on.
This happened partly because of the progressive depression of
agriculture and the stagnation of forest development, after the
ending of dependence upon hardwood trees. But the main influence
was the mushroom growth of an industrial economy based upon
the coalfields. There was no incentive to re-design the countryside
to meet the new requirements of extra food for an increasing
population or of softwood timbers for urban development. These
materials could be imported cheaply, and the nation's wealth was
provided from industry rather than land. The countryside was
maintained for a long time under aristocratic control in the
eighteenth century manner, but mainly as a preserve for private
sport and amenity. This was in sharp contrast to the industrial
and manufacturing towns, where more than half the population
was concentrated under conditions having little connection with
any standards save those of expediency.

When private pressure groups and societies were formed during the nineteenth century, seeking to adjust the balance of interests which had been upset by the establishment of an industrial economy, there was little co-ordination between them. Each group concentrated upon a particular field of national life and depended for success upon the energies and influence of members, or some fortuitous crisis which might help to force Government action. At the time, there seemed to be ample room in the country to accommodate each activity separately, without much need to consider overall plans for integration.

The improvement of living and working conditions in towns, the provision of public access to mountains and the establishment of a policy which would help England to catch up with other countries in the practice of softwood forestry, were among the causes which must have appeared widely divergent in those years. In the light of further developments during the present century, they can now be recognized as aspects of the total national environment, needing careful integration with other requirements including those of good design.

Much progress was made as a result of the separate efforts of the early pressure groups, but they paved the way for narrow legislation and professional administration, imbued with an exclusive attitude, in fields of activity which have since increasingly overlapped.

Planning

Planning grew initially from the desire to improve towns. It is still predominantly geared to and concerned with urban matters. The population has continued to multiply rapidly and towns have spread. The developments of electricity and motor transport have freed the siting of industry from its bonds with coal, and have enabled people to live further away from their jobs. Consequently, more and more demands for urban use have been made upon the countryside. Within the confines of urban development, whether these be large areas or isolated projects in rural districts, planners have tried to make sure that standards of good design have been taken into account equally with those of functional efficiency. Close team-work with architects, engineers and, lately, landscape architects, has been maintained and is, indeed, required for some procedures laid down by legislation.

A similar concern for aesthetic design and the co-ordination of interests has been lacking in legislation affecting the countryside. Major land-uses have been regarded as separate issues; the regular occurrence of financial and other crises has focussed attention predominantly upon their economic aspects. Forest policy was first made under siege conditions during one world war and reinforced by a repetition of those circumstances during the second conflict. It has been strongly influenced by strategic as well as economic requirements to secure the growing of softwood trees as rapidly and on as large a scale as possible. Agriculture, after periods of peacetime depression and wartime prosperity, has been granted an overriding priority in the interests of stabilization. This has enabled some revolutionary changes in the patterns of English landscape to be made without challenge. The development of both industries which, more than most others, can alter the appearance of the countryside at large for better or worse, has often taken place in a disjointed and fortuitous fashion in relation to landscape.

By comparison with urban affairs, therefore, rural planning has been fragmentary. Overall attention to design has been dominated by the material needs of agriculture and forestry, which are excluded from planning control, and have themselves been competitive rather than integrated with each other until recent years. The belated extension of planning to include the country-side was made at first almost solely to check ugly urban development in rural areas. In this it was reasonably successful within limited terms of reference. Later, after the Second World War, it was extended again, supposedly to safeguard amenity in the countryside at large and particularly in areas of special land-scape value, such as the new National Parks. In practice, the influence of planning, especially upon the conservation or creation of well-designed landscape, has been weakened by financial restrictions, cumbrousness and exemption clauses. There has been a lack of co-ordination between rural interests which has only been partly overcome by intricate but informal systems of consultation, however willingly these may have been undertaken.

Amenity

Amenity, in the sense of a pleasant environment, is something which most people consciously or subconsciously strive to attain throughout their lives. The co-ordination of all relevant interests including those of recreation and aesthetic design is implied by that word. Nevertheless, the acceptance of care for amenity within national legislation and policies for rural areas has been painfully slow and is still incomplete. The winning of this regard has remained primarily the province of private organizations which have had to appeal ceaselessly for attention. The need to secure access and land for public recreation in the physical sense was the first aspect of amenity to receive recognition. In the latter part of the last century it became the subject of separate legislation for specific areas; then, in the present century, it was incorporated in forest policy. It finally gained general, but administratively and financially uncertain, support under the National Parks Act. Scientific amenity, the conservation of wild life, has had an equally long struggle for attention but, with the establishment of the Nature Conservancy, became more strongly protected.

Aesthetic Amenity

Aesthetic amenity in rural landscapes may be described as the pleasant appearance of individual components, and their integration with one another to form overall designs which are visually attractive as well as functionally sound. It has been discussed endlessly but no provisions have so far been made which are fully satisfactory. Few critical studies have been made upon the techniques of rural landscape planning to suit modern requirements. The whole subject of design in the English countryside has become very confused, not least when trees and forestry are involved.

The eighteenth-century style of landscape, dominated by hardwood trees and still surviving in many parts of lowland England, although decimated by wartime and other inroads and fading with age, is a popularly acceptable criterion of good rural design. The preservationist attitude which amenity organizations maintained towards this type of landscape had a strong influence upon planning legislation. This trend developed in the last century when, for example, an attempt was made to protect parts of the New Forest from change solely by negative statutory means. The need for management in amenity woodland to keep the desired effects has since been recognized, notably through the work of the National Trust. Adequate provision for such management was overlooked, however, when power to make preservation orders upon trees and woods was added to planning.

The dislike of coniferous trees often expressed by amenity organizations has stemmed more from objections to the utilitarian manner in which they were first arranged in English uplands in the nineteen-twenties, than from a careful assessment of the aesthetic potentialities of the trees in landscape design. As a result, generally negative policies have also been evolved for the protection of wild and open land, where large-scale afforestation with conifers came as an entirely new landscape development. An interesting example is provided by the Lake District agreement for the division of land between forestry and amenity interests. Although an attempt was made later to integrate these interests in the Hardknott district, the negative policy was not reversed. This kind of exclusive approach has also influenced rural planning in the countryside at large. It has led to a proliferation upon maps of zones, belts and areas, indicating estimates of landscape value but providing little positive guidance to the principles of good design which should be followed within them. There is also the risk that undemarcated landscape may be looked upon as expendable.

Thus a situation developed and hardened wherein, on the one hand, forestry and farming were empowered to change the landscape in an unregulated manner with little or no brief of their own for design. At the same time, planning was unable to influence rural patterns much beyond the demarcation, preservation and occasional management of some of the best examples of the old unified types of landscape — as a kind of piecemeal antidote to utilitarian modern changes elsewhere in the countryside. That visual amenity is not necessarily a natural associate of forestry and farming practice, unless conscious and deliberate attention is paid to design, has only slowly been realized. The desirability of re-unifying landscape to suit modern requirements and tastes does not yet receive general support. Until it does, the negative attitude to landscape planning cannot be replaced by a positive overall policy for the integration of use and beauty.

Recreation

Since the Second World War, further social changes have helped to bring about a wider acceptance of these objectives. With spectacular increases in population, greater individual affluence, more leisure and almost universal car-ownership, public pressure upon the countryside for recreation of all kinds has given the amenity aspects of land planning a new importance. In addition, the attractions of English rural scenery to overseas visitors now possess a cash value in the national economy which cannot be lightly pushed aside.

The conservation of the countryside as a recreational and aesthetic as well as a material resource is made more difficult, in a small, overcrowded and highly urbanized country, by the limited amount of land available. From the material point of view alone, there is insufficient room to treat all our complex requirements separately. The concept of multiple land-use to integrate our needs as carefully as possible has won strong support in recent years. This calls for much greater attention to the intricacies of design, as the co-ordination of forestry and agricultural interests in some upland areas has already demonstrated. The added pressure to plan for leisure can no longer be treated as a minor issue, catered for by scattered reservations, but also has to be taken into account everywhere in schemes for multiple use.

Integration

Already there are signs that a more comprehensive approach to the overall planning of land-use, including aesthetics as well as function, is gaining favour. Forest policy has been greatly modified to have regard for visual amenity, and the part which the landscape architect can play in the matter is now accepted. Rural planning and forestry were, for a time, linked together under the same Ministerial control, which promised to consider the conservation of amenity values as an important national resource. At the time of writing a searching re-examination of amenity legislation, its financial provisions and the consultative processes stemming from it, has been put in hand. Agricultural policy seems likely to remain separated from landscape planning, but the subject is still under debate. Amenity problems arising from the effect of modern practices upon the old pattern of hedgerow trees, the reclamation of upland areas and the re-introduction of shelter belts, may yet receive closer attention. Such matters are of major importance if a balance is to be struck between use and beauty in national land policy. While their relationship with forestry, planning and amenity has been referred to, this book is concerned primarily with the development of major forest enterprises in the landscape.

In this field at least, it seems that the wheel may have nearly turned full circle and the whole and balanced view of landscape held by the old landowners may be restored. Our needs are much more numerous and complicated than they were two hundred years ago. The means by which they can be integrated depend upon democratic legislation instead of autocratic conviction. But the positive creation and conservation of fine country as an attractive environment for national life can still be achieved.

The fostering of aesthetic values in forestry is now an acknowledged part of national policy, but because the subject has been treated superficially for so long, there is a dearth of positive information about how it should be undertaken. Cost-benefit analyses are required of woodland areas of various types to measure amenity effects in economic terms, so that a clearer idea of justifiable expenditure upon them may be obtained. Such analyses would not, however, provide any aesthetic guidance upon which the layout of new work could be based.

If the future expansion of forestry, either as afforestation in upland areas or in the restocking of existing woods, is to be carried out with care for landscape, it is necessary to determine precisely what that care means — and then to define principles of forest design which may make it secure. The geological diversity of this country gives rise to many types of scenery in the form of distinct regions. A logical first step in planning forest development therefore seems to be to study each region as a whole, rather than to work within artificial administrative boundaries.

National Parks

The National Parks were marked out as just such examples of regional landscape. They have the added advantages, for study purposes, of containing large areas of the type of land where the expansion of forestry, the improvement of hill farms, the mounting pressure for recreation and the protection of landscape values have already come into conflict with each other. The need for multiple use planning is already apparent. The Exmoor National Park therefore provided an excellent sample area in which to examine the design problems involved in the further development of forestry, compatible with landscape values, and the various land uses and interests in that region.

Exmoor — Two Studies

Separate studies were made of afforestation on open land and restocking in existing woods. Each was based upon :

1. A review of administrative problems.
2. A survey of physical conditions and land-use.
3. An assessment of the requirements of competing interests, including recreation.
4. An analysis of landscape to define special qualities and characteristics.
5. The application of basic principles of landscape design.
6. The translation of aesthetic and material criteria into practical terms, to form an easily understandable grammar of principles for forest design in the areas finally recommended for new projects.

Plans drawn in accordance with the findings of this work, indicate that a substantial total area of open land and woods in Exmoor could be used for productive forestry, without detriment to other interests or undue extra cost, to the benefit of amenity. Such use, in the manner prescribed, could therefore enhance the attractions of the region in every sense. That such claims are valid is supported by the large measure of agreement which the ideas have received from all kinds of groups with interests in the future of the National Park. The principles have also been successfully applied in day-to-day negotiations about forestry projects.

The afforestation plan goes further than the terms of the Voluntary Scheme by insisting that it is not enough to agree broad zones for planting — specific sites should be marked out and, moreover, agreement upon planting designs within them is equally important. This has naturally led to a prolonged series of consultations with interested parties, but the findings of the survey have effectively survived repeated examination. As might be expected, there are a few outstanding differences about local detail but the principles have generally been accepted as the basis for a workable type of Voluntary Scheme. In the 15th Annual Report of the National Parks Commission for 1964, paragraph 25 reads :

'During the year we have had discussions with the Forestry Commission about the afforestation survey prepared by the Exmoor National Park authorities. The position is that this survey was completed before the voluntary scheme of consultation on afforestation of hitherto unplanted land in National Parks was thought of.

This Exmoor Survey is a detailed and sensitive study which adopted the more positive approach of showing carefully defined areas where afforestation would be accepted, having regard to the intimate landscape of the Park. We and the Forestry Commission hope that local consultations will settle any outstanding difference there may be between the various bodies concerned.'

As a corollary to the positive planning of well-designed and economic modern forestry projects, both studies reveal a hard core of traditional areas. These are either stretches of open moorland or areas of old woods. Their conservation is vital, at least in the first phase of an overall landscape development plan, if a critical framework of traditional character is to be kept in the Park. In relation to forest expansion, they can be pinpointed as precisely as the land best suited for productive use, and their management should be equally positive. Preservation, although a useful holding action at times, is not enough. Later, when new beauty has been created elsewhere, the value of the present amenity lands may lessen and their future can be reviewed in the light of changed circumstances and, perhaps, new tastes.

Unfortunately, while the afforestation survey shows up critical areas of open land, so far as tree planting is concerned, much of it is vulnerable to change from agricultural improvement. Some of it could be altered without spoiling the landscape, but other parts may have to be deliberately under-farmed if present National Park purposes are to be fulfilled. The matter requires a separate study but, while agriculture remains unco-ordinated with care for landscape, some vital areas of open moor will undoubtedly be lost. In existing woods, amenity management of critical sections is hampered by financial difficulties, and the subject has, surprisingly, not yet been recognized officially as of equal importance to afforestation.

Future

Much of the work done in Exmoor is therefore exploratory, to measure the size of such problems. But the main object has been to contribute to the study of techniques for expanding the forest industry so that harmony between use and beauty can be assured. The methods deduced are intended to be flexible to allow for aesthetic and material changes in the future. The plans stemming

Q

from them are for a particular stage in the history of the landscape and should be reviewed periodically in the light of new influences upon design.

The studies took place in a National Park, where, perhaps, the conservation of existing landscape character may be more demanding, and the integration of new patterns more difficult, than elsewhere. Yet there appears to be no reason why similar methods of planning forestry should not be used in other regions — even on derelict land where traditional patterns have vanished. The whole process of survey, analysis and deduction enables positive recommendations to be made upon the place of modern forestry in either the creation, maintenance or the improvement of landscape. In view of the increasing demand for recreation everywhere, including the enjoyment of visual amenity, good forest design should not be confined to those parts of the country which happen to have survived in an attractive form. It should also become part of a vigorous overall rural policy, directed as much to the deliberate creation of landscape beauty in a modern style as to the conservation of the well-loved remains of an older environment.

POSTSCRIPT

POSTSCRIPT

It is almost inevitable that, after an interval of time, there will be corrections to make or new information to add in a book of this kind. My last chance to do that — at proof stage before publication — has now arrived.

To begin with, the lack of any specific reference in the book to the Town and Country Planning Act of 1962 is rather obvious. It is, of course, a consolidating Act, embodying those amendments, chiefly financial, made to the Act of 1947 during the 'fifties. The main scheme of planning control remains virtually the same, certainly so far as measures affecting forestry, landscape and the rural problems examined here are concerned — although the appropriate Sections are numbered differently in the later Act.

The new *Memorandum on the Preservation of Trees and Woodlands*, issued by the Ministry of Land and Natural Resources in September 1966, also makes no fundamental planning changes about Tree Preservation Orders — only legislation can do that, as stated in the Ministry's Circular No. 1/66. In effect the Memorandum brings up to date, officially, arrangements such as those for consultation, which had been built up informally over the years. The Forestry Commission's new interest in maintaining the beauty of the countryside, following earlier policy changes, is mentioned.

During 1966, the Forestry Commission has added to the Bibliography by issuing Booklet No. 18 : *Forestry in the Landscape*. It is written by Sylvia Crowe, who was appointed landscape consultant to the Commission after the forest policy review of 1963. The advice in the booklet is warmly welcomed in a foreword by the Chairman. If it can also be accepted and applied by all ranks under the Commission, and by the private and contracting sectors in forestry as well, the appearance of productive woods and forests in the countryside could be vastly improved. But, as I have tried to point out, agriculturalists and planners would also have to play their full part, especially in the conservation of smaller features and hedge trees — upon the presence of which some of the maxims in the booklet depend, and concerning which the Forestry Commission has so far displayed less rather than more interest.

One disappointment in 1966 was the dissolution of the direct link between forestry and rural planning under the Ministry of Land and Natural Resources. Many of that Ministry's responsibilities have been reabsorbed by either the Agriculture or Housing Ministries. Also, the Government's proposals for the countryside, finally embodied in a White Paper: *Leisure in the Countryside* (*Cmd.* 2928), have not materialized in law. The National Parks Commission has been reorganized, ostensibly in readiness for new legislation, but it has already expressed some misgivings about the adequacy of certain proposals (*N.P.C.* 17th *Annual Report*, 1966). A more serious economic crisis than any which helped to delay action during the last decade, and other urgent issues, have postponed the likelihood of a new Bill being presented, at least until the next Parliamentary session.

Finally, in the Exmoor National Park, a separate study seeking to reconcile the needs of agricultural productivity with landscape design and conservation, mentioned in this book as desirable, has been started. That work, together with the earlier forestry surveys, may form a trilogy of positive studies from which a complete landscape development plan for the district can be made. This method of assessing amenity problems in rural areas may offer a sound basis for their co-ordination with economic regional planning which now seems to be the favoured administrative pattern for the future. Meanwhile, the whole subject of rural planning, in Exmoor as elsewhere, remains very unsettled.

January 1967.

APPENDICES

APPENDIX 1

Copy of Text of the Voluntary Scheme over Afforestation issued by the National Parks Commission, January 1961

c.236
1.61.   NPC/G/489.

AFFORESTATION IN NATIONAL PARKS

1. The Timber Growers' Organisation, the Country Landowners' Association, the Forestry Commission and the National Parks Commission are anxious to secure that in the future use of land in National Parks, proper regard should be given both to the needs of forestry and to the preservation and enhancement of the natural beauty of the landscape.

2. Under the provisions of the Town and Country Planning Act, 1947, the use of any land for the purposes of agriculture and forestry (including afforestation) is not deemed to involve development of the land. Proposals for afforestation do not, therefore, require planning permission. In National Parks, the Park Planning Authorities are statutorily responsible for the preservation and enhancement of the natural beauty of the area and for encouraging the provision of opportunities for open-air recreation, and they have a duty under Section 84 of the National Parks Act, 1949, to have due regard, in the exercise of their functions, to the needs of agriculture and forestry.

3. In order to try to avoid conflict between the needs of forestry and the preservation and enhancement of natural beauty, the parties to this agreement believe that the closest co-operation should be maintained between those concerned with afforestation and those responsible for accomplishing the purposes for which National Parks have been established. Accordingly, they agree that the Park Planning Authorities should be given the opportunity of commenting upon all proposals for the afforestation of any land which has hitherto not been planted.

4. In each National Park (except one or two where special arrangements have already been made) the National Parks Commission will advise the Park Planning Authority to carry out, in association with the Forestry Commission, a survey with a view to compiling maps which would divide the land in the park as far as possible into three categories :

(a) areas where there is a strong presumption that afforestation would be acceptable;

(b) areas where, although there is a presumption against afforestation, proposals might be acceptable; and

(c) areas where there is a strong presumption against afforestation.

5. These categories are devised as a general guide to policy and are not to be regarded as precise or rigid; they should be adjusted where necessary to meet the particular circumstances of individual parks.

6. The surveys should be discussed between the planning authorities and the National Parks Commission, who will as necessary consult amenity societies, and also between the Forestry Commission, the Timber Growers' Organisation and the Country Landowners' Association. The surveys, amended as necessary after these consultations, will be made public, and it is intended that private landowners will frame their afforestation proposals in accordance with them; the Forestry Commission will certainly do so.

7. In case of disagreement at any stage, the good offices of the Government Departments concerned will be available.

8. Pending the completion of the surveys, which must of necessity take a considerable time, the Timber Growers' Organisation and the Country Landowners' Association will advise members to consult the Park Planning Authorities about their afforestation proposals. Arrangements for such consultation will be made locally in each Park.

9. These arrangements will not apply outside National Parks, nor will they apply to proposals for the re-planting of existing woodlands, including felled, devastated and scrub woodlands.

12.1.61.

APPENDIX 2

List of Sites of Special Scientific Interest, within the Exmoor National Park, notified to Devon and Somerset County Councils by the Nature Conservancy under Section 23 of the National Parks Act, 1949

SOMERSET
1. *Dunkery Beacon, Holnicote and Homebush Wood.* (6,719 acres)
   North part of Exmoor
   A sample section of Exmoor, with boundaries chosen to include good examples of all the characteristic types of vegetation from hill-top moorland to valley-bottom woodland.
2. *Burridge Wood.* (54 acres)
   North-west of Dulverton
   A well preserved partly coppiced oakwood characteristic of the region.
3. *Knaplock and North Barton Woods.* (80 acres)
   In the parish of Winsford, Dulverton Rural District, south part of Exmoor.
   An area including deciduous woodland surviving on the steep valley slopes with interesting local variations in vegetation.

DEVONSHIRE
4. *Heddon's Mouth.* (404 acres)
   On the north coast
   An unspoilt valley remarkable for its steep sides and straight course. The area as a whole includes vegetation on both acid and base-rich soils, varying from damp ferny woodland to dry screes.
5. *Watersmeet.* (344 acres)
   South of Lynmouth
   Oak woodlands with a rich flora of ferns and mosses as well as flowering plants. Ash and Alder are associated on the damper flush sites. The summit heath completes the natural vegetational range of the district.

251

APPENDIX 3

The Exmoor Afforestation Survey and the Voluntary Scheme

During early rounds of consultation after the survey had been completed, there was a general feeling that the positive approach to the subject should be balanced by a clearer presentation of the negative aspects. Accordingly, the areas where large-scale planting would be unacceptable, because of over-riding aesthetic or other reasons, were hatched upon the map illustrating the report.

Immediately, a third category of land was demarcated on the plan by implication, namely the 'white' land. Most of this appeared over the relatively intensive agricultural land, especially the Brendon Hills, but some of the middle ground in the Park was included. The 'white' land represented an intermediate zone where afforestation was either not expected or not welcome for other reasons. But, clearly, objection could not be as strong as in the hatched zone. Thus, it might be assumed that planting proposals in 'white' areas, while not as immediately acceptable as they would be in the specific sites, would, nevertheless, have a better chance of acceptance than proposals in the hatched areas.

In some ways, the application of zones to the afforestation plan weakened the precision of the original concept. The subtleties of landscape are such that precision is necessary in forest design and broad zones do little of themselves to secure the attention to detail which is required if good effects are to be achieved. On the other hand, the hatched zone made clear the area where greatest opposition to planting might be expected and also introduced a note of flexibility into the 'white' land. It was foreseen that some flexibility might be needed, both to help reach agreement with other parties and to leave room for alterations, found desirable through practice, when the plan came under periodic review.

When the details of the Voluntary Scheme were circulated in 1961, the classification of land in three categories was called for officially, and some doubt was raised whether the specific planting sites on the Exmoor plan would be acceptable in place of a broad zone. Within a few months, however, the National Parks Commission confirmed that the plan satisfied official requirements. Paragraph 5 of the Voluntary Scheme (Appendix 1) allows, of course, for some flexibility in interpretation.

A more serious matter is the omission in the text of the Scheme of any mention of plantation design. On the other hand there is nothing in the Scheme to prevent Park Authorities, if they wish to do so, from supplementing their surveys with a full appreciation of design problems. Such work certainly proved necessary in Exmoor and, in my own opinion, the value of any Voluntary Scheme is likely to be seriously diminished without it.

Finally, the wisdom of the zonal approach to the subject may be questioned. The intimacy of much of the Exmoor country has been advanced as one reason for selecting precise planting sites instead of a general zone. The same argument applies against any further broad subdivisions. They tend to iron out the fine detail of the varied landscape compositions, upon which the very character of the Park depends.

In my view, the Voluntary Scheme contains an unnecessarily complicated administrative approach which overlooks essential design problems. Of course, it can be combined with the technical and artistic approaches made in Exmoor so that a workable compromise is reached. But it seems to me that the original plan to allocate land for a specific purpose, subject to a kind of design control, and to periodic review, was simpler and more in tune with the realities of the countryside.

NOTES

NOTES

Where a source, published or unpublished, is quoted more than once, the full title is given in the first instance — afterwards, it is given in shortened form. Command papers are identified by reference number, and date if necessary, after first description. Where several works by the same author are quoted, later references to each work are identified by publication dates. After their first full quotation the following abbreviations have been used :

C.P.R.E.   Council for the Preservation of Rural England.
F.C.   Forestry Commission.
N.C.   Nature Conservancy.
N.P.C.   National Parks Commission.

See also Bibliography, pp. 275–288, where sources are listed under authors alphabetically.

PART I

Chapter 1

1. *The Relation between Forest Policy and Economic Development, Part 1: England.* An unpublished D.Phil. thesis by A. A. Zukowski, 1951. Bodleian Library, Oxford
2. *Forests and Forestry in Great Britain*, by W. L. Taylor, p. 10. Crosby Lockwood, 1945
3. Only occasional consignments of oak were still obtainable from some of the smaller southern forests such as Bere, Whittlewood, Salcey, Rockingham, Windsor and Bushy Park. See Albion (Note 4 below, p. 107)
4. *Forests and Sea Power*, by R. G. Albion, pp. 132–134. Harvard University Press, 1926
5. *Ibid.*, pp. 370–388
6. *Ibid.*, pp. 30–31, 164ff. and 282ff.
7. *The Making of the English Landscape*, by Dr. W. G. Hoskins, p. 139. Hodder and Stoughton, 1957
8. *The Young Melbourne*, by Lord David Cecil, pp. 13–37 : Prologue. Grey Arrow Books, 1960 Edn.

9. *Tomorrow's Landscape*, by Sylvia Crowe, p. 81. Architectural Press, 1956

10. *Studies in Landscape Design*, by G. A. Jellicoe, p. 18. Oxford, 1960

11. *Some Directions about raising Forest Trees* by the 6th Earl of Haddington (1761) is a fine example. Edited by Professor M. L. Anderson, in whose introduction the influences of the period upon forestry are also described, the work was first published by Nelson in 1953

12. Albion, *op. cit.* pp. 5–10

13. *Trees, Woods and Man* by H. L. Edlin, p. 119. Collins, 1956

14. Albion, *op. cit.* pp. 32–33

15. Taylor, *op. cit.* p. 10

16. Zukowski, *op. cit.*, refers to these awards

17. *On Planting and Rural Ornament*, Vol. I, by Marshall (1803) as quoted by Zukowski

18. *British Forestry in 1790–1813* by Dr. E. W. Jones contains further information collected from contemporary reports of the Board of Agriculture. Quart. Jour. of For., Vol. LV, Nos. 1 and 2, 1961

19. *André Le Nôtre: Garden Architect to Kings* by Helen M. Fox. Batsford, 1962

20. *Capability Brown* by Dorothy Stroud. Country Life, 1950, (1957 Edn.)

21. From Christopher Hussey's Introduction to Dorothy Stroud's book on Brown

22. *The English Landscape Garden* by H. F. Clark, Pleiades, 1948, and *Gardening in Britain* by Miles Hadfield, Hutchinson, 1960, fully describe and analyse this phase of English landscape history

23. Clark, *op. cit.*, pp. 3–4

24. Crowe, *op. cit.*, 1956, p. 11

25. Edlin, *op. cit.*, 1956, p. 121

26. *Hedges as a Feature of Our Countryside* by J. M. Way and Dr. B. N. K. Davis. Jour. of the Min. of Ag., Vol. 70, No. 12, pp. 565–568, 1963

27. *Forestry Commission Census Report No. 2: Hedgerow and Park Timber and Woods under Five Acres*, 1951, pp. 31 and 59. H.M.S.O. 1953.

Chapter 2

1. Albion, *op. cit.*, pp. 408–411

2. *History of Ships since the Invention of Steamships* by Sir Phillip Watts, referred to under 'Ships', *Encyclopaedia Britannica*, 11th Edn., 1911

3. W. A. Gordon, of the Department of Forestry at Oxford, drew my attention to this curious state of affairs which is well documented by lawsuits during the nineteenth century

4. *Law of Forestry* by B. W. Adkin, pp. 100–111. Estates Gazette,

1914. Chapters I and II explain the meaning of timber and the doctrine of timber estates. See also *The Law of Forestry* by W. A. Gordon, pp. 102–116, for modern interpretations. H.M.S.O., 1955

5. *English Social History* by Professor G. M. Trevelyan, pp. 552–555. Longmans, 1942

6. *Practical British Forestry* by C. P. Ackers, Ch. IX, pp. 308–325. Oxford, 1938

7. Edlin, *op. cit.*, 1956, p. 133

8. Taylor, *op. cit.*, p. 11

9. *Forestry and Woodland Life* by H. L. Edlin, p. 86. Batsford, 1947

10. Edlin, *op. cit.*, 1956, p. 133

11. *Trees and Shrubs Hardy in the British Isles* by W. J. Bean, Vol. I, Ch. 1, pp. 3–19. Murray, 1950 Edn. Biographical notes upon many plant hunters are given in Vol. I; dates of discovery, introduction, etc. of trees are provided under species in Vols. I–III

12. *Westonbirt Arboretum:* Forestry Commission Guide Book, H.M.S.O., 1960

13. Taylor, *op. cit.*, p. 12

14. Hoskins, *op. cit.*, pp. 170–179

15. Information in this and several following paragraphs is drawn from *Planning Law and Procedure* by A. E. Telling, Ch. 1, pp. 3–7. Butterworths, 1963

16. Trevelyan, *op. cit.*, p. 537

17. See Part I, Ch. 3 (c), pp. 75–78, for further discussion of the Lake District

18. *The Common Lands of England and Wales* by Sir Dudley Stamp and Dr. W. G. Hoskins, especially Ch. 6 and 7. Collins, 1963. Also *English Commons and Forests* by G. Shaw-Lefevre, especially Ch. 3. Cassell, 1894. Both books contain detailed accounts of struggles to protect individual commons

19. *The Royal Parks of London* by Richard Church. Ministry of Works Guide Book, H.M.S.O. 1956

20. *Epping Forest* by Alfred Qvist, p. 9. Corporation of London, 1958

Chapter 3

1. 'Forests and Forestry' by Sir William Schlich in 1910. *Encyclopaedia Britannica*, 11th Edn., 1911

2. *F.C. Census of Woodlands*, 1924 and *Post-War Forest Policy, Cmd. 6447*, 1943, pp. 14–15, 35.

3. *Cmd. 6447*, 1943, pp. 10–11, reprints the original summary from the Acland Report, the full title of which is *Final Report of the Reconstruction Committee — Forestry Sub-Committee — Ministry of Reconstruction. Cmd. 8881*, 1918

4. F. M. G. Willson, in Part IV, pp. 41–56, of an unpublished D.Phil. thesis about Administrative Commissions in Britain, describes the Forestry Commission's difficulties. Bodleian Library, Oxford, 1953. See also Gordon, *op. cit.*, pp. 204–217

5. *F.C. 1st Annual Report*, 1920, pp. 12–13

6. *The Land: Now and Tomorrow* by Sir George Stapledon, Ch. VII, pp. 84–93. Faber, 1935

7. *Man and the Land*, by Sir Dudley Stamp, p. 197. Collins, 1955

8. Mostly situated in England, the largest being the New Forest in Hampshire and the Forest of Dean in Gloucestershire

9. Zukowski draws attention to these economic difficulties

10. *Improvement of Woodlands* by W. E. Hiley, pp. 38–41. Country Life, 1931

11. *Post-War Forestry:* A Report on Forestry Policy prepared by the Royal Scottish and English Forestry Societies, pp. 9–10, 1944

12. Notably *Forestry Practice*, first issued in 1933, *Home-Grown Timber*, 1933, and a series on *Timber Utilization*, issued in 1934–38

13. The Acland Committee had not ruled out the possibility of applying compulsion to neglectful landowners (*Cmd. 8881*, 1917, p. 32) and, in 1929, the Commissioners suggested that additional compulsory powers might have to be sought. (*F.C. 10th Annual Report*, p. 31). At Conferences in 1938–39 a more realistic policy began to emerge tempering control with better financial and technical encouragement. (*F.C. 18th Annual Report*, p. 14; *Cmd. 6447*, 1943, pp. 18–19)

14. Willson, *op. cit.*, Part IV, p. 63.

15. The proportion in private forestry was calculated from an analysis of areas planted with grant-aid recorded in *Cmd. 6447*, p. 98. The proportion in State forestry was derived from figures given in several *F.C. Annual Reports*, 1920–38, and in *Cmd. 6447*, pp. 94–95

16. The first National Park in the world to be established was the Yellowstone Park in America in 1872. By 1916, there were so many American parks that the United States National Park Service was created to manage them. Canada, South Africa, the Argentine and other countries, including many in Europe, established national parks between 1885 and 1945

17. *Cmd. 3851*, 1931

18. *Britain's National Parks* by Harold M. Abrahams, pp. 14–20. Country Life, 1959. These pages include a summary of the principal conclusions of the *Addison Report*

19. *Production of Hardwoods*, 1929. A memorandum issued by the Forestry Commissioners, published in the technical press in 1930

and reproduced as an Appendix to the *F.C. 15th Annual Report*, 1934. Pages 50–55 of this report also refer

20. *F.C. 15th Annual Report*, 1934, pp. 47–50

21. Gordon, *op. cit.*, pp. 221–225

22. *F.C. Report of the Forest of Dean Committee, Cmd. 686*, 1958, p. 37, para. 166

23. *F.C. Progress Report 1955–60*, prepared for the 8th Brit. Commonwealth For. Conf. in 1962, p. 17, para. 3

24. A number of these are listed in the Bibliography and I have drawn upon them freely for material

25. *Remarks on Forest Scenery and Other Woodland Views* by William Gilpin, 4th Edn. edited by Sir Thomas Lauder, Edinburgh, 1834. In 1791, Gilpin presented this work in three volumes — the first on trees, the second on ways of arranging them, including forests, and the third on the New Forest itself

26. *F.C. Report of the New Forest Committee, Cmd. 7245*, 1947, p. 11. This report provided much of the historical information quoted in succeeding pages

27. *The New Forest, A Symposium*. Galley Press, London, 1960. Ch. VII, by H. L. Edlin, pp. 112–113. See also Gordon, *op. cit.*, pp. 71–75

28. *Thirty-Five Years in the New Forest*, by Gerald Lascelles, describes this leisurely period. Arnold, 1915

29. *Cmd. 7245*, 1947, pp. 13–14

30. Edlin, in *The New Forest, A Symposium*, 1960, pp. 116–117

31. See Part I, Ch. 4 (b), pp. 107–111, on Tree Preservation Orders

32. G. B. Ryle, formerly Deputy Director of the Forestry Commission, also criticized such mechanical treatment in an address to the Society of Foresters in 1962 : *Forestry*, Vol. XXXVI, No. 1, 1963, p. 7. Incorrectly it seems, he attributed the invention of the roadside amenity belt to the planners

33. *F.C. 16th–19th Annual Reports*, 1935–38 contain acknowledgements of the Committee's advice, but no details

34. *The Lakers* by Norman Nicholson. Hale, 1956

35. *Report on National Parks in England and Wales, Cmd. 6628*, by John Dower, p. 19. Ministry of Town and Country Planning, 1945

36. H. L. Edlin supplied me with much information upon the protracted negotiations behind the discontinuance of Hardknott. There is no other comparable instance of the Commission withdrawing land from planting on such a scale after acquisition. Consultations upon amenity now take place regularly before acquisition

37. Crowe, *op. cit.*, 1956, p. 13

Chapter 4

1. *Timber Statistics* by J. J. MacGregor, Jour. R. Stat. Soc., Series A (Gen.) Vol. CXVI, Pt. III, 1953, pp. 298–322
2. *Home Timber Production*, 1939–45 by Russell Meiggs, 1949. Referred to in *F.C. Census of Woods 1947–49*, p. 17
3. *Cmd. 6447* and *Cmd. 6500* respectively
4. *Cmd. 6447*, 1943, p. 77
5. *The Future of Forests* by Prof. A. G. Tansley. *The Times*, 1945
6. Gordon, *op. cit.*, p. 240
7. *Ibid*, p. 271
8. *Ibid*, p. 288
9. *Memorandum on the Preservation of Trees and Woodlands* issued by the Ministry of Town and Country Planning, para. 34, p. 12. H.M.S.O., 1949. N.B. The designation of the Ministry responsible for planning changed a number of times after 1947 — from 'Town and Country Planning' to 'Housing and Local Government' in 1952, and lately it has been coupled with the Ministry of Land and Natural Resources. I have used the designation appropriate to each period described in my text
10. *Report on the Distribution of the Industrial Population*, Chairman: Sir Anderson Montague-Barlow, *Cmd. 6153*, 1940. *Final Report on Compensation and Betterment*, Chairman: Lord Justice Uthwatt, *Cmd. 6386*, 1942
    Report on Land Utilisation in Rural Areas, Chairman: Lord Justice Scott, *Cmd. 6378*, 1942
    Town and Country Planning 1943–51, a progress report issued by the Ministry of Local Government and Planning, *Cmd. 8204*, 1951, provides a succinct account of the main findings of these Reports
11. *Cmd. 8204*, 1951, pp. 8–11
12. Telling, *op. cit.*, pp. 12–15
13. *Cmd. 8204*, 1951, pp. 138–141, wherein interpretations of the word are discussed, commencing with its dictionary definition of 'pleasantness' or a quality 'agreeable to the mind, feelings or senses'
14. *Development by Government Departments*, Ministry of Local Government and Planning, Circular No. 100, 1950
15. *Cmd. 6628*, 1945
16. *Report of the National Parks Committee (England and Wales)* Cmd. 7121; *Conservation of Nature in England and Wales*, Cmd. 7122; and *Footpaths and Access to the Countryside*, Cmd. 7207
17. *Town Planning Control in Practice: IV, National Parks* by S. Lee Vincent. Jour. of Planning and Property Law, March 1962, pp. 148–160
    The National Parks of England and Wales by Arthur Blenkinsop.

Jour. of School of Planning, Newcastle University, Vol. VI, No. 1, 1964

18. *F.C. 32nd Annual Report*, 1951

19. *The Trend of Forest Workers' Wages, 1938–61* by F. E. Balman. Quart. Jour. of For. Vol. LV. No. 4, 1961. Also Gordon, *op. cit.* p. 242

20. *The Forestry Commission and the Use of Hill Land* by Dr. K. R. Walker. Reprint from the Scot. Jour. of Pol. Economy, Vol. VII, pp. 14–35, 1959

21. *Forestry, Agriculture and Marginal Land*, Report by the National Resources (Technical) Committee. Chairman: Professor Sir Solly Zuckerman. H.M.S.O., 1957

22. Reports *Cmd. 9631*, 1955, and *Cmd. 9091*, 1954, provide details for Wales and Scotland

23. Review of *The Zuckerman Report* by Dr. K. R. Walker. Jour. of Ag. Economics, Vol. XII, No. 4, 1957
    Also *Economics and the Use of Land for Forestry* by J. J. MacGregor, *Unasylva*, Vol. 14, No. 2, 1960. Reprinted Jour. of the R.I.C.S., March 1961

24. *F.C. Report of the Committee on Marketing of Woodland Produce*, Chairman: Mr. Hugh Watson, 1956

25. *F.C. 39th Annual Report*, 1958

26. *The Growing of Hardwoods for Pulpwood* by E. G. Richards. Quart. Jour. of For., Vol. LV, No. 3, 1961
    The Utilization of Small-sized Coniferous Thinnings in Great Britain. Paper presented by E. G. Richards at the 8th Brit. Commonwealth For. Conf., 1962

27. *The Survey of Private Forestry Costs: Summary Report for Forest Years 1951/52–1955/56*, published 1959, prepared jointly by Oxford and Aberdeen Universities contains supporting evidence

28. *Highland Landscape — A Survey*, by W. H. Murray. National Trust for Scotland, 1962. When the author criticizes forest development, it is usually the designs rather than the species which cause adverse comment

29. *The Desirable Balance Between Hardwood and Softwood Production in Great Britain.* Paper presented by H. M. Steven and W. M. McNeill at the 7th Brit. Commonwealth For. Conf., 1957

30. *F.C. Census Report No. 2: Hedgerow and Park Timber and Woods under Five Acres, 1951*, pp. 24, 31, 59. H.M.S.O., 1953

31. *F.C. Report of the Committee on Hedgerow and Farm Timber*, Chairman: Lord Merthyr. H.M.S.O., 1955

32. There have been a number of excellent publications on these subjects including: *The Establishment of Vegetation on Industrial Waste Land*

by R. O. Whyte and J. W. B. Sisam, Commonwealth Ag. Bureau, 1949; *Shelter Belts for Farmland*, Min. of Ag. Leaflet No. 15, 1951; *Shelterbelts and Microclimate*, F.C. Bulletin No. 29, 1957; *Tree Planting on Colliery Spoil Heaps*, F.C. Research Branch Paper No. 17, 1955; *New Life for Dead Lands*, Min. of Housing and Local Govt. Bulletin, 1963; *Shelterbelts and Windbreaks* by Dr. J. M. Caborn, Faber, 1965

33. H. Chapman, of the Ministry of Housing and Local Government, has assisted me with information which leads to this conclusion

34. *Memorandum on the Preservation of Trees and Woodlands*, Min. of Town and Country Planning, para. 8, p. 4, H.M.S.O., 1949

35. *Forestry and the Essex County Council*. Explanatory leaflet by the County Planning Adviser, 1961

36. *Trees in Worcestershire*. Bulletin by the County Planning Officer, 1957

37. *New Life for Dead Lands*, Min. of Housing and Local Govt. Bulletin 1963, and *Derelict Land*, by the Civic Trust, 1964, illustrate and describe some of these projects

38. Ministry of Housing and Local Govt. statistics

39. *Memorandum on Preservation*, 1949 (see note 34), para. 27, p. 10

40. *Cmd. 8204*, 1951, pp. 142–143

41. *The Preservation and Felling of Trees* by Anthony R. Mellows. Oyez Practice Notes No. 54, 1964

42. Ministry of Housing and Local Govt. *Circular No. 27/53*, p. 1

43. *Memorandum on Preservation*, 1949, para. 11, pp. 4–5

44. *Ibid*, para. 32, p. 12

45. *National Parks Commission Annual Reports, 1st–17th*, 1950–66 and the *Peak District National Park Annual Reports, 1st–14th*, 1951–66 contain references to such acquisitions and management programmes

46. *Somerset County Development Plan: Report of Survey*, First Review, 1964. Chapter III, particularly paras. 67–8, pp. 16–17

47. *F.C. 33rd–37th Annual Reports*, 1952–56 contain occasional references

48. *F.C. Pamphlet: Grants for Woodland Owners*, under constant revision, specifies that dedication does not exclude the reconciliation of amenity 'with the needs of good silviculture'. F.C. Booklet No 2, *The Dedication of Woodlands*, 1956 Edn., fully explains the scheme

49. *Somerset Development Plan Report, 1964*. Para. 73(e), p. 19. The arrangement is referred to again in Part III, Chap. 1 of my text

50. *N.P.C. 7th Annual Report*, 1956, pp. 29–30

51. *N.P.C. 10th Annual Report*, 1959, pp. 25–28. Also *N.P.C. 7th Annual Report*, 1956, pp. 30–31 and Appendix H, pp. 61–65, refer to proposed amendments to the Act

52. Nature Conservancy: *Nature Reserves and Sites of Special Scientific Interest*. Information Leaflet No. 1, 1954

53. *N.C. 15th Annual Report*, 1964, pp. 33–34 and map opposite p. 128, augmented by information from J. H. Hemsley of the N.C. in 1966

54. *Amenity and Forestry* by T. E. Edwardson. *Forestry* Vol. XXIX, No. 1, pp. 44–49, 1956. An account of the excursion of the Society of Foresters to the Lake District in 1955 to examine and discuss amenity problems

55. *Forestry in Relation to Landscape* by C. A. J. Barrington. Jour. of the F.C., No. 26, 1957. An address given to the Institute of Landscape Architects by one of the Commission's Conservators. It indicates a considerable change in outlook since the *Post-War Policy Report* of 1943

56. *F.C. Progress Report, 1955–60*, p. 17, para. 3

57. Tax arrangements in relation to forestry have been fully described in *Woodland Management* by W. E. Hiley, Chap. 23, Faber, 1954; *The Attractions of Woodlands* by O. Kelly, Supplement to *Stock Exchange Gazette*, 1962; and *Practical Forestry for the Agent and Surveyor* by C. E. Hart, Chap. 14, Estates Gazette, 1962. The last author has also published revised booklets upon *Taxation of Woodlands in England and Wales* from time to time

58. *F.C. 39th Annual Report*, 1958

59. A report in *The Times* in March 1960 focussed attention upon activities in the South-West. An address by Kenneth Rankin to the Forestry Section of the Federated Home Timber Associations, reported in *The Timber Trades Journal* in May 1960, indicated that commercial interest in the South-West had been somewhat magnified. Although economic woodland units, each of 10,000 acres within a 30 mile radius, were being sought, the search for land covered the whole of Southern England and parts of Wales

60. *The Case for Control of Afforestation of Open Land in National Parks*. C.P.R.E. Manifesto, 1961, prepared by John Coleman-Cooke

61. *N.P.C. 9th–12th Annual Reports*, 1958–61, refer. See Part II for detailed account. Some aspects of my survey and related work have been published elsewhere and include *New Trees Need Not Look Ugly*, *The Times*, Nov. 1959; *The Design of Forest Plantations*, *Town and Country Planning*, Dec. 1959; *Planning for Landscape*, *The Times*, Feb. 1960; *Forestry and Landscape in the Exmoor National Park*, *Forestry*, Vol. XXXIII, No. 1, 1960; and *Some Rural Problems*, *Prospect*, Jour. of the R. Inc. of Arch., Scotland, 1960

62. *N.P.C. 12th Annual Report*, 1961, pp. 35–37; 74–75 and Appendix I, pp. 89–91

63. *Ibid*, pp. 14–15. See Part III for detailed account

64. Currently (Feb. 1966) Voluntary Schemes are in operation in the Northumberland and Snowdonia Parks; under consideration in the Pembrokeshire Coast, Brecon Beacons, Dartmoor and Exmoor Parks; and believed to be deferred or rejected in the Yorkshire Dales, North York Moors, Lake District and Peak District Parks

65. *Integration of Forestry and the Hill Sheep Farm* by J. A. B. MacDonald. Quart. Jour. of For., Vol. LIII, No. 4, 1959, pp. 317–322

66. *Britain's Forest Resources.* Cantor lecture to R. Soc. of Arts by J. MacDonald reported in *The Timber Trades Journal*, May 1962

67. *Production Goals in Forestry with Special Reference to Great Britain.* Paper presented at the 8th Brit. Commonwealth For. Conf., 1962, by Dr. F. C. Hummel and A. J. Grayson

68. *State Hardwood Planting, 1952–62.* A letter by G. B. Ryle to *Country Life*, Feb. 1963

69. Hiley, *op. cit.*, 1954, p. 31, while recognizing the difficulties and expense of working 'dribs and drabs' of fertile land under trees, considers nevertheless that their potential productivity for hardwoods as well as softwoods should not be dismissed. A letter by P. W. Brine on *Export of Veneer Logs from Britain* in *The Timber Trades Journal*, March 1962, indicated the continuing demand for top-quality hardwoods

70. As recommended by the Merthyr Committee in 1955. Way and Davis, officers of the Nature Conservancy, thought in 1963 that the rate of hedge removal was disastrous and likely to prove disadvantageous to long-term agricultural interests

71. *A Sample Survey of Field and Other Boundaries in Great Britain* by G. M. Locke. Quart. Jour. of For., Vol. LVI, No. 2, 1962, pp. 137–144

72. MacDonald, 1962, who also refers to Locke's survey

73. *The Sudbrook Scheme for the Registration of Hardwood Areas for the Production of Hardwood Pulp.* Information booklet issued by Sudbrook Pulp Mill Ltd., Chepstow, 1961. Also *The Growing of Hardwoods for Pulpwood* by E. G. Richards. Quart. Jour. of For., Vol. LV, No. 3, 1961, pp. 206–222; *The Utilization of Small-Sized Coniferous Thinnings in Great Britain.* Paper presented by Richards at the 8th Brit. Commonwealth For. Conf., 1962

74. *Treatment of Degraded Hardwood Areas for Shelterwood Restocking* by G. B. Ryle and J. B. Stocks. Paper presented at F.A.O., Rome, 1960

75. *The Changing Use of Land in Britain* by R. H. Best and J. T. Coppock, Chap. 4, pp. 99–117 and p. 25. Faber, 1962

76. *Fourth Wave: The Challenge of Leisure* by Michael Dower. Civic Trust, 1965

77. I am indebted to the British Travel Association for this information. The income from American tourists alone is much more than that earned from our dollar sales of road vehicles and aircraft combined

78. *Forests and Parks* by G. B. Ryle. *The Countryman*, Vol. 58, No. 3, 1961, p. 560

79. *Now We're Creating Beauty*, by Laurence Easterbrook. Reprinted in Quart. Jour. of For., Vol. LIII, No. 1, 1959, pp. 27–29

80. The series of articles on *Forests and Parks* by G. B. Ryle, Mrs. Pauline Dower, Lt. Col. G. Haythornthwaite, Dr. W. J. Eggeling and others in *The Countryman*, Vol. 58, Nos. 3 and 4, 1961 and Vol. 59, No. 2, 1962, provides a good cross-section of thought upon forest amenity at the time

81. *Forestry as a Competitor for Land: Some Problems in Land-Use Decisions.* Paper presented by J. J. MacGregor at 8th Brit. Commonwealth For. Conf., 1962. Reprinted in Jour. of the R.I.C.S., Vol. 95, No. 3, Sept. 1962

82. *Landscape in Distress* by Lionel Brett. Architectural Press, 1965, pp. 150ff.

83. Detailed accounts of these systems are contained in *Planning and Control in the Managed Forest* by Prof. H. Knuchel and *Silviculture* by Prof. J. Kostler. Both works translated by Prof. M. L. Anderson, another authority, in 1953 and 1956. Oliver and Boyd. See also *Forests under Protection* by J. Jungo, *The Times*, Supplement on Switzerland, Feb. 1964. In *Degenerating Woodlands* by J. D. U. Ward, Quart. Jour. of For. Vol. LIII, No. 4, 1959, the lack of these methods in G.B. is considered. *In Favour of More Irregular Forestry in Britain* by R. L. Coke, Jour. C.L.A., Vol. 61, No. 4, 1962, is an account by a landowner in Norfolk who has successfully practised this type of forestry for many years

84. *The Dangerous Concept of the Natural Forest* by T. R. Peace. Quart. Jour. of For., Vol. LV, No. 1, 1961, pp. 12–23

85. A discussion with C. A. Connell of the Forestry Commission confirmed this point

86. *The Diverse Uses of Forests.* Address to the Society of Foresters by G. B. Ryle. *Forestry*, Vol. XXXVI, No. 1, 1963, pp. 3–9

87. Sir Dudley Stamp in his Foreword to Best and Coppock, 1962

88. *Conservation and Outdoor Recreation in the United States*, by J. J. MacGregor. *Nature*, Vol. 196, No. 4860, 1962, pp. 1134–1137

89. *The Chilterns as an Area of Outstanding Natural Beauty* by Dr. J. T. Coppock. Jour. of the T.P.I., Vol. 45, No. 6, 1959, pp. 137–141

90. The map was first published in *The Daily Telegraph* on 14th July 1960. A similar map appears in *Britons on Holiday* by G. D. M. Block. Conservative Political Centre, 1963

91. The point is made by J. and L. Sinden in a letter printed in *Forestry*, Vol. XXXVI, No. 2, 1963, pp. 261–262. In *The Public Use of Ashridge*, a report by J. F. Wager, Oxford Forest Library, 1963, an attempt is made to assess users' needs and tastes

92. *Amenity Values in British Forestry* by H. L. Edlin. *Forestry*, Vol. XXXVI, No. 1, pp. 65–89. *Outdoor Recreation in the British Countryside* by T. L. Burton and G. P. Wibberley. Report No. 5, Wye Coll. London, Dept. of Economics, 1965. The first of these references draws attention to several possible financial expressions of forest amenity; the second describes the cost-benefit approach in the evaluation of rural recreation projects

93. *F.C. 42nd Annual Report,* 1961

94. *Editorial Notes.* Quart. Jour. of For., Vol. LVII, No. 1, 1963, p. 3

95. *C.P.R.E. 37th Annual Report,* 1962–63, pp. 36–37. Society of Foresters: *Submission to Govt. Working Party on Forestry Policy,* 1962, para. 2 (e)

96. Ryle (Note 86) p. 8

97. *The Role of Forestry in the Economy of Britain.* Address by Sir Henry Beresford-Peirse at Third Discussion Meeting, Oxford, organized by the Soc. of Foresters. *Forestry*, Supplement 1963, p. 8

98. *Hansard, Commons,* Vol. 681, No. 600, Cols. 1467–1472, July 1963

99. *The Countryside in 1970.* Proceedings of the Study Conference, Nov. 1963. H.M.S.O.

100. The setting up of such a Council had been recommended in *The Trend Report on the Organization of Civil Science, Cmd. 2171,* 1963, Min. of Science

101. *Countryside in 1970,* Nov. 1963. Paper No. 20, pp. 264–271

102. *Ministry of Land and Natural Resources Order, 1965:* Circular No. 1/65 — Min. of Land and Natural Resources

103. *Estimates Committee: Eighth Special Report — The Forestry Commission,* Session 1964–65, page 8, Recommendation (XVII) (paragraph 88), Observation 28

104. Address by the Minister of Land and Natural Resources at the Annual Conference of National Park Authorities, Harrogate, May 1965

105. *The Development of Agriculture, Cmd. 2738,* August 1965. H.M.S.O.

106. Detailed recommendations made by the Minister included the establishment of Country Parks as subsidiary recreational areas to National Parks, better recreational use of water resources, care for coastal beauty, more access to the uplands, and additional expenditure upon derelict land and tree planting in copses and spinneys by public authorities

107. *Land Use Survey Handbook* by Alice Coleman and K. R. A. Maggs. 4th (Scottish) Edition, 1964. Isle of Thanet Geographical Association. *Panorama*, Vol. X, 1964. Jour. of the Isle of Thanet Geo. Assocn.

PART II

Chapter 1

1. *Somerset Development Plan Report, 1964,* Chap. III, contains a full account of the background and formation of County Council policy towards forestry. About 240 groups of woods and timbered features in the county were notified to the F.C. in 1949 as amenity areas. Thereafter, felling proposals affecting them were passed to the Planning Authority by the Commission for consultation. F.C. land acquisitions were subjected to the usual courtesy consultations between Govt. Depts. and Local Authorities. The Somerset policy has been to concentrate upon good liaison arrangements and to negotiate solutions to amenity problems rather than to use Tree Preservation Orders

2. The proportion was about 36%. This compares favourably with figures given in Part 1, Chap. 4(b). It is believed that the influence of the Planning Authority is reflected in the higher hardwood proportion

3. The decision was based upon Section 84 of the 1949 Act which lays down that Park Authorities, in carrying out their work, shall have due regard for forestry requirements

Chapter 2

1. Work upon the *Second Land Use Survey of Britain* was brought forward in Exmoor at the instigation of the Exmoor Society and a complete land-use map of the National Park was completed in 1963–1965. It is to be revised annually. I am indebted to Victor Bonham-Carter and Geoffrey Sinclair for advance information from the survey. In January 1966 preliminary calculations on this map showed 50,000 acres as moorland of all ecological types. The difference of 2,000 acres between this figure and that produced by myself is believed to be due to :

(a) the greater accuracy and ecological knowledge of the land-use surveyor and his team,

(b) the inclusion in the land-use survey of a number of small patches of a moorland type separated from the main highland, and included within otherwise relatively intensive farms. Such areas would not be 'open' land in a National Parks definition, unless reasonably accessible

2. The 1949 Act requires existing scenes to be 'preserved and enhanced'. Although the enhancement of scenery is a debatable matter, it is clear that, within the context of the Act, it should not be taken to mean widespread alterations to existing landscape patterns

3. It is very important to understand the various definitions of 'open land', 'moorland', etc. A complete lack of boundary hedges, banks and fences is of as much significance as the dominance of heather in defining truly open country in Exmoor for administrative purposes. The land-use map of Exmoor, which is strictly ecological with no administrative overtones, defines a total of 37,000 acres of heather moors *and* heaths. Much of this land is enclosed and has sufficient grass in the vegetation to be included in my second very broad sub-division of 'grass moorland'

4. Note 3 refers. The land-use survey defines 13,700 acres of grass moor in the National Park. These are ecologically pure and mixed stands of various moorland grasses and rushes. My 'grass moor' definition is broader and includes areas of enclosed grassy heaths

5. By January 1966 it could be estimated from the land-use map that probably 4,000 acres had been fully reclaimed from the moor for agricultural use. The refinement of detail in this map enabled it to be deduced that upwards of a further 3,000 acres had undergone agricultural 'interference' — i.e. enough superficial treatment to alter the appearance of the vegetation so that it could no longer be classified strictly as moorland. By the same date about 900 acres had been taken from moorland for afforestation in addition to the areas above. These figures show that agricultural improvement, which is not subject to consultation procedures with the Park Authorities, has caused far more change in the appearance of open country in Exmoor than has forestry during the last decade

6. *The Reclamation of Exmoor Forest* by Dr. C. S. Orwin. Oxford Univ. Press, 1929

7. *Forestry, Agriculture and Marginal Land,* Report by the Natural Resources (Technical) Committee. H.M.S.O. 1957

8. The Zuckerman Report of 1957 has now been revised 'in the light of changed economic circumstances and with a wider remit in terms of rural land use'. The revision is contained in the *Report of the Land Use Study Group: Forestry, Agriculture and the Multiple Use of Rural Land.* Dept. of Education and Science. H.M.S.O., 1966. Problems of amenity and recreation figure much more in this than in the earlier report

9. The figures for extensive agricultural use should be read in conjunction with Notes 1, 3 and 4, Chap. 2 (c), given above.

Chapter 3
1. Sylvia Crowe, in *Garden Design*, Country Life, 1958, has presented the principles of design with a clarity difficult to surpass; I wish to acknowledge the obvious influence which her account has had upon my application of the principles to forestry

PART III

Chapter 1
1. See Part I, Chap. 4 (c), pp. 116–118.
2. The membership of Forestry Consultative Panels includes representatives of the Park Authority, Nature Conservancy, T.G.O., C.L.A. and Forestry Commission. The functions of a Panel are advisory, both to the Park Committees and to the Forestry Commission

Chapter 2
1. See Part II, Chap. 2 (b), pp. 140–143.
2. The Minister of Land and Natural Resources in 1965 at the second conference on *The Countryside in 1970* was careful not to 'propose projects which would inevitably lead to an increase in expenditure'. But in the White Paper, *Leisure in the Countryside, Cmd. 2928,* presented by the Minister in February 1966, it is proposed to make grant-aid available for amenity work in the countryside at large, including the public purchase and management of woods. (Para. 53)
3. At the time of the F.C. Census, 1947–49, Somerset contained more scrub oak woodland, much of it degenerated coppice, than any other county in England. The total was 2,928 acres. Devon was second in area of oak scrub, having 2,361 acres, and third in area of birch scrub — 4,243 acres. *F.C. Census Report No. 5: English County Details*, 1953, pp. 60, 198
4. See Part II, Chap. 3, pp. 172–180.

Chapter 4
1. *Economic Survey of the South West* by Associated Industrial Consultants Ltd., 1965. Forestry sections

BIBLIOGRAPHY

BIBLIOGRAPHY

The list below includes the principal works consulted as well as those referred to in the Notes.

ABRAHAMS, H. M. (1959) 'Britain's National Parks', Country Life, London

ACKERS, C. P. (1938) 'Practical British Forestry', Oxford University Press, London
(1945) 'Our Woodlands: their Sacrifice and Renovation', Torch Stream Books, London

ACLAND, Sir Francis (1918) Final Report of the Forestry Sub-Committee Ministry of Reconstruction (Cmd. 8881), H.M.S.O., London, 'The Acland Report'

ADDISON, Lord (1931). See under MINISTRY OF HEALTH

ADKIN, B. W. (1914) 'Law of Forestry', Estates Gazette, London

ALBION, R. G. (1926) 'Forests and Sea Power', Harvard University Press, U.S.A.

ANDERSON, Prof. M. L. (1950) 'The Selection of Tree Species'. Oliver and Boyd, Edinburgh
See also under HADDINGTON, KNUCHEL and KOSTLER

ASSOCIATED INDUSTRIAL CONSULTANTS Ltd. (1965) 'Economic Survey of the South West'. Forestry sections

BALMAN, F. E. (1961) 'The Trend of Forest Workers' Wages 1938–61'. Quart. Jour. of For., Vol. LV : No. 4

BARRINGTON, C. A. J. (1957) 'Forestry in Relation to Landscape'. Jour. of the F.C. No. 26

BERESFORD-PEIRSE, Sir H. (1963) 'The Role of Forestry in the Economy of Britain'. Supplement to *Forestry*, reporting 3rd Discussion Meeting, Soc. of Foresters of G.B.

BEST, R. H. and COPPOCK, J. T. (1962) 'The Changing Use of Land in Britain'. Faber, London

BLENKINSOP, A. (1964) 'The National Parks of England and Wales'. Jour. of School of Planning, Newcastle, Vol. VI : No. 1

BLOCK, G. D. M. (1963) 'Britons on Holiday'. Conservative Political Centre, London

BOALER, S. B. (1962). A Reply to G. B. Ryle's 'Forests and Parks'. *Countryman*, Vol. 59 : No. 2

BOYCE, J. S. (1954) 'Forest Plantation Protection against Diseases and Insect Pests'. F.A.O. Forestry Development Paper No. 3, 1954

BRACEY, Dr. H. E. (1962) 'Industry and the Countryside'. Faber, London

BRETT, L. (1965) 'Landscape in Distress'. Architectural Press, London

BRIGGS, R. A. (1962) A Reply to G. B. Ryle's 'Forests and Parks', *Countryman*, Vol. 59 : No. 2

BRINE, P. W. (1962) Letter on Hardwood Exports. *Timber Trades Journal*, 17th March 1962

BRITISH TRAVEL ASSOCIATION. Personal correspondence 1964–66 and Annual Report 1964–65

BROWN, A. J. (1956) 'North York Moors National Park'. North Riding of Yorkshire C.C., Home Publishing Co., Croydon

BURTON, S. H. (1952) 'Exmoor'. Westerway Books, London

BURTON, T. L. and WIBBERLEY, G. P. (1965) 'Outdoor Recreation in the British Countryside'. Dept. of Economics, Wye College, University of London

CABORN, Dr. J. M. – Author of Forestry Commission Bulletin No. 29. (See under F.C.)
(1965) 'Shelterbelts and Windbreaks'. Faber, London

CADMAN, W. A. — Author of Forestry Commission Forest Record No. 22. (See under F.C.)
(1962) Deputy Surveyor, New Forest, F.C. Personal Correspondence

CARDIGAN, The EARL of (1949) 'The Wardens of Savernake Forest'. Routledge and Kegan Paul, London

CHAPMAN, H. (1964) Ministry of Housing and Local Government, Personal Correspondence

CECIL, Lord David (1960 Edn.) 'The Young Melbourne'. Grey Arrow Books, London

CHURCH, Richard (1956) 'The Royal Parks of London'. Ministry of Works Guide Book. H.M.S.O., London

CIVIC TRUST (1964) 'Derelict Land'. Civic Trust, London

CLARK, H. F. (1948) 'The English Landscape Garden'. Pleiades Books, London

COKE, Major R. L. (1962) 'In Favour of More Irregular Forestry in Britain'. Jour. C.L.A., Vol. 61, No. 4

COLVIN, Brenda (1948) 'Land and Landscape'. Murray, London
(1957) Review of 'Counter Attack'. Jour. of Inst. of Landscape Architects, March issue

COMMONS ACT of 1876

COMMONS REGISTRATION ACT of 1965

COMMONWEALTH FORESTRY INSTITUTE, OXFORD (1961–63) Land Use Course Reports

CONNELL, C. A. (1963) Conservator F.C. South-West England. Personal Correspondence

COPPOCK, J. T. (1959) 'The Chilterns as an Area of Outstanding Natural Beauty.' Jour. of the Town Planning Institute, Vol. 45 : No. 6

C.P.R.E. Manifesto (1961) 'The Case for Control of Afforestation of Open Land in National Parks'. London
Annual Reports, especially 1958–65
(1963) Standing Committee on National Parks. Notes on Tree Planting and Management in National Parks
(1965) Study No. 1 : 'Afforestation in National Parks'
(1965) Study No. 2 : 'The Future of National Parks and the Country-side'

COUNTRY LANDOWNER, The (1957) Golden Jubilee Issue in June of Jour. of the C.L.A.

COUNTRYSIDE IN 1970, The (1964) Proceedings of the Study Conference, Nov. 1963. H.M.S.O., London

CROWE, Sylvia (1956) 'Tomorrow's Landscape'. Architectural Press, London
(1958) 'Garden Design'. Country Life, London
(1961) (Ed.) 'Space for Living'. (7th I.F.L.A. Congress) Djambatan, Amsterdam
(1963) (Ed. with MILLER, Z.) 'Shaping Tomorrow's Landscape'. (8th I.F.L.A. Congress) Djambatan, Amsterdam

DEER REMOVAL ACT of 1851 (affecting management of New Forest)

DEPT. OF EDUCATION AND SCIENCE (1966) 'Report of the Land Use Study Group — Forestry, Agriculture and the Multiple Use of Rural Land'. (The Ellison Report). H.M.S.O., London

DOWER, J. (1945) See under MINISTRY OF TOWN & COUNTRY PLANNING

DOWER, M. (1964) 'The Function of Open Country'. Jour. of the Town Planning Institute, Vol. 50, No. 4
(1965) 'Fourth Wave' : The Challenge of Leisure. Civic Trust, London

DOWER, Pauline (1961) A Reply to G. B. Ryle's 'Forests and Parks', Countryman, Vol. 58, No. 4

EASTERBROOK, L. (1959) 'Now We're Creating Beauty'. Quart. Jour. of Forestry, Vol. LIII, No. 1

EDINBURGH, H.R.H. the DUKE of (1963) Presidential Address at Conference 'The Countryside in 1970'
Report in The Times of 4th Nov., 1963
(1963) Discussion with HARRIS, K. upon above Conference. Report

in *The Observer* of 24th Nov., 1963

EDLIN, H. L. (1947) 'Forestry and Woodland Life'. Batsford, London
(1949) 'Woodland Crafts in Britain'. Batsford, London
(1956) 'Trees, Woods and Man'. Collins, London
(1956) with NIMMO, M. 'Treasury of Trees'. Countrygoer Books, Manchester
(1958) 'England's Forests'. Faber, London
(1960) 'Silviculture in the New Forest'. Contributed to 'The New Forest : A Symposium'. Galley Press, London
(1962) Personal Correspondence on Forest Parks, especially Hardknott
(1963) 'Amenity Values in British Forestry'. *Forestry*, Vol. XXXVI : No. 1

EDWARDS, J. (1962) 'The Scenic Role of Forestry in National Parks'. Quart. Jour. of For., Vol. LVI, No. 1

EDWARDS, K. C. (1962) 'The Peak District'. Collins, London

EDWARDS, P. (1962) 'Trees and the English Landscape'. Bell, London

EDWARDSON, T. E. (1956) 'Amenity and Forestry'. *Forestry*, Vol. XXIX, No. 1

EGGELING, Dr. W. J. (1961) A Reply to G. B. Ryle's 'Forests and Parks'. *Countryman*, Vol. 58, No. 4

ELECTRICITY ACT of 1957. Section 37 — the amenity clause

ELLIOTT, G. K. (1962) Report on Section K, Forestry, of the British Association, 1962. *Forestry*, Vol. XXXVI : No. 1

ELLISON, Prof. W. See DEPT. OF EDUCATION AND SCIENCE

EPPING FOREST ACT of 1878

ESSEX (1961) 'Forestry and the Essex County Council'. Leaflet by County Planning Adviser, E.C.C., Chelmsford

ESTIMATES COMMITTEE (1965) 8th Special Report 1964–65 : The Forestry Commission. H.M.S.O.

EVELYN, John 'Silva, or a Discourse of Forest Trees and the Propagation of Timber in His Majesty's Dominions'. (Address to Royal Society in 1662; 1st edition 1664; Hunter's Edition of 1776 with Notes used here)

FINANCE ACTS of 1894, 1949, 1960, 1963

FORESTRY ACTS of 1919–51

FORESTRY COMMISSION (1919–65) All publications from H.M.S.O. or F.C., London
Annual Reports : 1st–46th, 1920–65
Census Reports : Of Woodlands and Production of Home Grown Timber, 1924
Of Woodlands of Five Acres and over, 1947–49
English County Details, 1947–49

Of Hedgerow and Park Timber and Woods under Five Acres, 1951

Special Reports : Interim Report of Inter-Departmental Home Grown Timber Committee, 1933

On Timber Utilization — In Boxes and Packing Cases; in the Coal Mines; in Turnery; in Ships and Docks, 1934–38

Of National Forest Park Committees, 1935–45

On Post-War Forest Policy, 1943. (Cmd. 6447)

On Post-War Forest Policy — Private Woodlands — Supplementary Report, 1944. (Cmd. 6500)

Of the New Forest Committee, 1947. (Cmd. 7245)

Agreements on Afforestation in the Lake District with the C.P.R.E. 1936 and 1954, published 1955

Of the Committee on Hedgerow and Farm Timber, 1955. 'The Merthyr Report'

Of the Committee on Marketing Woodland Produce 1956. 'The Watson Report'

Of the Forest of Dean Committee, 1958. (Cmd. 686)

Progress Report 1955–60 by F.C. of G.B., 1962. F.C., London

Booklets : No. 2, The Dedication of Woodlands, 4th Edn., 1956

No. 6, National Forest Parks, 1961

No. 10, The New Forests of Dartmoor. 1964

Bulletins : No. 14, Forestry Practice, 7th Edn. 1958

No. 23, Experiments in Tree Planting on Peat 1954

No. 29, Shelterbelts & Micro-climate, 1957

No. 30, Exotic Trees in G.B., 1957

No. 34, Chalk Down Afforestation, 1962

Britain's Forests : Thornthwaite (Cumberland) 1952

Cannock Chase (Staffs.) 1957

Guide Books : Bedgebury, Kent (National Pinetum and Forest Plots). 3rd Edn., 1961

New Forest, 1951

Westonbirt Arboretum, 1960

National Forest Park Guides : Hardknott, 1949

Dean Forest and Wye Valley, 1956

The Border, 1958

Forest Operations : Leaflets and Records : numerous consultations made, e.g. Leaflet No. 12 'Income Tax and Estate Duty on Woods', 1959 and Record No. 22 'Shelterbelts for Welsh (Western) Hill Farms', 1953, revised 1963

Statutory Instruments : No. 1725 (1951). The Forestry (Exceptions from Restriction of Felling) Regulations

No. 1726 (1951). The Forestry (Felling of Trees) Regulations

No. 96 (1959) The Forestry (Exceptions from Restriction of Felling) (Amendment) Regulations

Research Branch Papers: No. 17 (1955) Tree Planting on Colliery Spoil Heaps. (Wood and Thirgood)

Miscellaneous Pamphlets: Grants for Woodland Owners (under constant revision)

Britain's New Forests 1962

Forestry in England 1963

Fox, Helen M. (1962) 'André Le Nôtre'. Batsford, London

GARDINER, R. (1963) 'Need for Landscape Strategy'. *The Times*, 30th Nov., 1963

GILBERT, Prof. E. W. (1964) 'Vaughan Cornish' Lecture to Oxford Preservation Trust

GILL, C. (1961) 'Dartmoor National Park — The First Ten Years'. Devon County Council

GILPIN, William (1791) 'Remarks on Forest Scenery and Other Woodland Views'. 4th Edn., 1834. Edited by Sir Thomas Lauder. Fraser & Co., Edinburgh

GORDON, W. A. (1955) 'The Law of Forestry'. H.M.S.O., London

GRAYSON, A. J. (1961) 'The Place of Hardwoods in Britain's Forest Economy'. An unpublished B.Litt. thesis. Oxford University Forest Library

HADDINGTON, The 6th EARL of (1761) edited by Prof. M. L. Anderson (1953). 'Some Directions about raising Forest Trees'. Nelson, London

HADFIELD, Miles (1957) 'British Trees. A Guide for Everyman'. Dent, London

(1960) 'Gardening in Britain'. Hutchinson, London

HANSARD. COMMONS. (1963) Vol. 681, No. 600, cols. 1467–1472. Minister's Statement on Forest Policy

HARRIS, K. (1963) 'The Countryside in 1970'. Report of interview with H.R.H. The Duke of Edinburgh. *The Observer*, 24th Nov., 1963

HARROWBY, The EARL of (1962) A Reply to G. B. Ryle's 'Forests and Parks'. *Countryman*, Vol. 59, No. 2

HART, C. E. (1962) 'Practical Forestry for the Agent and Surveyor'. Estates Gazette, London

HAYTHORNTHWAITE, Lt. Col. G. (1961) A Reply to G. B. Ryle's 'Forests and Parks'. *Countryman*, Vol. 58, No. 4

HEALEY, D. (1962) 'Forestry and the Public in G.B.' Paper presented at 8th British Commonwealth Forestry Conference

HENNESSY, J. (1964) 'Preservation and Progress: An Economist Looks at the National Trust'. Lloyds Bank Review No. 72

HILEY, W. E. (1931) 'Improvement of Woodlands'. Country Life, London

(1954) 'Woodland Management', Faber, London

HOBHOUSE, Sir Arthur — See MINISTRY OF TOWN & COUNTRY PLANNING

HOLMES, K. D. (1962) 'Afforestation on the North Yorkshire Moors'. Private paper loaned by Y.H. Association

(1963) 'Further Visits to North Yorkshire'. Private paper loaned by Y.H. Association

HOSKINS, Dr. W. G. (1957) 'The Making of the English Landscape'. Hodder & Stoughton, London

HOWARD, Sir Ebenezer (1898) 'Garden Cities of To-morrow'. Faber, London. 1946 Edn.

HUMMEL, Dr. F. C. and GRAYSON, A. J. (1962) 'Production Goals in Forestry with Special Reference to G.B.'. Paper presented at 8th Brit. Commonwealth For. Confnce.

HUSSEY, C. (1950) Introduction to 'Capability Brown' by Dorothy Stroud. Country Life, London

JAMES, N. D. G. (1948) 'Working Plans for Estate Woodlands'. Blackwell, Oxford

(1955) 'The Forester's Companion'. Blackwell, Oxford

JELLICOE, G. A. (1960) 'Studies in Landscape Design'. Oxford Univ. Press, London

JONES, Dr. E. W. (1961) 'British Forestry in 1790–1813'. Quart. Jour. of For., Vol. LV., Nos. 1 and 2

JUNGO, J. (1964) 'Forests under Protection'. *The Times* Supplement on Switzerland, 15th Feb., 1964

KEABLE, Gladys (1963) 'Tomorrow Slowly Comes'. Town & Country Planning Assocn., London

KELLY, G. S. (1956) 'Afforestation v. Landscape'. Article in 'Counter Attack' edited by Ian Nairn. Architectural Press, London

KELLY, O. (1962) 'The Attractions of Woodlands'. Article in Supplement to *Stock Exchange Gazette*, London, 24th Aug., 1962

KISSIN, I. (1944) 'Cooperation in Forestry'. Tech. Communication No. 2. Imperial Forestry Bureau, Oxford

KNUCHEL, Prof. H. (1953) English Edn. translated by Prof. M. L. Anderson, 'Planning and Control in the Managed Forest'. Oliver and Boyd, Edinburgh

KOSTLER, Prof. J. (1956) English Edn. translated by Prof. M. L. Anderson, 'Silviculture'. Oliver and Boyd, Edinburgh

LAMB, L. (1948) 'The Art of Landscape'. Arts Council of G.B., London

LANGLEY-TAYLOR, G. (1963) 'New Forest Laws Need Revision'. *The Times*, 29th April, 1963

LASCELLES, The Hon. G. (1915) 'Thirty-Five Years in The New Forest'. Arnold, London

LAW OF PROPERTY ACT of 1925 as it affects public access and commons

LOCKE, G. M. (1962) 'A Sample Survey of Field and Other Boundaries in G.B.' Quart. Jour. of For., Vol. LVI, No. 2

MacDONALD, J. A. B. (1959) 'Integration of Forestry and the Hill Sheep Farm'. Quart. Jour. of For., Vol. LIII, No. 4

MacDONALD, J. (1962) 'Britain's Forest Resources'. Cantor Lecture to R. Soc. of Arts. Reported in *The Timber Trades Journal*, 26th May, 1962

MacGREGOR, J. J. (1948) 'The Dedication Scheme for Private Woodlands'. Jour. R. Agric. Soc. of Eng., Vol. 109

(1953) 'Timber Statistics'. Jour. R. Stat. Soc., Series A (Gen.), Vol. CXVI. Pt. III

(1960) 'Economics and the Use of Land for Forestry'. *Unasylva*, Vol. 14, No. 2. (Also reprinted in the Jour. of the R.I.C.S., March 1961)

(1962) 'Forestry as a Competitor for Land : Some Problems in Land Use Decisions'. Paper presented at 8th Brit. Commonwealth For. Confnce. (Also reprinted in the Jour. of the R.I.C.S., Sept. 1962)

(1962) 'Conservation and Outdoor Recreation in the United States'. *Nature*, Vol. 196, No. 4860, 22nd December, 1962

MARSHALL (1803) 'On Planting and Rural Ornament'. Vol. 1 (quoted by Zukowski)

MEIGGS, R. (1949) 'Home Timber Production 1939–45'. London Ref. p. 17, F.C. Census 1947–49

MELLOWS, Dr. A. R. (1964) 'The Preservation and Felling of Trees'. Oyez Practice Notes No. 54, London

METROPOLITAN COMMONS ACT of 1866

MILES, Roger (1959) 'New Trees Need Not Look Ugly'. *The Times*, 4th November, 1959

(1959) 'The Design of Forest Plantations'. *Town and Country Planning*, Dec. 1959

(1960) 'Planning for Landscape'. *The Times*, 2nd February, 1960

(1960) 'Forestry and Landscape in the Exmoor National Park'. *Forestry*, Vol. XXXIII, No. 1

(1960) 'Some Rural Problems'. Paper presented to I.L.A. Annual Conference. Reprinted in *Prospect*, the Jour. of the Royal Inc. of Architects in Scotland, Winter 1960

(1962) 'Amenity May Cost Money'. Jour. of Exmoor Society No. 4. (affiliated to C.P.R.E.)

MINISTRY OF AGRICULTURE (1951) 'Shelter Belts for Farmland'. Leaflet No. 15, H.M.S.O., London

(1954) 'Public Inquiry into the Disposal of Land at Crichel Down', Cmd. 9176, H.M.S.O., London

(1965) 'The Development of Agriculture', Cmd. 2738. H.M.S.O., London

MINISTRY OF HEALTH — The Addison Report of the National Parks Committee, Cmd. 3851 (1931). H.M.S.O., London

MINISTRY OF HOUSING AND LOCAL GOVERNMENT — See MINISTRY OF TOWN AND COUNTRY PLANNING

MINISTRY OF LAND AND NATURAL RESOURCES (1965) Circular No. 1/65. Min. of L. and N.R. Order, 1965

(1966) 'Leisure in the Countryside, England and Wales', Cmd. 2928. H.M.S.O., London

MINISTRY OF SCIENCE — The Trend Report on the Organization of Civil Science, Cmd. 2171 (1963). H.M.S.O., London

MINISTRY OF TOWN AND COUNTRY PLANNING :

The Dower Report on National Parks in England and Wales. Cmd. 6628 (1945). H.M.S.O., London

The Hobhouse Report of the National Parks Committee (Eng. and Wales) Cmd. 7121 (1947). H.M.S.O., London

Memorandum on the Preservation of Trees and Woodlands, 1949

Tree Preservation Orders : Regulations and Circulars, 1948–64

Town and Country Planning 1943–51. Progress Report, Cmd. 8204. H.M.S.O., London

'New Life for Dead Lands', with Circular 39/63; 'Derelict Land', 1963. H.M.S.O., London

MINISTRY OF WORKS. See CHURCH, Richard (1956)

MOBBS, Prof. E. C. (1962) 'The Forest for Leisure and Pleasure'. Paper presented at British Association, Section K, Forestry, 1962

(1962) 'Recruitment and Education'. Paper presented at 8th Brit. Commonwealth For. Confnce. 1962

MORLING, R. J. (1963) 'Trees'. Estates Gazette, London

MURRAY, W. H. (1962) 'Highland Landscape'. National Trust for Scotland, Edinburgh

NAIRN, I. (1955) 'Outrage'. Architectural Press, London

(1956) 'Counter-Attack against Subtopia', Architectural Press, London

NATIONAL PARK AUTHORITIES CONFERENCE REPORT (1965). Yorkshire Dales N.P. publication

NATIONAL PARKS AND ACCESS TO THE COUNTRYSIDE ACT of 1949

NATIONAL PARKS COMMISSION (1949–66). All publications from H.M.S.O., London

Annual Reports : 1st–17th (1950–66)

National Park Guides : No. 1 'Dartmoor', 1957
No. 2 'Snowdonia', 1958
No. 3 'Peak District', 1960

NATIONAL TRUST ACTS of 1907, 1937

NATURE CONSERVANCY (1949–64). All publications from H.M.S.O., London

Annual Reports : 1st–15th (1950–64)

Information Leaflet No. 1: Nature Reserves and Sites of Special Scientific Interest (1954)

NEW FOREST ACTS of 1698, 1877, 1949, 1964

NEWSPAPERS consulted for items, articles, reports etc. Principally, *The Times*, *The Guardian*, *The Telegraph*, (Map, 14th July 1960), *The Observer*

NICHOLSON, E. M. (1957) 'Britain's Nature Reserves', Country Life, London

NICHOLSON, N. (1955) 'The Lakers'. Robert Hale, London

NISBET, J. (1905) 'The Forester'. (7th Edn.) Blackwood, London

NUISANCE REMOVAL AND DISEASE PREVENTION ACT of 1848

ORWIN, Dr. C. S. (1929) 'The Reclamation of Exmoor Forest'. Oxford Univ. Press

OXFORD and ABERDEEN UNIVERSITIES (1959) 'Survey of Private Forestry Costs : Summary Report for Forest Years 1951/52 — 1955/56'

PEACE, T. R. (1961) 'The Dangerous Concept of the Natural Forest'. Quart. Jour. of For., Vol. LV., No. 1

PEAK DISTRICT NATIONAL PARK. Annual Reports, 1st–14th, 1951–66. 'Our Heritage of Trees', 1961

PERIODICALS consulted for items, articles, reports etc. Principally, *Country Life* and *The Countryman*

PLINY, THE ELDER (*c*. A.D. 23–79) 'Naturalis historia'. Probably Book XVI. 12, on coppice

POPERT, A. H. (1955) 'The Place of Broadleaved Trees in British Forestry'. Quart. Jour. of For., Vol. L. No. 3

PUBLIC HEALTH ACTS of 1848, 1875

QVIST, A. (1958) 'Epping Forest'. A Corporation of London Publication

RAMBLERS' ASSOCIATION, The (1964) 'The Right to Roam'. London

RANKIN, K. (1960) Address to F.H.T.A. Timber Trades Journal, May, 1960

RICHARDS, E. G. (1961) 'The Growing of Hardwoods for Pulpwood'. With Appendices. Quart. Jour. of For., Vol. LV., No. 3

(1962) 'The Utilization of Small-sized Coniferous Thinnings in G.B.' Paper presented to the 8th Brit. Commonwealth For. Confnce. 1962

ROYAL COMMISSION ON COMMON LAND (1958) Report. Cmd. 462, H.M.S.O., London

ROYAL FORESTRY SOCIETIES of England and of Scotland (1944), 'Post-War Forestry: A Report on Forest Policy'. Prepared and published by the Societies

RUCK-KEENE, Vice-Admiral P. (1962) A Reply to G. B. Ryle's 'Forests and Parks'. *Countryman*, Vol. 59, No. 2

RYLE, G. B. and STOCKS, J. B. (1960) 'Treatment of Degraded Hardwood Areas for Shelterwood Restocking'. ('Dappled Shade Technique'). Paper presented to F.A.O., Rome

RYLE, G. B. (1960) 'Forestry in the Economic Development of Wales'. Paper read at Brit. Assocn., Cardiff, 1960

(1961) 'Forests and Parks'. *Countryman*, Vol. 58, No. 3

(1962) 'National Forests and Parks'. Paper read at Brit. Assocn., Manchester, 1962. Reprinted in Jour. of the Town Planning Institute Vol. XLIX, No. 1., January 1963

(1962) 'The Diverse Uses of Forests'. Address given to Soc. of Foresters, Lyndhurst, 1962. *Forestry*, Vol. XXXVI, No. 1, 1963

(1963) 'State Hardwood Planting 1952–62'. Letter, *Country Life*, February 1963

SCHLICH, Sir W. (1910) 'Forests and Forestry'. Encyclopaedia Britannica, 11th Edn., 1911

SHAW-LEFEVRE, Rt. Hon. G. (1894) 'English Commons and Forests'. Cassell, London

SIMMONS, I. G. (1965) 'Americans for Open Space'. *Town and Country Planning*, June 1965

SINDEN, J. and L. (1963) A Reply to H. L. Edlin's 'Amenity Values in British Forestry'. *Forestry*, Vol. XXXVI, No. 2

SIXTEENTH REPORT from the Select Committee on Estimates, Session 1948–49, The Forestry Commission. Note p. 11 Q. 2730 on amenity and others on land costs, indifference to Regional Committees, etc. H.M.S.O., London

SOCIETY OF FORESTERS of G.B. (1962) 'Submission to Govt. Working Party on Forestry Policy', issued as a separate pamphlet to *Forestry*. (Royal English Forestry Society's statement on 'Long Term Forest Policy'. Quart. Jour. of For., Vol. LVII, No. 1)

(1963) 'The Road Ahead, a National Forest Policy', Editorial in *Forestry*, Vol. XXXVI, No. 2

SOMERSET (1964) 'County Development Plan: Report of Survey', First Review, S.C.C., Taunton

STAMP, Sir L. Dudley (1946) 'Britain's Structure and Scenery', 1st Edn. Collins, London. Fontana Library 1962

(1955) 'Man and the Land'. Collins, London

(1962) Foreword to 'The Changing Use of Land in Britain' by Best and Coppock

(1962) 'The Land of Britain — its Use and Misuse'. Longmans, London

STAMP, Sir L. Dudley and HOSKINS, Dr. W. G. (1963) 'The Common Lands of England and Wales'. Collins, London

STAPLEDON, Sir R. G. (1935) 'The Land: Now and Tomorrow'. Faber, London

(1964) 'Human Ecology', edited by Robert Waller. Faber, London

STEVEN, H. M. and MCNEILL, W. M. (1957) 'The Desirable Balance Between Hardwood and Softwood Production in G.B.' Paper presented to the 7th Brit. Commonwealth For. Confnce. 1957

STROUD, Dorothy (1950) (1957 Edn.) 'Capability Brown'. Country Life, London

(1962) 'Humphrey Repton', Country Life, London

SUDBROOK SCHEME for the Registration of Hardwood Areas for the Production of Hardwood Pulp and Conditions of Purchase (1961 Edn. sent out by Sudbrook Pulp Mill Ltd.)

TANSLEY, Prof. A. G. (1923) (1932 Edn.) 'Practical Plant Ecology'. Allen and Unwin, London

(1945) 'The Future of Forests'. Article in *The Times* during 1945

TAYLOR, W. L. (1945) 'Forests and Forestry in Great Britain'. Crosby Lockwood, London

TECHNICAL JOURNALS consulted for items, articles, reports, etc. include *Forestry, Quarterly Journal of the Royal Forestry Society, Journal of the Royal Institution of Chartered Surveyors, Agriculture, The Timber Trades Journal, Journal of the Town Planning Institute, Journal of the Institute of Landscape Architects, Nature, The Economist*

TELLING, A. E. (1963) 'Planning Law and Procedure'. Butterworths, London

THOM, J. R. (1962) 'Wealth and Beauty in New Forests'. Article in *The Times*, Survey of Wales and Monmouthshire, 31st January 1962

(1962) 'Forestry and Multiple Land Use in Wales'. Quart. Jour. of Forestry, Vol. LVI, No. 2

THOULESS, R. H. (1930) (1962 Pan Edn.) 'Straight and Crooked Thinking'. Pan Books, London

TIMBER GROWERS' ORGANISATION Ltd. 'Your Woodlands: Profit or Loss?' Publicity pamphlet circulated by T.G.O. in late 'fifties and early 'sixties

TIMBER GROWER, The (April 1962 and others re membership) Quart. Newsletter of T.G.O. Ltd.

TOWN AND COUNTRY PLANNING ACTS of 1932, 1947, 1962

TREVELYAN, Prof. G. M. (1942) (1946 Edn.) 'English Social History'. Longmans, London

TURNER, H. A. (1962) "The Inter-Relation between State, Communal and Private Forestry'. Paper presented to the 8th Brit. Commonwealth For. Confnce, 1962

VINCENT, S. Lee (1962) 'Town Planning Control in Practice: IV. National Parks'. Jour. of Planning and Property Law

WAGER, J. F. (1964) 'The Public Use of Ashridge.' Unpublished Report on a Study of Recreational Use. Oxford Forest Library

WALKER, Dr. K. R. (1957) Review of the 'Zuckerman Report'. Jour. of Ag. Economics, Vol. XII, No. 4

(1959) 'The Forestry Commission and the Use of Hill Land'. Reprint from the Scot. Jour. of Pol. Economy, Vol. VII, pp. 14–35

WARD, J. D. U. (1959) 'Degenerating Woodlands'. Quart. Jour. of For., Vol. LIII, No. 4

WATTS, Sir Phillip (1910) 'History of Ships since the Invention of Steamships'. Encyclopaedia Britannica, 11th Edn., 1911, under 'Ships'

WAY, J. M. and DAVIS, Dr. B. N. K. (1963) 'Hedges as a Feature of our Countryside'. Agriculture, Jour. of Min. of Ag., Vol. 70, No. 12. (See also LOCKE)

WHYTE, R. O. and SISAM, J. W. B. (1949) 'Establishment of Vegetation on Industrial Waste Land'. Commonwealth Agricultural Bureau, Aberystwyth

WILLIAMS, D. N. and CHAPMAN, S. (1955) 'The Clear Felling of an Oak Scrub Area'. Quart. Jour. of Forestry, Vol. XLIX, No. 2

WILLSON, F. M. G. (1953) An unpublished D.Phil. thesis: 'A Consideration of the Experience in Britain of Administrative Commissions, represented in Parliament by non-ministerial Commissioners, with special reference to the Ecclesiastical Commission, the Charity Commission and the Forestry Commission'. Part IV: The Forestry Commission and Part V: Parliament, Government and the three Commissions. Bodleian Library, Oxford

WOOD, R. F. and NIMMO, M. Authors of Forestry Commission: Bulletin No. 34. (See under F.C.)

WORCESTERSHIRE (1957) 'Trees in Worcestershire'. Report by County Planning Officer

WORDSWORTH, W. (1835) 'A Guide Through the District of the Lakes' and later expanded editions by Hudson (1842) and 4th Edn. (1853) containing geological letters from Prof. Sedgwick. (See also NICHOLSON, N.)

WORKMAN, J. (1961) 'The History of Landscape Planting in England'. Quart. Jour. of For., Vol. LV, No. 2

YOUNG, D. W. (1951) 'The Forest Woodlands'. Contribution to F.C. Guide: New Forest

ZEHETMAYR, J. W. L. Author of Forestry Commission Bulletin No. 23 (See under F.C.)

ZUCKERMAN, Prof. Sir S. (1957) Chairman of the Natural Resources (Technical) Committee Reporting upon 'Forestry, Agriculture and Marginal Land'. H.M.S.O., London. (Known as 'The Zuckerman Report' under the Office of the Lord President of the Council)

ZUKOWSKI, A. A. (1951) Part I — England, of unpublished D.Phil. thesis, 'The Relation between Forest Policy and Economic Development'. Bodleian Library, Oxford

INDEX

Material contained in the Notes *and* Bibliography *is not included but references to individual notes are given where appropriate.*

T

INDEX

Aberdeen University, 129

access to the countryside (*see also* footpaths, rambling, waymarking etc.), pressure and legislation for 53–8, 66–7, 93, 95–8, 236; in Forestry Commission lands, 66–7, 69–71, 165, 213, 236; problems arising from, 67, 69, 71, 199, 213–14; agreements, orders or land purchase for, 56–7, 143–7, 208, 211; Exmoor surveys and, 143–8, 161, 164–8, 180, 183–8, 199, 205–9, 211, 213–14, 221

Access to Mountains (Scotland) Bill, 1884 *et seq.* 56, 67

acknowledgements: *Foreword*, 7–8

Acland Report on Forestry, 1917, 60–1

Acland, Sir Francis, 60

acquisition of land, few early examples of, 27, 50; compulsory powers for, 65, (Note 13), 88, 90–1, 93–4, 99–100; by Forestry Commission, 61–2, Table 2, 69, 75, 82, 87, Table 4, 98, 105, 111–12, 115, 119, Table 5, Diag. F, 127 — in Exmoor, 137, 148, 161, Table 6, 202, 204–5, 227–8; by other public authorities, 55, 93–4, 97, 110–11, 114, 200 — in Exmoor, 149, 165, Table 6, 208, 211, 227–9; by private organizations, 116–18 — in Exmoor, 193; by National Trust, 56–7, 77–8 — in Exmoor, Table 6, 200, 208–9, 211, 228–9

Acts of Parliament: Access to Mountains, 1939, 67; Bank Holiday 1871, 54; Commons, 1876, 54; Deer Removal, 1851, 72; General Enclosure, 1845, 54 and local Acts of, 29, 54; Epping Forest, 1878, 55–6; Finance, 1960, 117; Forest of Dean, 1668, 27–8; Forestry, 1919, 61; 1927, 69; 1945, 90; 1947, 90–1; 1951, 91–2; Law of Property, 1925, 55; Metropolitan Commons, 1866, 54; National Parks and Access to the Countryside, 1949, 67, 96–8, 108, 114, 130, 135, 143–4, 168, 203, 208; National Trust, 1907, 57, 209; New Forest, 1698, 27–8; 1877, 72–3; 1949, 73–4; 1964, 74; Nuisance Removal and Disease Prevention, 1848, 52–3; Public Health, 1848, 52; 1875, 53; Restriction of Ribbon Development, 1935, 68; Rights of Way, 1932, 55; Southampton and Dorchester Railway, 1845, 72; Town and Country Planning, 1932, 68–9; 1947, 93–8, 245; 1962, 245; Town Planning, 1909, 53; Transfer of Woods, 1923, 62–3, Table 2

Addison, Lord, 68

Addison Report on National Parks, 1931, 68–9

aesthetic values (*see* amenity, visual)

afforest, to, in connection with Royal hunting grounds, 27

afforestation (planting new land with trees), in the 18th century manner, 26, 28–44; early need and tardy Govt. support for, 25–8, 36, 45, 47–51, 59–60; by Forestry Commission, 1919–39, 61–3, Table 2, 69; criticisms of, 61–2, 66–7, 75, 77–8, 89–90; early efforts to remedy amenity defects in, 69–81; 1939–45, setbacks to, 82–3; 1943–1944, expansion plans for, 87–8, Table 4; 1945 *et seq.* conflicts and consultations about, 90, 92, 94–6, 98–9, 104–5, 111–13, 122–7; integration with agriculture, 99–100; reduced pace of, in England, 115, Table 5, Diag. F; latest policy towards, 127–32, 245–6; 1958 *et seq.* by private organizations, 116–18, 121–2; Voluntary Scheme over, in National Parks, 117–18, 139, 193, 196, 240, Appendices 1 and 3. Exmoor survey of, Part II, 135–89, Sketches (i)–(x) (*see* Exmoor for breakdown)

age-classes of trees, 83–4, 120, 126

agriculture, reorganization of, 18th century, 29–32, 34, 43–4, 233; decline and collapse of, 19th century, 46–7, 49, 54; depressions and changes of tenure, 20th century, 62–4; recent attitudes to trees and hedges, 88, 106–7; 120–1; competition/integration with forestry, 19, 61–2, 90, 95, 99–100, 115, 119, 127, 235, 238; exemption from planning control, 21, 94, 108, 235, 237, 241, 246; impending reorganization of, 130–1, 238, 246; in Exmoor, 21, 135, 137, 141, 143–61, Table 6, 183, 198, 203, 206, 209, 212–13, 241, 246

alder, 35, 201